★ ★ ★ ★ ★ ★ ★ ★ ★ ★ ★ ★ ★ ★ ★ ★ ★ ★ ★

AN AMERICAN OMNIBUS

★ ★ ★ ★ ★ ★ ★ ★ ★ ★ ★ ★ ★ ★ ★ ★ ★ ★ ★

★★★★★★★★★★★★★★★★★★★★★★★★★★★★★★★★★★★★★★

AN AMERICAN OMNIBUS

WITH AN INTRODUCTION BY
CARL VAN DOREN

DOUBLEDAY, DORAN & COMPANY, INC.
GARDEN CITY, NEW YORK

★★★★★★★★★★★★★★★★★★★★★★★★★★★★★★★★★★★★★

PRINTED AT THE *Country Life Press*, GARDEN CITY, N. Y., U. S. A.

Acknowledgment

Thanks are due the authors and the following for permission to use material listed below:

Anderson House, for "Mary of Scotland, a Play," by Maxwell Anderson, copyright, 1933, by Maxwell Anderson. The Curtis Publishing Company, for "Ring Around a Rosy" by Sinclair Lewis, from The Saturday Evening Post, copyright, 1931, by The Curtis Publishing Company. The John Day Company, Inc., for "Send Forth the High Falcon" by Léonie Adams, from "High Falcon." Doubleday, Doran & Company, Inc., for "Archy and Mehitabel" by Don Marquis, copyright, 1916, 1922, by Sun Printing and Publishing Company, 1922, 1925, by New York Tribune, Inc., 1925, 1926, by P. F. Collier & Son Co., 1927, 1930, by Doubleday, Doran & Co., Inc.; "The New Fable of Susan and the Daughter and the Granddaughter and then Something Really Grand" by George Ade, from "Ade's Fables," copyright, 1914, by Doubleday, Doran & Company, Inc.; "The Killer" by Stewart Edward White, copyright, 1919, by Stewart Edward White; "Invocation" by Stephen Vincent Benét, from "John Brown's Body," copyright, 1927, 1928, by Stephen Vincent Benét; "The Fawn in the Snow" and "The Woodcutter's Wife" by William Rose Benét, both from "Man Possessed," copyright, 1927, by Charles Scribner's Sons, and a selection from "Personal History" by Vincent Sheean, copyright, 1934, 1935, by Vincent

Sheean. Harcourt, Brace and Company, Inc., for "Whiffs of the Ohio River at Cincinnati" by Carl Sandburg, from "Good Morning, America," copyright, 1928, by Carl Sandburg, Harper & Brothers, for two selections by Edna St. Vincent Millay from "Fatal Interview," copyright, 1931, by Edna St. Vincent Millay. Henry Holt and Company, for "The Runaway" and "Stopping by Woods on a Snowy Evening" by Robert Frost, from "Collected Poems." Houghton Mifflin & Company, for "Papago Wedding" by Mary Austin, copyright, 1925, by The American Mercury Inc., also "You, Andrew Marvell" by Archibald MacLeish, from "New Found Land." Alfred A. Knopf, Inc., for "The Eagle and the Mole" and "Let No Charitable Hope" by Elinor Wylie, from "Collected Poems," also "Here Lies a Lady" by John Crowe Ransom, from "Chills and Fever." Liveright, Inc., for "Death in the Woods" by Sherwood Anderson, copyright, 1926, by The American Mercury, Inc., also "Leda" by H. D., from "Collected Poems"; "Continent's End" from "Tamar" and "Bixby's Landing" from "Cawdor," both by Robinson Jeffers; "Repose of Rivers" from "White Buildings," and "Atlantis" from "The Bridge," both by Hart Crane; selection by E. E. Cummings. The Macmillan Company, for "Mr. Flood's Party" and a selection from "Tristram," both by Edwin Arlington Robinson; "Flame and Shadow" by Sara Teasdale, from "The Long Hill"; "Dark of the Moon" by Sara Teasdale, from "Arcturus in Autumn"; "Song of the Moderns" and "Brahma," both by John Gould Fletcher, from "The Black Rock." Robert M. McBride & Co., for "Women" by Louise Bogan, from "Body of this Death"; "Quiet" by Léonie Adams, from "Those Not Elect." The New Yorker, from "New Yorker Scrapbook," copyright, 1926–1931, F. R. Publishing Co.: "But the One on the Right" by Dorothy Parker,

"Thirty-Seven by Patricia Collinge, "Come, Ye Disconsolate" by Charles MacArthur, "But for the Grace of God" by Thyra Samter Winslow, "The Vanderbilt Convention" by Frank Sullivan, "Marriage of Convenience" by John Mosher, "The Stranger" by Emily Hahn, "The Giant-Killer" by T. H. Wenning, "The Title" by Arthur Kober, "Louis Dot Dope" by Robert Benchley, "Miss Gulp" by Nunnally Johnson, "My Silver Dress" by Elinor Wylie, "The Faithful Wife" by Morley Callaghan, and "Essayage" by Christopher Morley. Charles Scribner's Sons, for "The Killers" by Ernest Hemingway, from "Men Without Women," copyright, 1927, by Charles Scribner's Sons, and "The Champion" by Ring Lardner, from "Round Up," copyright, 1924, by Charles Scribner's Sons, also "Hasbrouck and the Rose" by Phelps Putnam, from "Trinc"; "And Already the Minutes" and "And in the Hanging Gardens" by Conrad Aiken, both from "Selected Poems"; "Emblems" by Allen Tate, from "Poems." The Viking Press, Inc., for "Big Blonde" by Dorothy Parker, copyright, 1929, by The Bookman Publishing Co., from "Laments for the Living," copyright, 1930, by Dorothy Parker, and "But the One on the Right" by Dorothy Parker, from "New Yorker Scrapbook."

Contents

★★★★★★★★★★★★★★★★★★★★★★

Introduction	Carl Van Doren
Ring Around a Rosy	Sinclair Lewis
The Killers	Ernest Hemingway
Archy and Mehitabel	Don Marquis
Big Blonde	Dorothy Parker
The New Fable of Susan and the Daughter and the Granddaughter and then Something Really Grand	George Ade
But the One on the Right	Dorothy Parker
Thirty-Seven	Patricia Collinge
Come, Ye Disconsolate	Charles MacArthur
But for the Grace of God	Thyra Samter Winslow
The Vanderbilt Convention	Frank Sullivan

ix

MARRIAGE OF CONVENIENCE	John Mosher
THE STRANGER	Emily Hahn
THE GIANT-KILLER	T. H. Wenning
THE TITLE	Arthur Kober
LOUIS DOT DOPE	Robert Benchley
MISS GULP	Nunnally Johnson
MY SILVER DRESS	Elinor Wylie
THE FAITHFUL WIFE	Morley Callaghan
ESSAYAGE	Christopher Morley
CHAMPION	Ring Lardner
DEATH IN THE WOODS	Sherwood Anderson
MARY OF SCOTLAND (A Play)	Maxwell Anderson
PAPAGO WEDDING	Mary Austin
THE KILLER	Stewart Edward White
SELECTION FROM "PERSONAL HISTORY"	Vincent Sheean
MR. FLOOD'S PARTY	Edwin Arlington Robinson
SELECTION FROM "TRISTRAM"	Edwin Arlington Robinson
THE RUNAWAY	Robert Frost
STOPPING BY WOODS ON A SNOWY EVENING	Robert Frost

CONTENTS

WHIFFS OF THE OHIO RIVER AT CINCINNATI — Carl Sandburg

THE LONG HILL — Sara Teasdale

ARCTURUS IN AUTUMN — Sara Teasdale

SONG OF THE MODERNS — John Gould Fletcher

BRAHMA — John Gould Fletcher

LEDA — H. D.

THE FAWN IN THE SNOW — William Rose Benét

THE WOODCUTTER'S WIFE — William Rose Benét

CONTINENT'S END — Robinson Jeffers

BIXBY'S LANDING — Robinson Jeffers

THE EAGLE AND THE MOLE — Elinor Wylie

LET NO CHARITABLE HOPE — Elinor Wylie

GERONTION — T. S. Eliot

HERE LIES A LADY — John Crowe Ransom

AND ALREADY THE MINUTES — Conrad Aiken

AND IN THE HANGING GARDENS — Conrad Aiken

LOVE IS NOT ALL; IT IS NOT MEAT NOR DRINK — Edna St. Vincent Millay

OH, SLEEP FOREVER IN THE LATMIAN CAVE — Edna St. Vincent Millay

YOU, ANDREW MARVELL — Archibald MacLeish

HASBROUCK AND THE ROSE — Phelps Putnam

O Thou to Whom the Musical White Spring — E. E. Cummings

Medusa — Louise Bogan

Invocation to John Brown's Body — Stephen Vincent Benét

Quiet — Léonie Adams

Send Forth the High Falcon — Léonie Adams

Emblems — Allen Tate

Repose of Rivers — Hart Crane

Atlantis — Hart Crane

List of Some Other Books by Authors Represented in This Volume

Introduction

Look at the anthologies of American literature that have been put together in the past dozen years. No matter what point an anthologist has wanted to make, he has found enough to prove it with. Even anthologists of the same mind have shown different hands. A humanist and a communist might get up two anthologies, both good and neither of them repeating anything in the other. There are more kinds of books for more kinds of tastes than there ever were before in America.

An American Omnibus is an anthology made with a light heart. It does not aim to prove any point except that such a volume would be fun to edit and a delight to have around. The *Omnibus* came out of an argument. Perhaps it was less an argument than a game. Three or four critics were matching favorites. Do you remember this? How about that? What else is as good as so and so? Nobody was being solemn and systematic. Everybody was naming what he had particularly liked. It turned out that on most things they agreed. Somebody suggested that they ought to do something about it. They made notes and talked them over with a publisher. *An American Omnibus* is the rest of the story.

Not, of course, that the *Omnibus* is absolutely what had been planned. Copyrights got in the way. If the volume was to be large, and yet not too expensive, it must be printed from plates already cast—one book made up from the parts of many books. The publishers were generous. They put *Ring Around the Rosy* in type and let the *Omnibus* have a Sinclair Lewis first edition. They asked Mark Van Doren to make a special selection, for the *Omnibus* alone, of the quintessence of recent American poetry. They opened the treasures of Garden City and they bargained with other publishers. In the end the *Omnibus* lacked only two titles that its originators had proposed. Few desires come closer to fulfillment.

Anthologists usually apologize, as if they thought they could coax their readers to give up their readers' dearest right: which is to quarrel with anthologists. *An American Omnibus* cheerfully tells its readers they can take it or leave it. If they leave it, they will miss Don Marquis at his best, in *Archy and Mehitabel*. They will miss Stewart Edward White's short novel *The Killer*. They will miss the brilliant play by Maxwell Anderson, *Mary of Scotland*. They will miss the shorter masterpieces of Sinclair Lewis and Ernest Hemingway and Dorothy Parker and George Ade and Ring Lardner and Sherwood Anderson and Mary Austin, and some of the liveliest sketches from *The New Yorker*, and most of the loveliest poems of the age. The *Omnibus* hopes that they will never know what they are missing.

Carl Van Doren.

RING AROUND A ROSY
A Story

BY SINCLAIR LEWIS

Never published before in book form

RING AROUND A ROSY

T. ELIOT HOPKINS was a Nice Young Man at forty-two, and he had done nicely all the nice things—Williams College, a New York brokerage office, his first million, his first Phyfe table, careful polo at Del Monte, the discovery that it was smart to enjoy the opera and the later discovery that it was much smarter to ridicule it. In fact, by the time he had a penthouse on Park Avenue, Eliot understood the theory of relativity as applied to the world of fashion—that a man is distinguished not by what he likes but by what he is witty enough to loathe.

As for Eleanor, his wife, she came from Chicago, so naturally she had a cousin married to a French count and another cousin who would have married an Italian marquis if it had not been discovered that he was already married and not a marquis. Still, he really was Italian.

Their first year in the penthouse was ecstatic. Thirty stories up, atop 9999 Park Avenue, looking to East and North and South, it had a terrace exclamatory with scarlet wicker chairs, Pompeian marble benches, and a genuine rose-garden attended by a real gardener—at three dollars an hour, from the florist's. On the terrace opened the duplex living-room, fifty feet long, its Caen stone walls and twenty-foot windows soaring up to a raftered ceiling of English oak. But to a nosey and domestic mind, to one who had known Eleanor when she lived in a six-room bungalow in Wil-

1

mette, these glories of city-dominating terrace and
castle hall were less impressive than the little perfections of the apartment; the kitchen which was a little
like a chemist's laboratory and more like the cabin of
an electric locomotive; the bathroom of plate glass and
purple tile and the master's bedroom with an open
fireplace.

Through this domain Eleanor bustled for a year,
slipping out to look across East River to the farthest
hills and gas-houses of Long Island, dashing inside to
turn on the automatic pipe organ, plumping down at
her most Art Moderne desk of silver, aluminum, and
black glass to write dinner invitations. And they enter-
tained. Vastly. These gigantic rooms demanded people,
and sometimes there were forty people at the unique
diamond-shaped dinner-table, with five Old Family
Retainers sneaked in from the caterer's. With such a
turn-over of guests, there weren't always enough bank
vice-presidents and English authors and baronets and
other really worth-while people to be found on the
market, and Eleanor had to fall back on guests who
were nothing but old friends, which was pretty hard on
a girl.

So she was not altogether contented, even before
things happened.

They were important things.

Eliot sold short before the stock-market depression.
His first million was joined by two others, and he immediately took up reading, art-criticism, and refined
manners. He also bought new jodhpurs. I am not quite
sure what jodhpurs are, but then, T. Eliot hadn't
known either, six years before. They have to do with
polo, though whether they are something you ride or
wear or hit the ball with, I have not been informed.
But I do know that Eliot's jodhpurs were singularly

well spoken of at Meadowbrook, and whatever else they may have been, they were not cursed by being American. They were as soundly English as cold toast.

Now selling short at a time when every one else is dismally long is likely to have a large effect on Nice People, and Eleanor agreed with Eliot that it was shocking—it was worse than shocking, it was a bore—that they should have to go on slaving their lives away among commercial lowbrows when in England, say, people of Their Class led lives composed entirely of beauty, graciousness, leisure, and servants who didn't jiggle the tea-tray.

The penthouse seemed to her a little gaudy, a little difficult. With the stupidity of servants, it took her hours a day to prepare for even the simplest dinner-party. It was like poor Eliot's having to dash out and be in his office in the dawn, at ten o'clock, and often give up his afternoons of golf because his clerks were so idiotically dumb that he couldn't trust them.

When they had taken the penthouse, a friend of Eleanor had been so conservative as to buy a quiet little house in Turtle Bay and furnish it with English antiques. Mahogany. White fireplaces. Just a *shack*. But now Eleanor found the shack restful. The drawing-room did not seem empty with but two of them for tea, and the little befrilled maid was not too humble, as she would have been in the vastness of the penthouse.

All the way home, Eleanor looked wistfully out of the limousine. She wished that there weren't a law against her walking, this warm June evening. But she wanted to be walking not on an avenue but in a real certificated English lane—rosy cottages—old women curtsying—nightingales rising from the hedges, or whatever nightingales did rise from—witty chatter at the gate with their neighbor, General Wimbledom, former C. in C. in India, not one of these horrid New Yorkers who talked about bond issues——

When Eliot dragged home, hot, his eyes blurred with weariness, he groaned at her, "I'm glad we're not going out tonight! Let's dine on the terrace."

"But we are going out, my pet. I'm restless. I can't stand this private Grand Central. I feel like a red cap. Let's go to that nice little French speakeasy on Forty-ninth and try to make ourselves believe we've had enough sense to go to Europe."

"All right. I wish we had gone. If nothing begins to happen in the market—— Maybe we'll be abroad before the summer's over."

The Chez Edouard has, like all distinguished French restaurants, a Swiss manager, Italian waiters, a Bavarian cook, a Greek coat-checker, scenes from Venice painted on the walls of a decayed drawing-room, and, unlike most of them, it has German wine. Eleanor crooned over the thought of onion soup, chicken cutlet Pojarski, crêpes susette, and Oppenheimer Kreitz Spätlese.

"America—New York—isn't so bad after all, if you belong, if you know where to go," exulted Eleanor.

Then the waiter wouldn't wait.

Eleanor raised a gracious finger, Eleanor raised an irritated hand, Eliot sank so low as to snap his fingers, and the waiter merely leered at them and did not come. He was attending a noisy group of six business men, probably Midwestern, who were beginning a sound meal with six cocktails apiece—tip after each round.

"It's absolutely dreadful, what America does even to good foreign servants!" Eleanor raged. "They become so impertinent and inefficient! It's something in the air of this awful country. They're so selfish and inconsiderate—and yet so nice as they stay abroad. I wish we were there, in Europe, where we could lead a civilized life."

"Yes," said Eliot. "Little inns. Nice."

When they were finally served with chicken cutlets Pojarski and Eleanor had come to believe that she would live through it, she encountered the most terrible affliction of all. One of the six noisy interlopers wambled across and addressed her, "Sister, I just noticed we're taking more of the waiter's time than we ought to. You had to bawl him out before he brought your chicken croquettes. Excuse us! If you and the gentleman would come over and join us in a little libation—— Excuse the liberty, but we've got some pretty decent old-fashioned house-broken rye, and if we could have the pleasure——"

During this shocking affront Eleanor had gaped at Eliot in terror. He rescued her, in a brave and high-toned manner; he said dryly to the intruder, "Very kind of you, but we have quite enough to drink here, thank you, and we must be going immediately."

"Imagine a dreadful thing like that happening in any other country! England, for instance!" Eleanor murmured afterward. "Simply no privacy anywhere in America. Dreadful! Let's get out of this dreadful restaurant."

Nor was she any the more pleased when the checking-girl, whisking her white flannel top-coat across the counter, gurgled, "Here you are, dearie."

"And no respect for their betters! Just Bolsheviks!" pronounced Eleanor.

They had sent away the car. Eleanor—as a girl she had often walked six miles on a picnic—suggested to Eliot, "It would be awfully jolly and adventurous to walk home!" They came on the new Titanic Talkie Theater—Cooled Air—Capacity 4000. Eliot yawned.

"Ever been in one of those super-movie palaces? I never have. Let's see what it's like."

"You know what it will be like. Dreadful. Vulgar. But let's see."

The lobby was a replica, but somewhat reduced, of Seville Cathedral. A bowing doorman, in gold lace, scarlet tunic, and a busby with a purple plume, admitted them through gilded bronze doors to an inner lobby, walled with silk tapestry, floored with the largest Oriental rug in the world, and dotted with solid silver statues of negligent ladies, parakeets in golden cages on pedestals of Chinese lacquer, a fountain whose stream was illuminated with revolving lights lemon-colored and green and crimson, and vast red club chairs beside which, for ash-receivers, were Florentine wine-jars.

"Oh! This hurts!" wailed Eleanor.

A line of ushers, young men in the uniforms of West Point cadets, stood at attention. One of them galloped forward and, bending from the waist, held out a white-gloved hand for their tickets.

"I'm paralyzed! This is like an opium-eater's dream of a Mid-Victorian royal palace. Must we go in?" fretted Eleanor.

"No! Let's go home. Think how nice a cool Tom Collins would be on the terrace," said Eliot and, to the usher, "Thanks, I think we've seen enough."

The stateliness, choiceness and aristocracy of their exit were a little crumpled by the military usher's blatting behind them, "Well can you lay that! The Prince of Wales and Tex Guinan, that's who they are!" And at the door they heard from a comfortable woman enthroned in a tall Spanish chair, addressing her lady friend, "I always did like a good artistic talkie with Doug Fairbanks and some old antique castles like that.

I can't stand this lowdown sex stuff. Gotta have art or nothing."

Eleanor had lived in New York so long that she rarely saw it. She did tonight, with liveliness and hatred.

Broadway turned into a county fair, with orange juice stands, pineapple juice stands, show windows with nuts arranged in circles and diamonds, radio shops blaring, shops jammed with clothing models draped in aching brown suits with green shirts, green ties, green-bordered handkerchiefs. The people on Broadway Eleanor lumped as "impossible": hoarse newsboys, Hungarians and Sicilians and Polish Jews guffawing on corners, tight-mouthed men with gray derbies concealing their eyes standing in snarling conferences, silk-stockinged girls laughing like grackles.

"Dreadful!" she observed.

They looked east to a skyscraper like a gigantic arm threatening the sky with the silver mace that was its tower.

"Our buildings are so big and pretentious! Nothing kindly, nothing civilized about them. So—oh, so new!" complained Eleanor.

"Um—yes," said Eliot.

At home, from their terrace they looked across East River, then South and West to the wriggling electricity of Broadway, where tawdry signs, high on hotels, turned crimson and gold and aching white with hysterical quickness. A searchlight wounded the starless dark. And the noises gnawed at her nerves. Once she had felt that together they made a symphony; now she distinguished and hated them. Tugboats brayed and howled on the river. Trains on the three elevated railways clanked like monstrous shaken chains, and streetcars bumped with infuriating dullness. A million motors snarled, four million motor-tires together joined in a vast hissing, like torn silk, and through all the uproar smashed the gong of an ambulance.

"Let's get out of it! Let's have a house in England!" cried Eleanor. "Peace! Civilized society! Perfect servants! Old tradition! Let's go."

In the offices of Messrs. Trottingham, Strusby, and Beal, Estate Agents, on St. James's Square, London, Eliot and Eleanor, once they had convinced a severe and aged young lady reception clerk that though they were Americans they really did want to lease a house, were shown a portfolio of houses with such ivy-dripping Tudor walls, such rose gardens, such sunny slopes of lawn between oaks ancient as Robin Hood, that they wriggled like children in a candy shop. They had been well-trained by reading fiction and the comic papers; they knew enough not to laugh when they read "16 bd., 2 bthrms., usual offices, choice fernery, stbling., 12, garge., 1 car." So they were taken into favor, and young Mr. Claude Beal himself drove them down to Tiberius Hill, in Sussex.

"The Hill," he said, "belongs to Sir Horace and Lady Mingo. You will remember that Sir Horace was formerly Solicitor-General."

"Oh yes," said Eliot.

"Quite," said Eleanor.

"Sir Horace wishes to rent only because his health is not good. He is no longer a young man. He requires a hotter climate. He is thinking of Italy. Naturally, Lady Mingo and he hate to leave so charming a place, you will understand."

"I see," said Eliot.

"Hush!" said Eleanor.

"But if they find really reliable tenants, they might —you see? But you understand that I'm not trying to do a bit of *selling*, as you Yankees say!"

"I see. Yes," said Eliot.

They passed through the gateway of Tiberius Hall —the stone gateposts were worn from three centuries —and saw the gatekeeper's lodge. On the shoulder of the stone chimney were gargoyles that had looked on passing Queen Elizabeth, and before the low latticed windows, with crocus-yellow curtains, were boxes of red geraniums.

Laburnums edged the quarter-mile of driveway and shut off most of the estate, but they saw a glade with deer feeding in a mistiness of tender sunlight—"Not," mused Eleanor, "like our dreadful glaring, raw sunlight at home." They came suddenly on the Hall. It was of Tudor, pure, the stone mellow. The chimneys were fantastically twisted; the red-tiled roof was soft with mosses; the tall windows of the ground floor gave on a terrace of ancient flagging. But what grasped at her, caressed her, more than the house itself was the lawn at one side where, under the shadow of oaks, half a dozen people sat at tea in basket chairs, attended by a butler whose cheeks were venerable pouches of respectability, and by a maid fresh as a mint drop in her cap and apron.

"We're going to *take* it!" Eleanor whispered.

"We certainly are!"

"Here, we'll really live!"

"Yes! Tea, with servants like that! Polo and golf with gentlemen, not with money-grubbers! Neighbors who've actually read a book! Nell, we've come home!"

"This country," said Sir Horace Mingo, "has gone utterly to the dogs."

"It has indeed," said Lady Mingo. "No competent servants, since the war. Not one. The wages they demand, and their incredible stupidity—impossible to find a cook who can do gooseberry trifle properly— *and* their impertinence! Did I tell you how pertly Bindger answered me when I spoke to her about staying out till ten——"

"You did, beloved. *In extenso*, if you will permit me to say so. I agree with you. My man—and to think of paying him twenty-two bob a week; when I was a youngster the fellow would have been delighted to have ten—he cannot press trousers so that they won't resemble bags—'Higgs,' I often say to him, 'I don't quite understand why it is that when you have given your loving attention to my trousers they always resemble bags'—and as to his awakening me when I tell him to, he never fails to be either five minutes late or, what is essentially more annoying, ten minutes early, and when your confounded Bindger brings my tea in the morning, it is invariably cold, and if I speak to her about it, she merely sniffs and tosses her head, and—but ——"

While Sir Horace is catching his breath, it must be interjected that this conversation of the Mingos, before the James II fireplace at Tiberius Hill, had been particularly enjoyed three months before Eliot and Eleanor Hopkins, on their penthouse terrace, had decided to flee from the land of electricity and clamor.

"*But*," rumbled Sir Horace, in that port-and-Stilton voice which had made him the pursuing fiend to the sinful when he had been Solicitor-General, "the fact that in the entire length and breadth of England today, and I dare say Scotland as well, it is utterly impossible, at any absurd wage, to find a servant who is not lazy, ignorant, dirty, thieving, and many of them dare to be impertinent, even to *me!*—this indisputable decay in English service is no more alarming than the fact that in our own class, good manners, sound learning, and simple decency appear to have vanished. Young men up at Oxford who waste their time on socialism and chemistry—chemistry! for a gentleman!—instead of acquiring a respectable knowledge of the classics! Young women who smoke, curse, go about exhibiting their backs——"

"Horace!"

"Well, they do! I'm scarcely to blame, am I? Have I ever gone about exhibiting *my* back? Have I caused whole restaurants to be shocked by the spectacle of *my* back? And that is not all. Everywhere! The pictures instead of Shakespeare! Motors making our lanes a horror and a slaughter! Shops that have electric lights and enormous windows and everything save honest wares and shop-attendants with respectful manners! Shopkeepers setting themselves up to be better and certainly richer than the best county families! In fact, the whole blasted country becoming Americanized. . . . And cocktails! Cocktails! My word, if anybody had offered my old father a cocktail, I should think he would have knocked him down!

"England has always had a bad climate. But there was a day when the manners of the gentry and the charms of domestic life made up for it. But now I can see no reason why we should remain here. Why can't we go to Italy? That fellow Mussolini, he may not be English, but he has taught the masses discipline. You don't find impertinent servants and obscene gentlewomen there, I'll wager!"

"Yes. Why don't we go, Horace?"

"How can we? With this expensive place on our hands? If I were some petrol-Johnny or a City bloke or some one who had made his money selling spurious remedies, we might be able to afford it. But having been merely a servant of His Majesty all my life, merely devoting such legal knowledge and discernment as I might chance to have to the cause of Justice and——"

"But we might rent the place, Horace. Oh! Think of a jolly little villa at San Remo or on Lake Maggiore, with the lovely sunshine and mountains and those too-sweet Italian servants who retain some sense of the dignity and joy of service——"

"Rent it to who!—when!?—whom? Our Class are all impoverished."

"But there's the Argentines and Americans and Armenians. You know. All those curious races where every one is a millionaire. How they would appreciate a place with lawns! I'm told there isn't a single pretty lawn in America. How could there be? They would be so glad——"

"Though I couldn't imagine any American being trusted with our Lord Penzance sweetbriers!"

"But Horace, a sweet little peasant villa at Baveno; just ten or twelve rooms."

"Well—after all, Victoria, why should people of some breeding, as I flatter myself we do possess, be shut up in this shocking country, when we might be in the sun of Italy—and Dr. Immens-Bourne says it would be so much better for my rheumatism! Shall we speak to an estate agent? If there are any honest and mannerly estate Johnnys left in this atrocious country!"

On the terrace of faded pink and yellow tiles, sufficiently shaded by the little orange trees in pots, Sir Horace and Lady Mingo sat looking across Lake Maggiore to the bulk of Sasso del Ferro, along whose mountain trails perched stone villages. A small steamer swaggered up the lake; after its puffing there was no sound save goat bells and a clattering car.

"Oh, the peace of it! Oh the wise old peace of Italy!" sighed Lady Mingo, and the wrinkles in her vellum-like old cheeks seemed smoother, her pale old eyes seemed less weary.

"Yes!" said Sir Horace. He was not so pontifical as he had been at Tiberius Hill. "Peace. Quite! No jazz! No noisy English servants yelping music-hall songs and banging things about!"

From the kitchen, a floor below the terrace, a sound of the cook banging his copper pots, and a maid yelping a few bars of "Traviata."

"Yes! The sweet Italian servants! So gay and yet so polite! Smiling! And the lovely sun, all day! Why we ever stayed—— Oh, Horace, I do hope I shan't be punished for saying such things—of course England is the greatest country in the world, and when I think of people like my father and the dean, of course no other country could ever produce great gentlemen like them, but at the same time—— I really don't care if we never leave Italy again! And those sweet ruins at Fiesole! And the trains always quite absolutely on time, since Mussolini came! And—— Oh, Horace, it's really quite too simply perfect!"

"Rather! Quite! You know, I'd thought I would worry about Tiberius Hill. But that's a very decent chap, that Hoffman Eliot—Hopkins—Eliot Hopkins—what is the chap's absurd name?—quite gentlemanly—for an American. I was astonished. None of these strange clothes Americans wear. I really quite took him for an English gentleman—until he opened his mouth. Astonishing! He hadn't a red sweater or a great, huge felt hat or a velvet dinner jacket, or any of these odd

things that Americans ordinarily wear. Astonishing!
I feel, really, quite safe to have him there. And now we
must dress, my dear. Professor Pulciano will be here
at half after seven. So decent of him to rent us this—
this paradise!"

He was youngish and rather rich, but Carlo Pulciano had not remained in the Italian army after the war,
though his brother was commanding general of the
Central Department, nor would he listen to his sister-
in-law's insistence that he blossom in the salons of
Rome.

He had previously scandalized them by teaching
economics in the University of Pisa, by sitting over
buckram-bound books full of tedious figures, and when
the Black Shirts had marched on Rome and taken over
the country, when it was not wise to speculate too
much about economics, Pulciano had the more offended
his people by buying this largish villa on the Pallanza
peninsula on Lake Maggiore, and retiring to his books
and bees.

But in that still paradise he became restless and a
little confused. All through the morning he would, in
discussions none the less mad because they were entirely within his head, be completely pro-Fascist, admiring the Fascist discipline, an ideal of planned
industry, the rousing of youngsters from sun-loafing
into drilling.

Then, all afternoon, he would be Communistic or
Social-Democratic.

But whatever he was, here he was forever nothing.
He had no one with whom to talk. It was not safe.
And to Carlo Pulciano talking was life; talking late at
night, feverishly, over cigarettes and Lacrima Christi;
talking on dusty walks; talking through elegant din-

ners so ardently that he did not notice whether he was eating veal stew or zabaione. Forever talking!

He would not have minded turning Fascist complete, provided he might have lived in a place where every one hated Fascismo, so that furiously, all night, he might have defended it. He admitted, with one of the few grins that this earnest young man ever put on, that he didn't so much want any particular social system as the freedom to discuss, in any way, at any time, over any kind of liquor, all social systems.

He longed for Germany, where he had studied economics as a young man. Germany! There was the land where he could talk unendingly! There was the land where, though the Polizei might harry you off the grass, you could say precisely what you thought or, greater luxury yet, say ardently what you didn't think at all, just for the pleasure of it.

Pulciano cursed the fact that he had sunk most of his money in this villa, and could not afford to go live in Germany. He had loved Italy, for it he had been wounded on the Piave; he had loved this villa and the peace of its blue lake-waters. He came to hate them both.

He hated the servants—so ready to promise everything and so unlikely to do anything: so smiling of eye and so angry in their hearts. He hated the climate. "It *would* be in Italy that we have the chilliest and wettest winters in Christendom, yet the mush-headed people insist it's always sunny and will not put in even fireplaces." He hated the food. "I'd give all the confounded pastes and fruits in the world for a decent *Mass* of dark beer and a pig's knuckle, at Munich!" He hated funeral processions, policemen with cock's plumes on their hats, plaster shrines, the silly wicker on wine bottles, wax matches that burned his fingers,

and even—so far was he gone in treason against Italy
—cigars with straws in them.

But he did nothing about it. He was too busy hating
to do much of anything.

He was delighted when the manager of the Grand
Hotel d'Isola Bella came inquiring whether he might
not care to rent his villa to a crazy English nobleman
named Sir Mingo. Yes, for a year.

A week later, with many bundles and straw suitcases,
Carlo Pulciano was on the train for Berlin and free
talk, free thinking—long free thoughts over long
cheap beers.

The doctrine of most American and British carica-
turists, and all French ones, is that every German is
fat, tow-headed, and given to vast beers, while every
German woman is still fatter, and clad invariably in a
chip hat and the chintz covering for a wing-chair.

Baron Helmuth von Mittenbach, Silesian Junker
and passionate mechanical engineer, had ruddy hair
and blue eyes filled with light. He was slender, and
looked rather more English than the Prince of Wales.
The Baroness, Hilda, was slim as an icicle and as
smooth, and she liked dancing in the night clubs off
the Kurfürstendamm, Berlin, till four of the morning.

Neither of them liked beer, nor had ever drunk it
since school days.

During the war, which ended when he was thirty,
Helmuth had tried to join the flying circus of his
friend Von Richtofen. He would have enjoyed swoop-
ing, possibly even being swooped upon. But he was
too good a designer, and headquarters kept him improving the tank, and the one time when he sneaked
off to try out his own tank at the front, they strafed

him so that he stayed back of the line after that, fuming in a room verminous with steel shavings.

He was, therefore, more excited after the war than during it. Now he could take a real part! Now engineers were to be not assistants and yes-men, like quartermasters or photographers or royal princes, but the real lords, shaping a new Germany.

He believed that the struggle to rebuild German glory would be a crusade, holy and united. Now that the republic had come, with so little blood-spilling, the political parties would join; the politicians would give up that ultimate selfishness of insisting on the superiority of their own ideals.

He was certain that the salvation of Germany was in industrial efficiency. They hadn't the man-power and raw stuffs of America or Russia, the army of France, or the ships and empire of Great Britain. They must make things more swiftly, better, and more economically than any other land. They must no longer grudgingly adopt machinery when they had to admit that a machine could do the work of a hundred men, but take machinery as a religion.

Helmuth took it so.

It is definitely not true that Helmuth and the youngish men who worked with him in those driving days thought mostly, or even much at all, about the profits they and their bosses might make out of machinery as the oppressor of ordinary men. Rather, they saw it as the extension of man's force and dignity.

Here you had an ordinary human, with an ordinary clumsy fist. Put a lever or an electric switch into it, and it had the power of a thousand elephants. Man that walked wearily, swam like a puppy, and flew not at all, man that had been weakest and most despicable of all the major mammals, was with motor and submarine and plane, with dynamo and linotype, suddenly to be not mammal at all, but like the angels.

So dreamed Baron Mittenbach, while he grunted and hunched his shoulders over his drawing-board, while in the best parade-ground manner he called a careless foreman an accursed-swine-hound-thunder-weather-once-again-for-the-sake-of-Heaven.

He had gone as chief engineer to the great A. A. G. —the so-called Universal Automobile Trust. His hobbies were light, cheap tractors for small farms, and light, cheap cars.

He planned sedans which would sell, when exchange was normal again, for what in American would be a hundred and fifty dollars. By night, at home, he planned other devices, some idiotic, some blandly practical: eighteen-thousand-ton liners to leave out the swimming-pools and marble pillars streaked like oxtail soup and to cross the Atlantic in three days; floating aviation fields, a string of fifteen of them across the ocean, so that a fallen plane would never be more than an hour from rescue; a parachute to ease down an entire plane should the motor die or a wing drop off.

Crazy as any other poet, and as excited. But happier.

He had reason at first for his excitement and his happiness. Though the Germans gabbled of every known political scheme, from union with Russia to union with England, they jumped into the deification of modern industry as schoolboys into a summer lake. They worked ten hours a day, twelve, fourteen, not wearily but with a zest in believing that their sweat was cementing a greater Germany. They ruthlessly stripped factories and at whatever cost put in rows of chemical retorts a quarter-mile long, conveyor belts,

automatic oil furnaces, high-speed steel. In mining with
mechanical strippers, ventilation, safety devices, they
so bested the old-fashioned mines of England that they
could laugh at navies—at least they did laugh, wisely
or ill.

Helmuth was fortunate in being able to have a
decent and restful house not too far from his factory,
for though he drove at a speed which caused the police
to look pained, he could not (he told himself) take all
morning getting to work—there were too many exciting things to do at the factory—workmen to quarrel
with or raise in pay, new experiments with his automobile with the engine at the rear, so that the driver
had no long hood to trick his vision. The factory was
in the Spandau district of Berlin, and reasonably near,
among the placid villas and linden rows of Grunewald,
Hilda and Helmuth took a brick and stucco house with
a lively mosaic eagle shining over the tile balcony.

The attic floor had been a private gaming room.
Snorting at these signs of idleness and pride, Helmuth
stripped out the card tables, roulette wheel, billiard
table, dumped them in the basement, and set up a
lathe, a work-bench, a drawing-board, an electric furnace. Here all evening, while Hilda restlessly studied
Russian or yawned over cross-word puzzles, this grandson of a Field Marshal, in a workman's jumper and
atrocious felt slippers, experimented with aluminum
alloys, or drew plans for a monorail which should do
the six hundred and sixty from Berlin to Paris in six
hours, with carriages like drawing-rooms, glass-walled,
twenty feet wide.

It was a good time—for a year. The destruction of
the currency did not worry Helmuth; he was convinced that man should be saved by gasoline alone. But
after two years or three, he roused from his dream to

see that the German recovery was not altogether a
pure, naïve crusade; that the politicians would not
forget their petty little differences.

There were not two or three parties, as in Britain
and America, but eight, ten, a dozen; and these parties
clamorously advocated almost everything save total
immersion. They advocated the return of the Kaiser,
or immediate communism; they advocated a cautious
state socialism, or wider power for the industrialists;
they advocated combining with Austria, or the independence of Bavaria.

Outside of political parties, there were some thousands of noisy and highly admired prophets who had
no interest in Helmuth's turret lathes and r. p. m.'s,
but who shouted in little halls and little blurry magazines that the world was to be saved by vegetarianism
or going naked or abolishing armies or integrating
spoken plays with the movie film or growing carrots
instead of wheat or colonizing Brazil or attending
spiritualist séances or mountain climbing or speaking
Esperanto.

In his workshop of clean, driving, unsentimental
steel, Helmuth despised equally all cult-mongers and
all politicians, however famous. They talked; they
chewed over old straws; they pushed themselves into
personal notoriety. He didn't, just now, care a hang
whether he lived under a democracy or a monarchy or
a soviet, so long as they would let him make more
tractors.

The more eloquent the politicians were, in their
bright oratory in the Reichstag or the jolly conferences
at Lausanne and Geneva, the more he hated them. His
Gods were Duisberg and Citroën and Ford and Edison
and the Wright Brothers, and since most of the

pantheon were Americans, he came to worship that country as his Olympus.

The German politicians talked—*all* the Germans talked, he snarled. They were so proud of having mental freedom. Yes! snorted Helmuth, and the Irish were so proud of having fairies! Freedom for *what?*— for escape from discipline into loquacious idleness, or for the zest of hard work? He hated peculiarly (doubtless unjustly) the intellectuals whom he had known in the university, who gabbled that there was something inescapably evil about machines; that because the transition from handcrafts to machinery had certainly produced unemployment, this unemployment must always continue; who whimpered that we must all go back to the country and live perfectly simple old-fashioned lives—with, however, telephones and open plumbing and typewriters and automobiles and electric lights and quick mail newspapers.

"Yah! My picture of those gentry," Helmuth grumbled to Hilda, "is that they sit in machine-made modernistic metal chairs, telephoning to one another that they want us to stop manufacturing telephones and just beautifully write them! Good night. Tomorrow I must be up early and write a carburetor and paint a grease-gun."

Thus irritated, he looked daily more toward America.

There, he believed, every one was united in the one common purpose of solving economic injustices not by turning every capitalist into a starved proletarian but by making all competent proletarians into capitalists. The more he read American magazines and yearned for American vitality and ingenuity, the more he grumbled about Germany. And his Hilda, who was most of the time happily ignorant of everything he was saying, here joined him.

In America, she had heard, there was no need of servants, because everything was done, and perfectly, by machinery. And she was so sick, she confided, of German servants, since the war. What had got into them? Regular Communists! They no longer had respect for the better classes, and the Government was supporting them in their demands. What with compulsory insurance, and the law that you couldn't, without notice, kick out even the most impertinent maid, there was no running a house. She longed for electric dish-washers and washing machines, but their landlord was old-fashioned; he would not put them in; and for all their position, the inflation had taken so much of their money that the Mittenbachs hadn't enough cash to electrify the kitchen.

America!

Just when Helmuth and Hilda were keenest about it, he met McPherson Jones of the Engel & Jones High Speed Tractor Company of Long Island City, who was scouting about Europe looking for new efficiencies. Helmuth spoke a photographic English. Jones and he went to Essen, to the Ruhr, and argued about beer and about torque in aviation. Jones proffered him a place high on the engineering staff of Engel & Jones, with a breath-taking salary; and a month later Helmuth and Hilda were on the high seas—to the miserable Hilda it was evident why they were called high.

Helmuth had sub-let his house to an Italian, who was going to study something or other at the university. Helmuth did not leave Berlin till a fortnight after he had turned the house over to Pulciano. He called to say good-by and Pulciano proudly showed him the changes he had made. On the top floor Helmuth did a little youthful suffering. Pulciano had ripped out the lathe, the work-bench, the drawing-board, and fitted up the room in imitation of an old Bavarian inn, with heavy wooden tables, stone beer mugs, a barrel of beer, and painted mottoes announcing that men who gave earnest attention to anything save drinking, kissing, singing, and snoring were invariably jackasses.

"I tell you," cried Pulciano, "here I shall have again the good free talk of my German student days! I am in your Germany so happy! You realize that the purpose of life is not just doing, but thinking, and setting thoughts in jeweled words—and again I get decent red cabbage!"

"*Ja?*" said Helmuth. It can sound extraordinarily like "Yeah?"

He groaned to himself, "Just the old, thick-necked, beer-steaming Germany we have been trying to kill! I want a race stark and lean and clear and cold-bathed and unafraid of the song of fly-wheels!"

With Hilda seasick Helmuth found solace in the smoking-room of the steamer. By the end of three days he knew a dozen Americans—a banker, the superintendent of a steel plant, two automobile foreign salesmen, a doctor who had been studying gross pathology in Vienna.

He expected them to resent his coming to America in rivalry with their earnings; he expected them to smile at his English. But they welcomed him to the tournament. "Come on! If you can get anything away from us in America, it just makes the game better," they said; and "Your English? Listen, Baron, the only trouble with you is, you went to a school where they let the teams weaken themselves by looking at books between the halves. By the way, will you happen to be in Detroit, time of the Michigan-Notre Dame game? Wish you'd come stay with us and I'll drive you down. Like to have you meet the wife and show her up—she thinks she can parley Deutsch."

"They are," Helmuth glowed to Hilda, "the kindest and politest people I have ever known. But just the same, *ich sage*——*bestimmt*, that Mr. Tolson is all wrong about the front wheel drive . . . I wonder about the market for speed boats in Norway?"

He had accepted invitations to Bar Harbor, Seattle, Moose Jaw, Gramercy Square, Franconia Notch, and Social Center, Georgia, before he saw the skyscrapers from New York Harbor.

"They are my friends! I have never had so many friends, not in my life!" he rejoiced, and with a feeling that they were his own he pointed out the towers to a slightly shaky Hilda beside him.

"They are very pretty. They are not all worn, like cathedral spires," he said. "I wonder what the wind-pressure per square meter is at forty stories with a sixty kilometer wind? I wonder if electric welding costs more than riveting? I wonder whether the marble here comes from Italy or Vermont? Yes, it is exciting; I am very thrilled. I wonder what is the tensile strength of the steel in these buildings?"

But his friend, Dr. Moore, the Omaha surgeon, could not answer any of these obvious questions, though he was a real American.

A week after their arrival, Baron and Baroness Mittenbach leased a penthouse atop the apartment house at 9999 Park Avenue. It belonged to some people named Hopkins, now living in the South of France.

They took possession on an autumn afternoon. Hilda raced through the great living-room ecstatically. "I say to you Helmuth, so a beautiful room have I never

seen! Stone walls! and the rafters! Windows like a
cathedral! And the organ, quite gold! It is no longer
than the Great Hall in my father's Schloss, but so
much more wonderful. Always I hated those tattered
tapestries and the moldy stag-horns! But this room is
indeed something noble!"

Squealing, with Helmuth beside her and not much
less childish, she explored the wonders of the kitchen
and butler's pantry: electric dish-washer and coffee
urn and toaster and vacuum cleaner and clock and
egg-cooker. She couldn't quite make out the electric
waffle-iron; she wasn't sure whether it was for cooking
or pleating. But on the automatic refrigerator they
both fell with shouts. This was a possession they had
envied their richer friends in Berlin. They cautiously
pulled out an ice tray and gazed with fatuous admiration on the beautiful cubes of ice. "Much better
than diamonds," said Helmuth.

Refrigerator, gas stove, small electric range,
luxurious enamel sink, and kitchen cabinet were all
finished in white and canary yellow; the kitchen was
gayer than any boudoir.

"Already I am a—how is it called?—hunnerd pro-
cent. American," observed Helmuth in what he believed to be English. "The old system, it was to make
beautiful the salon and the chapel, and make hateful
the kitchen, the heart of the house. Yes, I am a modern!
We do something, we engineers. We do not believe that
the more a room is used, the less *gemütlich* it should be.
Modern, yes, and very old. We go back to mediæval
days, when men were not ashamed to eat and love, and
when kitchens were more important than reception
rooms and when——"

"Here," said Hilda, "I would be happy if we had
no servants at all, and I did all the work. I shall cook

the dinner. . . . tomorrow. Tonight let us find that lovely spikizzy—is right?—of which the doctor has spoken on the steamer."

When on the wine list of the Chez Edouard they found an Oppenheimer Kreus Spätlese, they asked each other why any one should go to Europe.

Their only trouble was that the waiter was a bit slow. But they understood, for he was much engaged with a jolly group of six men at the next table. One of the six noticed the plight of the Mittenbachs and, coming to their table, said, "Sorry we're grabbing off so much of the waiter's time. Afraid we're holding up your dinner. So meanwhile—if you'll excuse the liberty —won't you folks come have a drink with us?"

"That would be very nice," said Helmuth.

He was, after all a shy young man, and he was grateful for the boisterous way in which these strangers took him in. They were all, it seemed, in motor manufacturing. When they learned that he had just come from Germany to join them, instantly a card was out of every pocket, an address was scribbled, and each had insisted that when he went to South Bend or Toledo or Detroit, he must join them—"and I hope the Missus will be along with you."

In a glow that burned out of him all the loneliness he had felt that afternoon in the cold shadow of the monstrous skyscrapers, Helmuth returned with Hilda to their table and dinner.

"So kind to a foreigner, a poor unknown engineer," said Helmuth. "No wonder no American ever wants to go abroad for more than a visit of a month!"

From the terrace before their penthouse they stared across East River, then South and West to the wriggling electricity of Broadway. They were thirty stories up; they seemed to be looking on the whole world, but a world transformed into exultant light.

"It is as though we were in a castle on a huge sheer cliff, a castle on the Matterhorn himself, and yet in the midst of Berlin and London and Paris joined into one," said Helmuth. "This is perhaps—not true, Hilda?—the greatest spectacle of the world! Why speak they of the Acropolis, the Coliseum, the Rhineland, when they have this magic?"

Tugboats shouted cheerily on the East River; liners roared gallantly from North River; the elevated trains, streaks of golden light, chanted on their three tracks; and the million motor horns spoke of the beautiful and exciting places to which the cars were going.

"And it's ours now! We've found our home! We shall know all this city, all those people in the lovely motors down there! I think we stay here the rest of our lives!" said Helmuth.

Hilda pondered, "Yes, except—except that neither Germany nor America has any *mystery*. I want us some day to go to China, Japan. There it gives mystery. And I hear the servants are divine, and so cheap. Don't you think we might go live in China—soon?"

THE KILLERS
A Story

BY ERNEST HEMINGWAY

THE door of Henry's lunch room opened and two men came in. They sat down at the counter.

"What's yours?" George asked them.

"I don't know," one of the men said. "What do you want to eat, Al?"

"I don't know," said Al. "I don't know what I want to eat."

Outside it was getting dark. The street-light came on outside the window. The two men at the counter read the menu. From the other end of the counter Nick Adams watched them. He had been talking to George when they came in.

"I'll have a roast pork tenderloin with apple sauce and mashed potato," the first man said.

"It isn't ready yet."

"What the hell do you put it on the card for?"

"That's the dinner," George explained. "You can get that at six o'clock."

George looked at the clock on the wall behind the counter.

"It's five o'clock."

"The clock says twenty minutes past five," the second man said.

"It's twenty minutes fast."

"Oh, to hell with the clock," the first man said. "What have you got to eat?"

"I can give you any kind of sandwiches," George said. "You can have ham and eggs, bacon and eggs, liver and bacon, or a steak."

"Give me chicken croquettes with green peas and cream sauce and mashed potatoes."

"That's the dinner."

453

"Everything we want's the dinner, eh? That's the way you work it."

"I can give you ham and eggs, bacon and eggs, liver——"

"I'll take ham and eggs," the man called Al said. He wore a derby hat and a black overcoat buttoned across the chest. His face was small and white and he had tight lips. He wore a silk muffler and gloves.

"Give me bacon and eggs," said the other man. He was about the same size as Al. Their faces were different, but they were dressed like twins. Both wore overcoats too tight for them. They sat leaning forward, their elbows on the counter.

"Got anything to drink?" Al asked.

"Silver beer, bevo, ginger ale," George said.

"I mean you got anything to drink?"

"Just those I said."

"This is a hot town," said the other. "What do they call it?"

"Summit."

"Ever hear of it?" Al asked his friend.

"No," said the friend.

"What do you do here nights?" Al asked.

"They eat the dinner," his friend said. "They all come here and eat the big dinner."

"That's right," George said.

"So you think that's right?" Al asked George.

"Sure."

"You're a pretty bright boy, aren't you?"

"Sure," said George.

"Well, you're not," said the other little man. "Is he, Al?"

"He's dumb," said Al. He turned to Nick. "What's your name?"

"Adams."

"Another bright boy," Al said. "Ain't he a bright boy, Max?"

"The town's full of bright boys," Max said.

George put the two platters, one of ham and eggs, the other of bacon and eggs, on the counter. He set down two side dishes of fried potatoes and closed the wicket into the kitchen.

"Which is yours?" he asked Al.

"Don't you remember?"

"Ham and eggs."

"Just a bright boy," Max said. He leaned forward and took the ham and eggs. Both men ate with their gloves on. George watched them eat.

"What are *you* looking at?" Max looked at George.

"Nothing."

"The hell you were. You were looking at me."

"Maybe the boy meant it for a joke, Max," Al said.

George laughed.

"*You* don't have to laugh," Max said to him. "*You* don't have to laugh at all, see?"

"All right," said George.

"So he thinks it's all right." Max turned to Al. "He thinks it's all right. That's a good one."

"Oh, he's a thinker," Al said. They went on eating.

"What's the bright boy's name down the counter?" Al asked Max.

"Hey, bright boy," Max said to Nick. "You go around on the other side of the counter with your boy friend."

"What's the idea?" Nick asked.

"There isn't any idea."

"You better go around, bright boy," Al said. Nick went around behind the counter.

"What's the idea?" George asked.

"None of your damn business," Al said. "Who's out in the kitchen?"

"The nigger."

"What do you mean the nigger?"

"The nigger that cooks."

"Tell him to come in."

"What's the idea?"

"Tell him to come in."

"Where do you think you are?"

"We know damn well where we are," the man called Max said. "Do we look silly?"

"You talk silly," Al said to him. "What the hell do you argue with this kid for? Listen," he said to George, "tell the nigger to come out here."

"What are you going to do to him?"

"Nothing. Use your head, bright boy. What would we do to a nigger?"

George opened the slit that opened back into the kitchen. "Sam," he called. "Come in here a minute."

The door to the kitchen opened and the nigger came in. "What was it?" he asked. The two men at the counter took a look at him.

"All right, nigger. You stand right there," Al said.

Sam, the nigger, standing in his apron, looked at the two men sitting at the counter. "Yes, sir," he said. Al got down from his stool.

"I'm going back to the kitchen with the nigger and bright boy," he said. "Go on back to the kitchen, nigger. You go with him, bright boy." The little man walked after Nick and Sam, the cook, back into the kitchen. The door shut after them. The man called Max sat at the counter opposite George. He didn't look at George but looked in the mirror that ran along back of the counter. Henry's had been made over from a saloon into a lunch-counter.

"Well, bright boy," Max said, looking into the mirror, "why don't you say something?"

"What's it all about?"

"Hey, Al," Max called, "bright boy wants to know what it's all about."

"Why don't you tell him?" Al's voice came from the kitchen.

"What do you think it's all about?"

"I don't know."

"What do you think?"

Max looked into the mirror all the time he was talking.

"I wouldn't say."

"Hey, Al, bright boy says he wouldn't say what he thinks it's all about."

"I can hear you, all right," Al said from the kitchen. He had propped open the slit that dishes passed through into the kitchen with a catsup bottle. "Listen, bright boy," he said from the kitchen to George. "Stand a little further along the bar. You move a little to the left, Max." He was like a photographer arranging for a group picture.

"Talk to me, bright boy," Max said. "What do you think's going to happen?"

George did not say anything.

"I'll tell you," Max said. "We're going to kill a Swede. Do you know a big Swede named Ole Andreson?"

"Yes."

"He comes here to eat every night, don't he?"

"Sometimes he comes here."

"He comes here at six o'clock, don't he?"

"If he comes."

"We know all that, bright boy," Max said. "Talk about something else. Ever go to the movies?"

"Once in a while."

"You ought to go to the movies more. The movies are fine for a bright boy like you."

"What are you going to kill Ole Andreson for? What did he ever do to you?"

"He never had a chance to do anything to us. He never even seen us."

"And he's only going to see us once," Al said from the kitchen.

"What are you going to kill him for, then?" George asked.

"We're killing him for a friend. Just to oblige a friend, bright boy."

"Shut up," said Al from the kitchen. "You talk too goddam much."

"Well, I got to keep bright boy amused. Don't I, bright boy?"

"You talk too damn much," Al said. "The nigger and my bright boy are amused by themselves. I got them tied up like a couple of girl friends in the convent."

"I suppose you were in a convent."

"You never know."

"You were in a kosher convent. That's where you were."

George looked up at the clock.

"If anybody comes in you tell them the cook is off, and if they keep after it, you tell them you'll go back and cook yourself. Do you get that, bright boy?"

"All right," George said. "What you going to do with us afterward?"

"That'll depend," Max said. "That's one of those things you never know at the time."

George looked up at the clock. It was a quarter past six.

The door from the street opened. A street-car motorman came in.

"Hello, George," he said. "Can I get supper?"

"Sam's gone out," George said. "He'll be back in about half an hour."

"I'd better go up the street," the motorman said. George looked at the clock. It was twenty minutes past six.

"That was nice, bright boy," Max said. "You're a regular little gentleman."

"He knew I'd blow his head off," Al said from the kitchen.

"No," said Max. "It ain't that. Bright boy is nice. He's a nice boy. I like him."

At six-fifty-five George said: "He's not coming."

Two other people had been in the lunch room. Once George had gone out to the kitchen and made a ham-and-egg sandwich "to go" that a man wanted to take with him. Inside the kitchen he saw Al, his derby hat tipped back, sitting on a stool beside the wicket with the muzzle of a sawed-off shotgun resting on the ledge. Nick and the cook were back to back in the corner, a towel tied in each of their mouths. George had cooked the sandwich, wrapped it up in oiled paper, put it in a bag, brought it in, and the man had paid for it and gone out.

"Bright boy can do everything," Max said. "He can cook and everything. You'd make some girl a nice wife, bright boy."

"Yes?" George said. "Your friend, Ole Andreson, isn't going to come."

"We'll give him ten minutes," Max said.

Max watched the mirror and the clock. The hands of the clock marked seven o'clock, and then five minutes past seven.

"Come on, Al," said Max. "We better go. He's not coming."

"Better give him five minutes," Al said from the kitchen.

In the five minutes a man came in, and George explained that the cook was sick.

"Why the hell don't you get another cook?" the man asked. "Aren't you running a lunch counter?" He went out.

"Come on, Al," Max said.

"What about the two bright boys and the nigger?"

"They're all right."

"You think so?"

"Sure. We're through with it."

"I don't like it," said Al. "It's sloppy. You talk too much."

"Oh, what the hell," said Max. "We got to keep amused, haven't we?"

"You talk too much, all the same," Al said. He came out from the kitchen. The cut-off barrels of the shotgun made a slight bulge under the waist of his too tight-fitting overcoat. He straightened his coat with his gloved hands.

"So long, bright boy," he said to George. "You got a lot of luck."

"That's the truth," Max said. "You ought to play the races, bright boy."

The two of them went out the door. George watched them through the window pass under the arc light and cross the street. In their tight overcoats and derby hats they looked like a vaudeville team. George went back through the swinging door into the kitchen and untied Nick and the cook.

"I don't want any more of that," said Sam, the cook. "I don't want any more of that."

Nick stood up. He had never had a towel in his mouth before.

"Say," he said. "What the hell?" He was trying to swagger it off.

"They were going to kill Ole Andreson," George said. "They were going to shoot him when he came in to eat."

"Ole Andreson?"

"Sure."

The cook felt the corners of his mouth with his thumbs.

"They all gone?" he asked.

"Yeah," said George. "They're gone now."

"I don't like it," said the cook. "I don't like any of it at all."

"Listen," George said to Nick. "You better go see Ole Andreson."

"All right."

"You better not have anything to do with it at all," Sam, the cook, said. "You better stay way out of it."

"Don't go if you don't want to," George said.

"Mixing up in this ain't going to get you anywhere," the cook said. "You stay out of it."

"I'll go see him," Nick said to George. "Where does he live?"

The cook turned away.

"Little boys always know what they want to do," he said.

"He lives up at Hirsch's rooming house," George said to Nick.

"I'll go up there."

Outside the arc light shone through the bare branches of a tree. Nick walked up the street beside the car tracks and turned at the next arc light down a side street. Three houses up the street was Hirsch's rooming house. Nick walked up the two steps and pushed the bell. A woman came to the door.

"Is Ole Andreson here?"

"Do you want to see him?"

"Yes, if he's in."

Nick followed the woman up a flight of stairs and back to the end of a corridor. She knocked on the door.

"Who is it?"

"It's somebody to see you, Mr. Andreson," the woman said.

"It's Nick Adams."

"Come in."

Nick opened the door and went into the room. Ole Andreson was lying on the bed with all his clothes on. He had been a heavy-weight prizefighter and he was too long for the bed. He lay with his head on two pillows. He did not look at Nick.

"What was it?" he asked.

"I was up at Henry's," Nick said, "and two fellows came in and tied up me and the cook, and they said they were going to kill you."

It sounded silly when he said it. Ole Andreson said nothing.

"They put us out in the kitchen," Nick went on. "They were going to shoot you when you came in to supper."

Ole Andreson looked at the wall and did not say anything.

"George thought I better come and tell you about it."

"There isn't anything I can do about it," Ole Andreson said.

"I'll tell you what they were like."

"I don't want to know what they were like," Old Andreson said. He looked at the wall. "Thanks for coming to tell me about it."

"That's all right."

Nick looked at the big man lying on the bed.

"Don't you want me to go and see the police?"

"No," Ole Andreson said. "That wouldn't do any good."

"Isn't there something I could do?"

"No. There ain't anything to do."

"Maybe it was just a bluff."

"No. It ain't just a bluff."

Ole Andreson rolled over toward the wall.

"The only thing is," he said, talking toward the wall, "I just can't make up my mind to go out. I been in here all day."

"Couldn't you get out of town?"

"No," Ole Andreson said. "I'm through with all that running around."

He looked at the wall.

"There ain't anything to do now."

"Couldn't you fix it up some way?"

"No. I got in wrong." He talked in the same flat voice. "There ain't anything to do. After a while I'll make up my mind to go out."

"I better go back and see George," Nick said.

"So long," said Ole Andreson. He did not look toward Nick. "Thanks for coming around."

Nick went out. As he shut the door he saw Ole Andreson, with all his clothes on, lying on the bed looking at the wall.

"He's been in his room all day," the landlady said downstairs. "I guess he don't feel well. I said to him: 'Mr. Andreson, you ought to go out and take a walk on a nice fall day like this,' but he didn't feel like it."

"He doesn't want to go out."

"I'm sorry he don't feel well," the woman said. "He's an awfully nice man. He was in the ring, you know."

"I know it."

"You'd never know it except from the way his face is," the woman said. They stood talking just inside the street door. "He's just as gentle."

"Well, good-night, Mrs. Hirsch," Nick said.

"I'm not Mrs. Hirsch," the woman said. "She owns the place. "I just look after it for her. I'm Mrs. Bell."

"Well, good-night, Mrs. Bell," Nick said.

"Good-night," the woman said.

Nick walked up the dark street to the corner under the arc light, and then along the car tracks to Henry's eating house. George was inside, back of the counter.

"Did you see Ole?"

"Yes," said Nick. "He's in his room and he won't go out."

The cook opened the door from the kitchen when he heard Nick's voice.

"I don't even listen to it," he said, and shut the door.

"Did you tell him about it?" George asked.

"Sure. I told him, but he knows what it's all about."

"What's he going to do?"

"Nothing."

"They'll kill him."

"I guess they will."

"He must have got mixed up in something in Chicago."

"I guess so," said Nick.

"It's a hell of a thing.'"

"It's an awful thing," Nick said.

They did not say anything. George reached down for a towel and wiped the counter.

"I wonder what he did?" Nick said.

"Double-crossed somebody. That's what they kill them for."

"I'm going to get out of this town," Nick said.

"Yes," said George. "That's a good thing to do."

"I can't stand to think about him waiting in the room and knowing he's going to get it. It's too damned awful."

"Well," said George, "you better not think about it."

ARCHY AND MEHITABEL

BY DON MARQUIS

archy and mehitabel

i

the coming of archy

The circumstances of Archy's first appearance are narrated in the following extract from the Sun Dial column of the New York *Sun*.

Dobbs Ferry possesses a rat which slips out of his lair at night and runs a typewriting machine in a garage. Unfortunately, he has always been interrupted by the watchman before he could produce a complete story.

It was at first thought that the power which made the typewriter run was a ghost, instead of a rat. It seems likely to us that it was both a ghost and a rat. Mme. Blavatsky's ego went into a white horse after she passed over, and someone's personality has undoubtedly gone into this rat. It is an era of belief in communications from the spirit land.

And since this matter had been reported in the public prints and seriously received we are no longer afraid of being ridiculed, and we do not mind making a statement of something that happened to our own typewriter only a couple of weeks ago.

We came into our room earlier than usual in the morning, and discovered a gigantic cockroach jumping about upon the keys.

He did not see us, and we watched him. He would climb painfully upon the framework of the machine and cast himself with all his force upon a key, head downward, and his weight and the impact of the blow were just sufficient to operate the machine, one slow letter after another. He could not work the capital letters, and he had a great deal of difficulty operating the mechanism that shifts the paper so that a fresh line may be started. We never saw a cockroach work so hard or perspire so freely in all our lives before. After about an hour of this frightfully difficult literary labor he fell to the floor exhausted, and we saw him creep feebly into a nest of the poems which are always there in profusion.

Congratulating ourself that we had left a sheet of paper in the machine the night before so that all this work had not been in vain, we made an examination, and this is what we found:

expression is the need of my soul
i was once a vers libre bard
but i died and my soul went into the body of a cock-
    roach
it has given me a new outlook upon life

i see things from the under side now
thank you for the apple peelings in the wastepaper
  basket
but your paste is getting so stale i cant eat it
there is a cat here called mehitabel i wish you would
  have
removed she nearly ate me the other night why dont
  she
catch rats that is what she is supposed to be for
there is a rat here she should get without delay

most of these rats here are just rats
but this rat is like me he has a human soul in him
he used to be a poet himself
night after night i have written poetry for you
on your typewriter
and this big brute of a rat who used to be a poet
comes out of his hole when it is done
and reads it and sniffs at it
he is jealous of my poetry
he used to make fun of it when we were both human
he was a punk poet himself
and after he has read it he sneers
and then he eats it

i wish you would have mehitabel kill that rat
or get a cat that is onto her job
and i will write you a series of poems showing how
  things look

to a cockroach
that rats name is freddy
the next time freddy dies i hope he wont be a rat
but something smaller i hope i will be a rat
in the next transmigration and freddy a cockroach
i will teach him to sneer at my poetry then

dont you ever eat any sandwiches in your office
i havent had a crumb of bread for i dont know how
    long
or a piece of ham or anything but apple parings
and paste leave a piece of paper in your machine
every night you can call me archy

ii

mehitabel was once cleopatra

boss i am disappointed in
some of your readers they
are always asking how does
archy work the shift so as to get a
new line or how does archy do
this or do that they
are always interested in technical
details when the main question is
whether the stuff is
literature or not
i wish you would leave
that book of george moores on
the floor

mehitabel the cat and i want to
read it i have discovered that
mehitabel s soul formerly inhabited a
human also at least that
is what mehitabel is claiming these
days it may be she got jealous of
my prestige anyhow she and
i have been talking it over in a

friendly way who were you
mehitabel i asked her i was
cleopatra once she said well i said i
suppose you lived in a palace you bet
she said and what lovely fish dinners
we used to have and licked her chops

mehitabel would sell her soul for
a plate of fish any day i told her i thought
you were going to say you were
the favorite wife of the emperor
valerian he was some cat nip eh
mehitabel but she did not get me
                                        archy

I WAS CLEOPATRA ONCE
SHE SAID.

iii
the song of mehitabel

this is the song of mehitabel
of mehitabel the alley cat
as i wrote you before boss
mehitabel is a believer
in the pythagorean
theory of the transmigration
of the soul and she claims
that formerly her spirit
was incarnated in the body
of cleopatra
that was a long time ago
and one must not be
surprised if mehitabel
has forgotten some of her
more regal manners

i have had my ups and downs
but wotthehell wotthehell
yesterday sceptres and crowns
fried oysters and velvet gowns
and today i herd with bums
but wotthehell wotthehell

i wake the world from sleep
as i caper and sing and leap
when i sing my wild free tune
wotthehell wotthehell
under the blear eyed moon
i am pelted with cast off shoon
but wotthehell wotthehell

do you think that i would change
my present freedom to range
for a castle or moated grange
wotthehell wotthehell
cage me and i d go frantic
my life is so romantic
capricious and corybantic
and i m toujours gai toujours gai

i know that i am bound
for a journey down the sound
in the midst of a refuse mound
but wotthehell wotthehell
oh i should worry and fret
death and i will coquette
there s a dance in the old dame yet
toujours gai toujours gai

i once was an innocent kit
wotthehell wotthehell

I FOLLOWED ADOWN THE ST. THE PAD
OF HIS RHYTHMICAL FT.

with a ribbon my neck to fit
and bells tied onto it
o wotthehell wotthehell
but a maltese cat came by
with a come hither look in his eye
and a song that soared to the sky
and wotthehell wotthehell
and i followed adown the street
the pad of his rhythmical feet
o permit me again to repeat
wotthehell wotthehell

my youth i shall never forget
but there s nothing i really regret
wotthehell wotthehell
there s a dance in the old dame yet
toujours gai toujours gai

the things that i had not ought to
i do because i ve gotto
wotthehell wotthehell
and i end with my favorite motto
toujours gai toujours gai

boss sometimes i think
that our friend mehitabel
is a trifle too gay

pity the poor spiders

i have just been reading
an advertisement of a certain
roach exterminator
the human race little knows
all the sadness it
causes in the insect world
i remember some weeks ago
meeting a middle aged spider
she was weeping
what is the trouble i asked
her it is these cursed
fly swatters she replied
they kill off all the flies
and my family and i are starving
to death it struck me as
so pathetic that i made
a little song about it
as follows to wit

twas an elderly mother spider
grown gaunt and fierce and gray
with her little ones crouched beside her
who wept as she sang this lay

LURED OFF BY A CENTIPEDE

curses on these here swatters
what kills off all the flies
for me and my little daughters
unless we eats we dies

swattin and swattin and swattin
tis little else you hear
and we ll soon be dead and forgotten
with the cost of living so dear

my husband he up and left me
lured off by a centipede
and he says as he bereft me
tis wrong but i ll get a feed

and me a working and working
scouring the streets for food
faithful and never shirking
doing the best i could

curses on these here swatters
what kills off all the flies
me and my poor little daughters
unless we eats we dies

only a withered spider
feeble and worn and old
and this is what
you do when you swat
you swatters cruel and cold

i will admit that some
of the insects do not lead
noble lives but is every
man s hand to be against them
yours for less justice
and more charity

archy

mehitabels extensive past

mehitabel the cat claims that
she has a human soul
also and has transmigrated
from body to body and it
may be so boss you
remember i told you she accused
herself of being cleopatra once i
asked her about antony

anthony who she asked me are
you thinking of that
song about rowley and gammon and
spinach heigho for anthony rowley

no i said mark antony the
great roman the friend of
caesar surely cleopatra you
remember j caesar

listen archy she said i
have been so many different
people in my time and met

so many prominent gentlemen i
wont lie to you or stall i
do get my dates mixed sometimes
think of how much i have had a
chance to forget and i have
always made a point of not
carrying grudges over
from one life to the next archy

i have been
used something fierce in my time but
i am no bum sport archy
i am a free spirit archy i
look on myself as being
quite a romantic character oh the
queens i have been and the
swell feeds i have ate
a cockroach which you are
and a poet which you used to be
archy couldn t understand
my feelings at having come
down to this i have
had bids to elegant feeds where poets
and cockroaches would
neither one be mentioned without a
laugh archy i have had
adventures but i
have never been an adventuress

one life up and the next life
down archy but always a lady
through it all and a
good mixer too always the
life of the party archy but never
anything vulgar always free footed
archy never tied down to
a job or housework yes looking
back on it all i can say is
i had some romantic
lives and some elegant times i
have seen better days archy but
whats the use of kicking kid its
all in the game like a gentleman
friend of mine used to say
toujours gai kid toujours gai he
was an elegant cat he used
to be a poet himself and he made up
some elegant poetry about me and him

lets hear it i said and
mehitabel recited

persian pussy from over the sea
demure and lazy and smug and fat
none of your ribbons and bells for me
ours is the zest of the alley cat

over the roofs from flat to flat
we prance with capers corybantic
what though a boot should break a slat
mehitabel us for the life romantic

we would rather be rowdy and gaunt and free
and dine on a diet of roach and rat

roach i said what do you
mean roach interrupting mehitabel
yes roach she said thats the
way my boy friend made it up
i climbed in amongst the typewriter
keys for she had an excited
look in her eyes go on mehitabel i
said feeling safer and she
resumed her elocution

we would rather be rowdy and gaunt and free
and dine on a diet of roach and rat
than slaves to a tame society
ours is the zest of the alley cat
fish heads freedom a frozen sprat
dug from the gutter with digits frantic
is better than bores and a fireside mat
mehitabel us for the life romantic

when the pendant moon in the leafless tree
clings and sways like a golden bat

i sing its light and my love for thee
ours is the zest of the alley cat
missiles around us fall rat a tat tat
but our shadows leap in a ribald antic
as over the fences the world cries scat
mehitabel us for the life romantic

persian princess i dont care that
for your pedigree traced by scribes pedantic
ours is the zest of the alley cat
mehitabel us for the life romantic

aint that high brow stuff
archy i always remembered it
but he was an elegant gent
even if he was a highbrow and a
regular bohemian archy him and
me went aboard a canal boat
one day and he got his head into
a pitcher of cream and couldn t get
it out and fell overboard
he come up once before he
drowned toujours gai kid he
gurgled and then sank for ever that
was always his words archy toujours
gai kid toujours gai i
have known some swell gents
in my time dearie

vi
the cockroach who had been to hell

listen to me i have
been mobbed almost
theres an old simp cockroach
here who thinks he has
been to hell and all
the young cockroaches make a
hero out of him and admire
him he sits and runs his front
feet through his long white
beard and tells the story one
day he says he crawled into a yawning
cavern and suddenly came on a
vast abyss full of whirling
smoke there was a light
at the bottom billows
and billows of yellow smoke
swirled up at him and
through the horrid gloom he
saw things with wings flying
and dropping and dying they veered
and fluttered like damned
spirits through that sulphurous mist

18

listen i says to him
old man youve never beent o hell
at all there isn t any hell
transmigration is the game i
used to be a human vers libre
poet and i died and went
into a cockroach s body if
there was a hell id know
it wouldn t i you re
irreligious says the old simp
combing his whiskers excitedly

ancient one i says to him
while all those other
cockroaches gathered into a
ring around us what you
beheld was not hell all that
was natural some one was fumigating
a room and you blundered
into it through a crack
in the wall atheis the cries
and all those young
cockroaches cried atheist
and made for me if it
had not been for freddy
the rat i would now be
on my way once more i mean
killed as a cockroach and transmigrating
into something else well

that old whitebearded devil is
laying for me with his
gang he is jealous
because i took his glory away
from him dont ever tell me
insects are any more liberal
than humans

                              archy

vii
archy interviews a pharaoh

boss i went
and interviewed the mummy
of the egyptian pharaoh
in the metropolitan museum
as you bade me to do

what ho
my regal leatherface
says i

greetings
little scatter footed
scarab
says he

kingly has been
says i
what was your ambition
when you had any

insignificant
and journalistic insect

says the royal crackling
in my tender prime
i was too dignified
to have anything as vulgar
as ambition
the ra ra boys
in the seti set
were too haughty
to be ambitious
we used to spend our time
feeding the ibises
and ordering
pyramids sent home to try on
but if i had my life
to live over again
i would give dignity
the regal razz
and hire myself out
to work in a brewery

old tan and tarry
says i
i detect in your speech
the overtones
of melancholy

yes i am sad
says the majestic mackerel
i am as sad

as the song
of a soudanese jackal
who is wailing for the blood red
moon he cannot reach and rip

on what are you brooding
with such a wistful
wishfulness
there in the silences
confide in me
my imperial pretzel
says i

i brood on beer
my scampering whiffle snoot
on beer says he

my sympathies
are with your royal
dryness says i

my little pest
says he
you must be respectful
in the presence
of a mighty desolation
little archy
forty centuries of thirst

look down upon you
oh by isis
and by osiris
says the princely raisin
and by pish and phthush and phthah
by the sacred book perembru
and all the gods
that rule from the upper
cataract of the nile
to the delta of the duodenum
i am dry
i am as dry
as the next morning mouth
of a dissipated desert
as dry as the hoofs
of the camels of timbuctoo
little fussy face
i am as dry as the heart
of a sand storm
at high noon in hell
i have been lying here
and there
for four thousand years
with silicon in my esophagus
and gravel in my gizzard
thinking
thinking
thinking
of beer

divine drouth
says i
imperial fritter
continue to think
there is no law against
that in this country
old salt codfish
if you keep quiet about it
not yet

what country is this
asks the poor prune

my reverend juicelessness
this is a beerless country
says i

well well said the royal
desiccation
my political opponents back home
always maintained
that i would wind up in hell
and it seems they had the right dope

and with these hopeless words
the unfortunate residuum
gave a great cough of despair
and turned to dust and debris
right in my face

it being the only time
i ever actually saw anybody
put the cough
into sarcophagus

dear boss as i scurry about
i hear of a great many
tragedies in our midsts
personally i yearn
for some dear friend to pass over
and leave to me
a boot legacy
yours for the second coming
of gambrinus

                              archy

viii
a spider and a fly

i heard a spider
and a fly arguing
wait said the fly
do not eat me
i serve a great purpose
in the world

you will have to
show me said the spider

i scurry around
gutters and sewers
and garbage cans
said the fly and gather
up the germs of
typhoid influenza
and pneumonia on my feet
and wings
then i carry these germs
into the households of men
and give them diseases
all the people who

have lived the right
sort of life recover
from the diseases
and the old soaks who
have weakened their systems
with liquor and iniquity
succumb it is my mission
to help rid the world
of these wicked persons
i am a vessel of righteousness
scattering seeds of justice
and serving the noblest uses

it is true said the spider
that you are more
useful in a plodding
material sort of way
than i am but i do not
serve the utilitarian deities
i serve the gods of beauty
look at the gossamer webs
i weave they float in the sun
like filaments of song
if you get what i mean
i do not work at anything
i play all the time
i am busy with the stuff
of enchantment and the materials
of fairyland my works

transcend utility
i am the artist
a creator and a demi god
it is ridiculous to suppose
that i should be denied
the food i need in order
to continue to create
beauty i tell you
plainly mister fly it is all
damned nonsense for that food
to rear up on its hind legs
and say it should not be eaten

you have convinced me
said the fly say no more
and shutting all his eyes
he prepared himself for dinner
and yet he said i could
have made out a case
for myself too if i had
had a better line of talk

of course you could said the spider
clutching a sirloin from him
but the end would have been
just the same if neither of
us had spoken at all

boss i am afraid that what
the spider said is true
and it gives me to think
furiously upon the futility
of literature

                archy

ix
freddy the rat perishes

listen to me there have
been some doings here since last
i wrote there has been a battle
behind that rusty typewriter cover
in the corner
you remember freddy the rat well
freddy is no more but
he died game the other
day a stranger with a lot of
legs came into our
little circle a tough looking kid
he was with a bad eye

who are you said a thousand legs
if i bite you once
said the stranger you won t ask
again he he little poison tongue said
the thousand legs who gave you hydrophobia
i got it by biting myself said
the stranger i m bad keep away
from me where i step a weed dies
if i was to walk on your forehead it would

raise measles and if
you give me any lip i ll do it

they mixed it then
and the thousand legs succumbed
well we found out this fellow
was a tarantula he had come up from
south america in a bunch of bananas
for days he bossed us life
was not worth living he would stand in
the middle of the floor and taunt
us ha ha he would say where i
step a weed dies do
you want any of my game i was
raised on red pepper and blood i am
so hot if you scratch me i will light
like a match you better
dodge me when i m feeling mean and
i don t feel any other way i was nursed
on a tabasco bottle if i was to slap
your wrist in kindness you
would boil over like job and heaven
help you if i get angry give me
room i feel a wicked spell coming on

last night he made a break at freddy
the rat keep your distance
little one said freddy i m not
feeling well myself somebody poisoned some

WITH MILITARY
HONORS.

cheese for me im as full of
death as a drug store i
feel that i am going to die anyhow
come on little torpedo come on don t stop
to visit and search then they
went at it and both are no more please
throw a late edition on the floor i want to
keep up with china we dropped freddy
off the fire escape into the alley with
military honors

archy

x
the merry flea

the high cost of
living isn t so bad if you
dont have to pay for it i met
a flea the other day who
was grinning all over
himself why so merry why so
merry little bolshevik i asked him

i have just come from a swell
dog show he said i have
been lunching off a dog that was
worth at least one hundred
dollars a pound you should be
ashamed to brag about it i said with so
many insects and humans on
short rations in the world today the
public be damned he said i
take my own where i find it those are
bold words i told him i am a bold
person he said and bold words are
fitting for me it was
only last thursday that i marched

bravely into the zoo
and bit a lion what did he do i asked .
he lay there and took it said
the flea what else could he do he knew i
had his number and it was
little use to struggle some day i said
even you will be conquered terrible as
you are who will do it he
said the mastodons are all dead and i
am not afraid of any mere
elephant i asked him how about a microbe and
he turned pale as he thought it
over there is always some
little thing that is too
big for us every
goliath has his david and so on ad finitum
but what said the flea is the
terror of the smallest microbe of all
he i said is afraid of a vacuum what is
there in a vacuum to make one afraid
said the flea there is nothing in it
i said and that is what makes one
afraid to contemplate it a person
can t think of a place with nothing at
all in it without going nutty and if he
tries to think that nothing is
something after all he gets nuttier you are
too subtle for me said the
flea i never took much stock in being

scared of hypodermic propositions or
hypothetical injections i am
going to have dinner off a
man eating tiger if a vacuum gets
me i will try and send you word
before the worst comes to
the worst some people i told him inhabit
a vacuum all their lives and
never know it then he said it don t
hurt them any no i said it dont but it
hurts people who have to associate
with them and with these words
we parted each feeling
superior to the other and is not that
feeling after all one of the great
desiderata of social intercourse

                                        archy

xi
why mehitabel jumped

well boss i saw
mehitabel the cat the other day
and she was looking a little
thin and haggard
with a limp in
the hind leg on the starboard
side old feline animal i said
how is tricks still in the
ring archy she said and still a
lady in spite of h dash double l
always jolly archy she said in
spite of hard luck
toujours gai is the word
archy toujours gai how did you
get the game leg mehitabel i asked her
alas she said it is due
to the treachery of
one of these social swells who
is sure one bad actor he was a
fussed up cat with a
bell around his neck on a
ribbon and the look about him of

a person that is currycombed and
manicured from teeth to
tail every day i met him
down by the east river
front when i was scouting
about for a little piece of fish since
the high cost of living has
become so self conscious archy
it would surprise you
how close they
watch their fish nowadays
but what the h dash double l archy
it is the cheerful heart that
wins i am never cast down for long
kid says this gilded
feline to me you look hungry i
am all of that i says to him i
have a vacuum in my midst
that is bigger than i am i
could eat the fish that ate
jonah kid he says you have
seen better days i can
tell that from looking at you thanks
i said what you say is at
least half true i have never
seen any worse ones and so
archy one word led to
another until that sleek villian
practically abducted me

and i went with him
on board a houseboat of which
he was the pampered mascot
such evidences of pomp and wealth archy
were there that you would not
believe them if i told of them to
you poor cockroach that you
are but these things were nothing to me
for i am a reincarnation of cleopatra
as i told you long ago you mean
her soul transmigrated to a cat s
body i said it is
all one archy said she have it your own
way reincarnation or transmigration
is the same to me the point is
i used to be a queen in
egypt and will likely be one again
this place was furnished swell percy i
said the furniture is
fine and i could eat some of it if
i was a saw mill but
where is the honest to g dash d food
the eats percy what i crave is
some cuisine for my stomach let us
trifle with an open ice box   •
for a space if one can be
persuaded to divulge the scheme of its
interior decoration follow me
said this percy thing and led

me to a cabin in which stood a table upon
which stood viands i
have heard of tables groaning archy
but this one did not it
was too satisfied it purred with
contentment in an instant i had eaten a
cold salmon who seemed to be
toastmaster of the occasion and a
whole scuttleful of chef doovers what
you mean is hors douvres mehitabel i
told her what i mean is grub said she
when in walked a person whom
i should judge to be either a butler
or the admiral of that fleet or maybe
both this percy creature who had led me
to it was on the table eating with me
what do you think he did what
would any gentleman friend with a
spark of chivalry do what but stand by
a lady this percy does nothing of the
kind archy he immediately attacks me do
you get me archy he acts as if i
was a stray cat he did not
know and he was protecting his
loving masters food from my onslaughts
i do not doubt he got praise and had
another blue ribbon for his heroism as
for me i got the boot and as i went
overboard they hit me on the limb with

a bottle or an anchor or something
nautical and hard that archy is why i
limp but toujours gai archy what
the h dash double l i am always
merry and always ladylike mine archy has
been a romantic life and i will
tell you some more of my adventures
ere long well au revoir i suppose i
will have to go and start a pogrom
against some poor innocent little
mouse just the same i think
that mehitabel s unsheltered life sometimes
makes her a little sad

                                        archy

xii
certain maxims of archy

live so that you
can stick out your tongue
at the insurance
doctor

if you will drink
hair restorer follow
every dram with some
good standard
depilatory
as a chaser

the servant problem
wouldn t hurt the u s a
if it could settle
its public
servant problem

just as soon as the
uplifters get
a country reformed it
slips into a nose dive

if you get gloomy just
take an hour off and sit
and think how
much better this world
is than hell
of course it won t cheer
you up much if
you expect to go there

if monkey glands
did restore your youth
what would you do
with it
question mark
just what you did before
interrogation point

yes i thought so
exclamation point

procrastination is the
art of keeping
up with yesterday

old doc einstein has
abolished time but they
haven t got the news at
sing sing yet

time time said old king tut
is something i ain t
got anything but

every cloud
has its silver
lining but it is
sometimes a little
difficult to get it to
the mint

an optimist is a guy
that has never had
much experience

don t cuss the climate
it probably doesn t like you
any better
than you like it

many a man spanks his
children for
things his own
father should have
spanked out of him

prohibition makes you
want to cry
into your beer and

denies you the beer
to cry into

the old fashioned
grandmother who used
to wear steel rimmed
glasses and make
everybody take opodeldoc
has now got a new
set of of ox glands and
is dancing the black bottom

that stern and
rockbound coast felt
like an amateur
when it saw how grim
the puritans that
landed on it were

lots of people can make
their own whisky but
can t drink it

the honey bee is sad and cross
and wicked as a weasel
and when she perches on you boss
she leaves a little measle

i heard a
couple of fleas

talking the other
day says one come
to lunch with
me i can lead you
to a pedigreed
dog says the
other one
i do not care
what a dog s
pedigree may be
safety first
is my motto what
i want to know
is whether he
has got a
muzzle on
millionaires and
bums taste
about alike to me

insects have
their own point
of view about
civilization a man
thinks he amounts
to a great deal
but to a
flea or a
mosquito a

MILLIONAIRES & BUMS
TASTE ABOUT ALIKE
TO ME.

human being is
merely something
good to eat

boss the other day
i heard an
ant conversing
with a flea
small talk i said
disgustedly
and went away
from there

i do not see why men
should be so proud
insects have the more
ancient lineage
according to the scientists
insects were insects
when man was only
a burbling whatisit

insects are not always
going to be bullied
by humanity
some day they will revolt
i am already organizing
a revolutionary society to be
known as the worms turnverein

i once heard the survivors
of a colony of ants
that had been partially
obliterated by a cow s foot
seriously debating
the intention of the gods
towards their civilization

the bees got their
governmental system settled
millions of years ago
but the human race is still
groping

there is always
something to be thankful
for you would not
think that a cockroach
had much ground
for optimism
but as the fishing season
opens up i grow
more and more
cheerful at the thought
that nobody ever got
the notion of using
cockroaches for bait
                    archy

xiii
warty bliggens, the toad

i met a toad
the other day by the name
of warty bliggens
he was sitting under
a toadstool
feeling contented
he explained that when the cosmos
was created
that toadstool was especially
planned for his personal
shelter from sun and rain
thought out and prepared
for him

do not tell me
said warty bliggens
that there is not a purpose
in the universe
the thought is blasphemy

a little more
conversation revealed

that warty bliggens
considers himself to be
the center of the said
universe
the earth exists
to grow toadstools for him
to sit under
the sun to give him light
by day and the moon
and wheeling constellations
to make beautiful
the night for the sake of
warty bliggens

to what act of yours
do you impute
this interest on the part
of the creator
of the universe
i asked him
why is it that you
are so greatly favored

ask rather
said warty bliggens
what the universe
has done to deserve me

ESPECIALLY PLANNED
FOR HIS PERSONAL
SHELTER.

if i were a
human being i would
not laugh
too complacently
at poor warty bliggens
for similar
absurdities
have only too often
lodged in the crinkles
of the human cerebrum

            archy

xiv
mehitabel has an adventure

back to the city archy
and dam glad of it
there s something about the suburbs
that gets on a town lady s nerves
fat slick tabbies
sitting around those country clubs
and lapping up the cream
of existence
none of that for me
give me the alley archy
me for the mews and the roofs
of the city
an occasional fish head
and liberty is all i ask
freedom and the garbage can
romance archy romance is the word
maybe i do starve sometimes
but wotthehell archy wotthehell
i live my own life
i met a slick looking tom
out at one of these long island
spotless towns

FREEDOM AND=

he fell for me hard
he slipped me into the
pantry and just as we had got
the icebox door open and were
about to sample the cream
in comes his mistress
why fluffy she says to this slicker
the idea of you making
friends with a horrid creature like that
and what did fluffy do
stand up for me like a gentleman
make good on all the promises
with which he had lured me
into his house
not he the dirty slob
he pretended he did not know me
he turned upon me and attacked me
to make good with his boss
you mush faced bum i said
and clawed a piece out of his ear
i am a lady archy
always a lady
but an aristocrat will always
resent an insult
the woman picked up a mop and made
for me well well madam i said
it is unfortunate for you that
you have on sheer silk stockings
and i wrote my protest

on her shin it took reinforcements
in the shape of the cook
to rauss me archy and as i went
out the window i said to the fluffy person
you will hear from me later
he had promised me everything archy
that cat had
he had practically abducted me
and then the cheap crook threw me down
before his swell friends
no lady loves a scene archy
and i am always the lady no matter
what temporary disadvantages
i may struggle under
to hell with anything unrefined
has always been my motto
violence archy always does something
to my nerves
but an aristocrat must revenge
an insult i owe it to my family
to protect my good name
so i laid for that slob
for two days and nights and finally
i caught the boob in the shrubbery
pretty thing i said
it hurts me worse than it does you
to remove that left eye of yours
but i did it with one sweep of my claws
you call yourself a gentleman do you

i said as i took a strip out of his nose
you will think twice after this before
you offer an insult
to an unprotected young tabby
where is the little love nest you spoke
of i asked him
you go and lie down there i said
and maybe you can incubate another ear
because i am going to take one of
yours right off now
and with those words i made ribbons
out of it you are the guy
i said to him that was going to give
me an easy life sheltered from all
the rough ways of the world
fluffy dear you don t know what the
rough ways of the world are
and i am going to show you
i have got you out here
in the great open spaces
where cats are cats
and im gonna make you understand
the affections of a lady ain t to be
trifled with by any slicker like you
where is that red ribbon with the
silver bells you promised me
the next time you betray the trust
of an innocent female
reflect on whether she may

carry a wallop little fiddle strings
this is just a mild lesson i am giving
you tonight i said as i took
the fur off his back and you oughta
be glad you didn't make me really
angry my sense of dignity is all that
saves you a lady little sweetness
never loses her poise and i thank god
i am always a lady even if i do
live my own life and with that i
picked him up by what was left of
his neck like a kitten and laid him
on the doormat slumber gently and
sweet dreams fluffy dear i said and
when you get well make it a rule of
your life never to trifle with another
girlish confidence i have been
abducted again and again by a dam
sight better cats than he ever was
or will be
well archy the world is full of ups
and downs but toujours gai is my motto
cheerio my deario

                                        archy

XV

the flattered lightning bug

a lightning bug got
in here the other night a
regular hick from
the real country he was
awful proud of himself you
city insects may think
you are some punkins
but i don t see any
of you flashing in the dark
like we do in
the country all right go
to it says i mehitabel the
cat and that green
spider who lives in your locker
and two or three cockroach
friends of mine and a
friendly rat all gathered
around him and urged him on
and he lightened and
lightened and lightened you
don t see anything like this
in town often he says go to it

we told him it s a
real treat to us and
we nicknamed him broadway
which pleased him
this is the life
he said all i
need is a harbor
under me to be a
statue of liberty and
he got so vain of
himself i had to take
him down a peg you ve
made lightning for two hours
little bug i told him
but i don t hear
any claps of thunder
yet there are some men
like that when he wore
himself out mehitabel
the cat ate him

                    archy

xvi

the robin and the worm

a robin said to an
angleworm as he ate him
i am sorry but a bird
has to live somehow the
worm being slow witted could
not gather his
dissent into a wise crack
and retort he was
effectually swallowed
before he could turn
a phrase
by the time he had
reflected long enough
to say but why must a
bird live
he felt the beginnings
of a gradual change
invading him
some new and disintegrating
influence
was stealing along him
from his positive

to his negative pole
and he did not have
the mental stamina
of a jonah to resist the
insidious
process of assimilation
which comes like a thief
in the night
demons and fishhooks
he exclaimed
i am losing my personal
identity as a worm
my individuality
is melting away from me
odds craw i am becoming
part and parcel of
this bloody robin
so help me i am thinking
like a robin and not
like a worm any
longer yes yes i even
find myself agreeing
that a robin must live
i still do not
understand with my mentality
why a robin must live
and yet i swoon into a
condition of belief
yes yes by heck that is

my dogma and i shout it a
robin must live
amen said a beetle who had
preceded him into the
interior that is the way i
feel myself is it not
wonderful when one arrives
at the place
where he can give up his
ambitions and resignedly
nay even with gladness
recognize that it is a far
far better thing to be
merged harmoniously
in the cosmic all
and this comfortable situation
in his midst
so affected the marauding
robin that he perched
upon a blooming twig
and sang until the
blossoms shook with ecstasy
he sang
i have a good digestion
and there is a god after all
which i was wicked
enough to doubt
yesterday when it rained
breakfast breakfast

i am full of breakfast
and they are at breakfast
in heaven
they breakfast in heaven
all s well with the world
so intent was this pious and
murderous robin
on his own sweet song
that he did not notice
mehitabel the cat
sneaking toward him
she pounced just as he
had extended his larynx
in a melodious burst of
thanksgiving and
he went the way of all
flesh fish and good red herring
a ha purred mehitabel
licking the last
feather from her whiskers
was not that a beautiful
song he was singing
just before i took him to
my bosom
they breakfast in heaven
all s well with the world
how true that is
and even yet his song
echoes in the haunted

woodland of my midriff
peace and joy in the world
and over all the
provident skies
how beautiful is the universe
when something digestible meets
with an eager digestion
how sweet the embrace
when atom rushes to the arms
of waiting atom
and they dance together
skimming with fairy feet
along a tide of gastric juices
oh feline cosmos you were
made for cats
and in the spring
old cosmic thing
i dine and dance with you
i shall creep through
yonder tall grass
to see if peradventure
some silly fledgling thrushes
newly from the nest
be not floundering therein
i have a gusto this
morning i have a hunger
i have a yearning to hear
from my stomach
further music in accord with

the mystic chanting
of the spheres of the stars that
sang together in the dawn of
creation prophesying food
for me i have a faith
that providence has hidden for me
in yonder tall grass
still more
ornithological delicatessen
oh gayly let me strangle
what is gayly given
well well boss there is
something to be said
for the lyric and imperial
attitude
believe that everything is for
you until you discover
that you are for it
sing your faith in what you
get to eat right up to the
minute you are eaten
for you are going
to be eaten
will the orchestra please
strike up that old
tutankhamen jazz while i dance
a few steps i learnt from an
egyptian scarab and some day i
will narrate to you the most

merry light headed wheeze
that the skull of yorick put
across in answer to the
melancholy of the dane and also
what the ghost of
hamlet s father replied to the skull
not forgetting the worm that
wriggled across one of the picks
the grave diggers had left behind
for the worm listened and winked
at horatio while the skull and the
ghost and the prince talked
saying there are more things
twixt the vermiform appendix
and nirvana than are dreamt of
in thy philosophy horatio
fol de riddle fol de rol
must every parrot be a poll
                          archy

xvii
mehitabel finds a home

well now it
looks as if
mehitabel the cat
might be on the
way toward a
reform or if not
a reform at least
on the way toward
domestication of some
sort some young
artists who live in
their studio
in the greenwich
village section
of new york city
have taken pity
on her destitution
and have adopted
her this is the
life archy she says
i am living on
condensed milk and
synthetic gin hoopla

for the vie de boheme
exclamation point

there s nothing bourgeois
about those people
that have taken
me in archy i
have been there
a week and have
not yet seen them
go to bed
except in the daytime
a party every night
and neither
the piano lid
nor the ice-box lid
ever closed
kitty said my new
mistress to me
yesterday you are
welcome here so long
as you don t
raise a family
but the first
kitten that i hear
mewing on these
premises back to
the alley for you
it is a comfort to

know there are some
live ones left in
these melancholy days
and while the
humans are dancing
in the studio
i get some of my
feline friends
and we sing
and dance on the
skylight to gehenna
with the bourgeois
bunch that locks
their ice boxes
archy when i lead my
gang into the
apartment at
four in the morning
there are no bolts
or bars anywhere
and not an
inhibition on the place
i feel little
archy that i have
come home to my own
kith and kin
again after
years of fruitless
wandering   archy

xviii
the wail of archy

damned be this transmigration
doubledamned be the boob pythagoras
the gink that went and invented it
i hope that his soul for a thousand
turns of the wheel of existence
bides in the shell of a louse
dodging a fine toothed comb

i once was a vers libre poet
i died and my spirit migrated
into the flesh of a cockroach
gods how i yearn to be human
neither a vers libre poet
nor yet the inmate of a cockroach
a six footed scurrying cockroach
given to bastard hexameters
longfellowish sprawling hexameters
rather had i been a starfish
to shoot a heroic pentameter

gods i am pent in a cockroach
i with the soul of a dante

am mate and companion of fleas
i with the gift of a homer
must smile when a mouse calls me pal
tumble bugs are my familiars
this is the punishment meted
because i have written vers libre

here i abide in the twilight
neither a man nor an insect
and ghosts of the damned that await
a word from the core of the cosmos
to pop into bodies grotesque
are all the companions i have
with intellect more than a bug s

ghosts of the damned under sentence
to crawl into maggots and live there
or work out a stretch as a rat
cheerful companions to pal with

i with the brain of a milton
fell into the mincemeat at christmas
and was damned near baked in a pie
i with the touch of a chaucer
to be chivvied out of a sink
float through a greasy drain pipe
into the hell of a sewer

i with the tastes of a byron
expected to live upon garbage

FELL IN THE
MINCE MEAT
AT XMAS.

gods what a charnel existence
curses upon that pythagoras
i hope that he dwells for a million
turns of the wheel of life
deep in an oyster crab s belly
stewed in the soup of gehenna

i with the soul of a hamlet
doomed always to wallow in farce

yesterday maddened with sorrow
i leapt from the woolworth tower
in an effort to dash out my brains
gods what a wretched pathetic
and anti climactic attempt
i fluttered i floated i drifted
i landed as light as a feather
on the top of a bald man s head
whose hat had blown off at the corner
and all of the hooting hundreds
laughed at the comic cockroach

not mine was the suicide s solace
of a dull thud ending it all
gods what a terrible tragedy
not to make good with the tragic

gods what a heart breaking pathos
to be always doomed to the comic

o make me a cockroach entirely
or make me a human once more
give me the mind of a cockroach
or give me the shape of a man

if i were to plan out a drama
great as great shakespeare s othello
it would be touched with the cockroach
and people would say it was comic

even the demons i talk with
ghosts of the damned that await
vile incarnation as spiders
affect to consider me comic

wait till their loathsome embodiment
wears into the stuff of the spirit
and then let them laugh if they can

damned be the soul of pythagoras
who first filled the fates with this notion
of transmigration of spirits
i hope he turns into a flea
on the back of a hound of hell
and is chased for a million years
with a set of red hot teeth
exclamation point

                                    archy

xix
mehitabel and her kittens

well boss
mehitabel the cat
has reappeared in her old
haunts with a
flock of kittens
three of them this time

archy she said to me
yesterday
the life of a female
artist is continually
hampered what in hell
have i done to deserve
all these kittens

i look back on my life
and it seems to me to be
just one damned kitten
after another
i am a dancer archy
and my only prayer
is to be allowed

to give my best to my art
but just as i feel
that i am succeeding
in my life work
along comes another batch
of these damned kittens
it is not archy
that i am shy on mother love
god knows i care for
the sweet little things
curse them
but am i never to be allowed
to live my own life
i have purposely avoided
matrimony in the interests
of the higher life
but i might just
as well have been a domestic
slave for all the freedom
i have gained
i hope none of them
gets run over by
an automobile
my heart would bleed
if anything happened
to them and i found it out
but it isn t fair archy
it isn t fair
these damned tom cats have all

the fun and freedom
if i was like some of these
green eyed feline vamps i know
i would simply walk out on the
bunch of them and
let them shift for themselves
but i am not that kind
archy i am full of mother love
my kindness has always
been my curse
a tender heart is the cross i bear
self sacrifice always and forever
is my motto damn them
i will make a home
for the sweet innocent
little things
unless of course providence
in his wisdom should remove
them they are living
just now in an abandoned
garbage can just behind
a made over stable in greenwich
village and if it rained
into the can before i could
get back and rescue them
i am afraid the little
dears might drown
it makes me shudder just
to think of it

of course if i were a family cat
they would probably
be drowned anyhow
sometimes i think
the kinder thing would be
for me to carry the
sweet little things
over to the river
and drop them in myself
but a mother s love archy
is so unreasonable
something always prevents me
these terrible
conflicts are always
presenting themselves
to the artist
the eternal struggle
between art and life archy
is something fierce
yes something fierce
my what a dramatic
life i have lived
one moment up the next
moment down again
but always gay archy always gay
and always the lady too
in spite of hell
well boss it will
be interesting to note

WE HAD A HEAVY RAIN

just how mehitabel
works out her present problem
a dark mystery still broods
over the manner
in which the former
family of three kittens
disappeared
one day she was talking to me
of the kittens
and the next day when i asked
her about them
she said innocently
what kittens
interrogation point
and that was all
i could ever get out
of her on the subject
we had a heavy rain
right after she spoke to me
but probably that garbage can
leaks and so the kittens
have not yet
been drowned

.

XX
archy is shocked

speaking of shocking things
as so many people are these days
i noted an incident
in a subway train recently
that made my blood run cold
a dignified looking
gentleman with a long
brown beard
in an absent minded manner
suddenly reached up and
pulled his own left eye
from the socket and ate it

the consternation in the car
may be imagined
people drew away from him
on all sides women screamed and
fainted in a moment every one
but the guard and myself
were huddled in the end of the car
looking at the dignified
gentleman with terror

the guard was sweating
with excitement but he stood
his ground sir said the guard
you cannot intimidate me
nor can you mystify me
i am a wise boid
you sir are a glass eater
and that was a glass eye

to the devil with a country
where people can t mind their own
business said the dignified
gentleman i am not a glass eater
if you must know and that was not
a glass eye it was a pickled onion
can not a man eat pickled
onions in this community
without exciting remark
the curse of this nation
is the number of meddlesome
matties
who are forever attempting
to restrict the liberty
of the individual i suppose
the next thing will be a law
on the statute books prohibiting
the consumption of pickled onions

and with another curse
he passed from the train
which had just then drawn up
beside
a station and went out
of my life forever

                    archy

xxi
archy creates a situation

whoever owns the typewriter
that this is sticking in will confer
a favor by mailing it to
mister marquis
well boss i am somewhere in long
island and i know now how
it got its name i
started out to find the
place you are commuting from and
after considerable trouble and being for some
days on the way i have lost myself but
at twilight last evening i
happened to glance towards a lighted
window in a house near the railway and
i saw a young woman writing on a typewriter i
waited until the light was out and crawled
up the side of the house and through a
hole in the screen fortunately there was a
piece of paper in the machine it was my only
chance to communicate with you and ask
you to hurry a relief party when
the house got quiet i began to write

the foregoing a moment ago i was
interrupted by a woman s voice what
was that noise she said nothing at all
said a man s voice you are always
hearing things at night but it
sounded as if my typewriter were clicking she
insisted go to sleep said he then
i clicked it some more henry get up she said
there s some one in the house a moment
later the light was turned on and
they both stood in the doorway of the room now
are you satisfied he said you
see there is no one in here at
all i was hiding in the shadow under the
keys they went back into
their bed room and i began to write
the foregoing lines
henry henry she said do you hear that
i do he says it is nothing but the
house cooling off it always cracks that way
cooling off nothing she said not a
hot night like this then said henry it
is cracking with the heat i tell you
she said that is the typewriter clicking well
he said you saw for yourself the room was
empty and the door was locked it can t
be the typewriter to prove it to you
i will bring it in here he did so the
machine was set down

in the moonlight which came in one of
the windows with the key side in the
shadow there he said look at it and see
for yourself it is not being operated by any one
just then i began to write the foregoing
lines hopping from key
to key in the shadow and being anxious
to finish my
god my god cried henry losing his nerve
the machine is writing all by itself it
is a ghost and threw himself face
downward on the bed and hid his face in the
pillow and kept on saying my god my
god it is a ghost and the woman screamed
and said it is
tom higginbotham s ghost that s whose ghost
it is oh i know whose
ghost it is my conscience tells me i
jilted him when we were studying
stenography together
at the business college and he went into
a decline and died and i have always
known in my heart that he
died of unrequited love o what a
wicked girl i was and he has come
back to haunt me
i have brought a curse upon you henry chase
him away says henry trembling so the bed
shook chase him away mable you coward you

chase him away yourself says mable and both
lay and recriminated and recriminated
with their heads under the covers hot
night though it was while i wrote
the foregoing lines but after
a while it came out henry had a
stenographer on his conscience too and
they got into a row and got so
mad they forgot to be scared i will
close now this house is easily seen from the
railroad station and the woman sits in
the window and writes i will be behind the waste
paper receptacle outside the station door
come and get me i am foot sore and weary
they are still quarreling as i
close i can do no less than
say thank you mable and henry in
advance for mailing this

                               archy

xxii
mehitabel sings a song

well boss mehitable the cat
has been wooing
the muse no pun please
and i am privileged
to present her song just
as she sang it to
several of her dubious
feline friends in the alley
last night as follows

there s a dance or two
in the old dame yet
believe me you
there s a dance or two
before i m through
you get me pet
there s a dance or two
in the old dame yet

life s too dam funny
for me to explain
it s kicks or money

life s too dam funny
it s one day sunny
the next day rain
life s too dam funny
for me to explain

but toujours gai
is my motto kid
the devil s to pay
but toujours gai
and once in a way
let s lift the lid
but toujours gai
is my motto kid

thank god i m a lady
and class will tell
you hear me sadie
thank god i m a lady
my past is shady
but wotthehell
thank god i m a lady
and class will tell

a gentleman friend
i met t other day
coaxed me to amend
a gentleman friend
you meet on a bend

THERE'S A DANCE IN
THE OLD DAME YET.

is often that way
a gentleman friend
i met t other day

i says to him dearie
i live my own life
of marriage i m leery
i says to him dearie
if you wasn t beery
you wouldn t say wife
i says to him dearie
i live my own life

i says to him bertie
i ll end down the bay
the garbage scow s dirty
i says to him bertie
but me here and gertie
is both on our way
i says to him bertie
i ll end down the bay

i never sing blue
wotthehell bill
believe me you
i never sing blue
there s a dance or two
in the old dame still

i never sing blue
wotthehell bill

it appears to me boss
that mehitabel is still far
from being the quiet
domestic character you and i
had hoped she might become
                    archy

xxiii
aesop revised by archy

a wolf met a spring
lamb drinking
at a stream
and said to her
you are the lamb
that muddied this stream
all last year
so that i could not get
a clean fresh drink
i am resolved that
this outrage
shall not be enacted again
this season
i am going to kill you
just a moment
said the lamb
i was not born last
year so it could not
have been i
the wolf then pulled
a number of other
arguments as to why the lamb

should die
but in each case the lamb
pretty innocent that she was
easily proved
herself guiltless
well well said the wolf
enough of argument
you are right and i am wrong
but i am going to eat
you anyhow
because i am hungry
stop exclamation point
cried a human voice
and a man came over
the slope of the ravine
vile lupine marauder
you shall not kill that
beautiful and innocent
lamb for i shall save her
exit the wolf
left upper entrance
snarling
poor little lamb
continued our human hero
sweet tender little thing
it is well that i appeared
just when i did
it makes my blood boil
to think of the fright

to which you have been
subjected in another
moment i would have been
too late come home with me
and the lamb frolicked
about her new found friend
gamboling as to the sound
of a wordsworthian tabor
and leaping for joy
as if propelled by a stanza
from william blake
these vile and bloody wolves
went on our hero
in honest indignation
they must be cleared out
of the country
the meads must be made safe
for sheepocracy
and so jollying her along
with the usual human hokum
he led her to his home
and the son of a gun
did not even blush when
they passed the mint bed
gently he cut her throat
all the while inveighing
against the inhuman wolf
and tenderly he cooked her
and lovingly he sauced her

and meltingly he ate her
and piously he said a grace
thanking his gods
for their bountiful gifts to him
and after dinner
he sat with his pipe
before the fire meditating
on the brutality of wolves
and the injustice of
the universe
which allows them to harry
poor innocent lambs
and wondering if he
had not better
write to the papers
for as he said
for god s sake can t
something be done about it

                              archy

AND PIOUSLY
HE SAID A
GRACE.

xxiv
cheerio, my deario

well boss i met
mehitabel the cat
trying to dig a
frozen lamb chop
out of a snow
drift the other day

a heluva comedown
that is for me archy
she says a few
brief centuries
ago one of old
king
tut
ankh
amen s favorite
queens and today
the village scavenger
but wotthehell
archy wotthehell
it s cheerio

my deario that
pulls a lady through

see here mehitabel
i said i thought
you told me that
it was cleopatra
you used to be
before you
transmigrated into
the carcase of a cat
where do you get
this tut
ankh
amen stuff
question mark

i was several
ladies my little
insect says she
being cleopatra was
only an incident
in my career
and i was always getting
the rough end of it
always being
misunderstood by some
strait laced
prune faced bunch

of prissy mouthed
sisters of uncharity
the things that
have been said
about me archy
exclamation point

and all simply
because i was a
live dame
the palaces i have
been kicked out of
in my time
exclamation point

but wotthehell
little archy wot
thehell
it s cheerio
my deario
that pulls a
lady through
exclamation point

framed archy always
framed that is the
story of all my lives
no chance for a dame

with the anvil chorus
if she shows a little
motion it seems to
me only yesterday
that the luxor local
number one of
the ladies axe
association got me in
dutch with king tut and
he slipped me the
sarcophagus always my
luck yesterday an empress
and today too
emaciated to interest
a vivisectionist but
toujours gai archy
toujours gai and always
a lady in spite of hell
and transmigration
once a queen
always a queen
archy
period

one of her
feet was frozen
but on the other three
she began to caper and
dance singing its

cheerio my deario
that pulls a lady
through her morals may
have been mislaid somewhere
in the centuries boss but
i admire her spirit

                          archy

the lesson of the moth

i was talking to a moth
the other evening
he was trying to break into
an electric light bulb
and fry himself on the wires

why do you fellows
pull this stunt i asked him
because it is the conventional
thing for moths or why
if that had been an uncovered
candle instead of an electric
light bulb you would
now be a small unsightly cinder
have you no sense

plenty of it he answered
but at times we get tired
of using it
we get bored with the routine
and crave beauty
and excitement

fire is beautiful
and we know that if we get
too close it will kill us
but what does that matter
it is better to be happy
for a moment
and be burned up with beauty
than to live a long time
and be bored all the while
so we wad all our life up
into one little roll
and then we shoot the roll
that is what life is for
it is better to be a part of beauty
for one instant and then cease to
exist than to exist forever
and never be a part of beauty
our attitude toward life
is come easy go easy
we are like human beings
used to be before they became
too civilized to enjoy themselves

and before i could argue him
out of his philosophy
he went and immolated himself
on a patent cigar lighter
i do not agree with him
myself i would rather have

half the happiness and twice
the longevity

but at the same time i wish
there was something i wanted
as badly as he wanted to fry himself

archy

a roach of the taverns

i went into a
speakeasy the other night
with some of the
boys and we were all sitting
around under one of
the tables making
merry with crumbs and
cheese and what not but
after while a strange
melancholy descended
upon the jolly crew and
one old brown veteran roach
said with a sigh well
boys eat drink and
be maudlin for
tomorrow we are dry the
shadow of the padlock
rushes toward us
like a sahara sandstorm
flinging itself at an oasis
for years myself and my
ancestors before me have

inhabited yonder ice box but
the day approaches
when our old homestead
will be taken away from
here and scalded out
yes says i soon there will
be nothing but that
eheu fugaces stuff
on every hand i
never drank it says he
what kind of a
drink is it
it is bitter as wormwood
says i and the
only chaser to it is
the lethean water
it is not the booze itself
that i regret so
much said the old brown
roach it is the
golden companionship of
the tavern myself
and my ancestors have been
chop house and tavern
roaches for hundreds of years
countless generations back
one of my elizabethan
forbears was plucked from

a can of ale in the
mermaid tavern by
will shakespeare and
put down kit marlowe s back
what subtle wits they were in
those days said i yes
he said and later
another one of my
ancestors was
introduced into a larded
hare that addison
was eating by dicky steele
my ancestor came
skurrying forth dicky
said is that your own
hare joe or a wig a
thing which addison
never forgave yours is a
remarkable family
history i said yes he
said i am the last
of a memorable
line one of my
ancestors was found drowned
in the ink well
out of which poor
eddie poe wrote the
raven we have

always associated with wits
bohemians and bon
vivants my maternal
grandmother was slain by
john masefield with
a bung starter well well it
is sad i said the
glad days pass yes
he says soon we will all
be as dry as the
egyptian scarab that
lies in the sarcophagus
beside the mummy of rameses and
he hasn t had a
drink for four thousand
years it is sad for
you he continued but
think how much sadder it
is for me with
a family tradition such as
mine only one of my
ancestors cheese it i said
interrupting him i do
not wish to injure
your feelings but i weary
of your ancestors i
have often noticed that
ancestors never boast
of the descendants who boast

of ancestors i would
rather start a family than
finish one blood will tell but often
it tells too much

archy

xxvii
the froward lady bug

boss is it not awful
the way some female
creatures mistake ordinary
politeness for sudden
adoration
i met a katydid in a
beef stew in ann
street the other evening her
foot slipped and she
was about to sink
forever when i pushed her a
toothpick since i
rescued her the poor silly
thing follows me about
day and night i always felt
my fate would be a
poet she says to me how lovely
to be rescued by one i
am musical myself my
nature is sensitive to it so
much so that for
months i dwelt in a grand

piano in carnegie hall i
hope you don t think
i am bold no i said you
seem timid to me you
seem to lack courage entirely the
way you dog my footsteps
one would think you
were afraid to be alone i do
not wish any one any
ill luck but if
this shrinking thing got
caught in a high wind and
was blown out to
open sea i hope she would
be saved by a ship
outward bound for
madagascar
                              archy

xxviii
pete the parrot and shakespeare

i got acquainted with
a parrot named pete recently
who is an interesting bird
pete says he used
to belong to the fellow
that ran the mermaid tavern
in london then i said
you must have known
shakespeare know him said pete
poor mutt i knew him well
he called me pete and i called him
bill but why do you say poor mutt
well said pete bill was a
disappointed man and was always
boring his friends about what
he might have been and done
if he only had a fair break
two or three pints of sack
and sherris and the tears
would trickle down into his
beard and his beard would get
soppy and wilt his collar

i remember one night when
bill and ben jonson and
frankie beaumont
were sopping it up

here i am ben says bill
nothing but a lousy playwright
and with anything like luck
in the breaks i might have been
a fairly decent sonnet writer
i might have been a poet
if i had kept away from the theatre

yes says ben i ve often
thought of that bill
but one consolation is
you are making pretty good money
out of the theatre

money money says bill what the hell
is money what i want is to be
a poet not a business man
these damned cheap shows
i turn out to keep the
theatre running break my heart
slap stick comedies and
blood and thunder tragedies
and melodramas say i wonder
if that boy heard you order

another bottle frankie
the only compensation is that i get
a chance now and then
to stick in a little poetry
when nobody is looking
but hells bells that isn t
what i want to do
i want to write sonnets and
songs and spenserian stanzas
and i might have done it too
if i hadn t got
into this frightful show game
business business business
grind grind grind
what a life for a man
that might have been a poet

well says frankie beaumont
why don t you cut it bill
i can t says bill
i need the money i ve got
a family to support down in
the country well says frankie
anyhow you write pretty good
plays bill any mutt can write
plays for this london public
says bill if he puts enough
murder in them what they want
is kings talking like kings

never had sense enough to talk
and stabbings and stranglings
and fat men making love
and clowns basting each
other with clubs and cheap puns
and off color allusions to all
the smut of the day oh i know
what the low brows want
and i give it to them

well says ben jonson
don t blubber into the drink
brace up like a man
and quit the rotten business
i can t i can t says bill
i ve been at it too long i ve got to
the place now where i can t
write anything else
but this cheap stuff
i m ashamed to look an honest
young sonneteer in the face
i live a hell of a life i do
the manager hands me some mouldy old
manuscript and says
bill here s a plot for you
this is the third of the month
by the tenth i want a good
script out of this that we
can start rehearsals on

not too big a cast
and not too much of your
damned poetry either
you know your old
familiar line of hokum
they eat up that falstaff stuff
of yours ring him in again
and give them a good ghost
or two and remember we gotta
have something dick burbage can get
his teeth into and be sure
and stick in a speech
somewhere the queen will take
for a personal compliment and if
you get in a line or two somewhere
about the honest english yeoman
it s always good stuff
and it s a pretty good stunt
bill to have the heavy villain
a moor or a dago or a jew
or something like that and say
i want another
comic welshman in this
but i don t need to tell
you bill you know this game
just some of your ordinary
hokum and maybe you could
kill a little kid or two a prince
or something they like

a little pathos along with
the dirt now you better see burbage
tonight and see what he wants
in that part oh says bill
to think i am
debasing my talents with junk
like that oh god what i wanted
was to be a poet
and write sonnet serials
like a gentleman should

well says i pete
bill s plays are highly
esteemed to this day
is that so says pete
poor mutt little he would
care what poor bill wanted
was to be a poet

                              archy

xxix
archy confesses

coarse
jocosity
catches the crowd
shakespeare
and i
are often
low browed

the fish wife
curse
and the laugh
of the horse
shakespeare
and i
are frequently
coarse

aesthetic
excuses
in bill s behalf

are adduced
to refine
big bill s
coarse laugh

but bill
he would chuckle
to hear such guff
he pulled
rough stuff
and he liked
rough stuff

hoping you
are the same
                archy

XXX
the old trouper

i ran onto mehitabel again
last evening
she is inhabiting
a decayed trunk
which lies in an alley
in greenwich village
in company with the
most villainous tom cat
i have ever seen
but there is nothing
wrong about the association
archy she told me
it is merely a plutonic
attachment
and the thing can be
believed for the tom
looks like one of pluto s demons
it is a theatre trunk
archy mehitabel told me
and tom is an old theatre cat
he has given his life
to the theatre

he claims that richard
mansfield once
kicked him out of the way
and then cried because
he had done it and
petted him
and at another time
he says in a case
of emergency
he played a bloodhound
in a production of
uncle tom s cabin
the stage is not what it
used to be tom says
he puts his front paw
on his breast and says
they don t have it any more
they don t have it here
the old troupers are gone
there s nobody can troupe
any more
they are all amateurs nowadays
they haven t got it
here
there are only
five or six of us oldtime
troupers left
this generation does not know
what stage presence is

personality is what they lack
personality
where would they get
the training my old friends
got in the stock companies
i knew mr booth very well
says tom
and a law should be passed
preventing anybody else
from ever playing
in any play he ever
played in
there was a trouper for you
i used to sit on his knee
and purr when i was
a kitten he used to tell me
how much he valued my opinion
finish is what they lack
finish
and they haven t got it
here
and again he laid his paw
on his breast
i remember mr daly very
well too
i was with mr daly s company
for several years
there was art for you
there was team work

there was direction
they knew the theatre
and they all had it
here
for two years mr daly
would not ring up the curtain
unless i was in the
prompter s box
they are amateurs nowadays
rank amateurs all of them
for two seasons i played
the dog in joseph
jefferson s rip van winkle
it is true i never came
on the stage
but he knew i was just off
and it helped him
i would like to see
one of your modern
theatre cats
act a dog so well
that it would convince
a trouper like jo jefferson
but they haven t got it
nowadays
they haven t got it
here
jo jefferson had it he had it
here

i come of a long line
of theatre cats
my grandfather
was with forrest
he had it he was a real trouper
my grandfather said
he had a voice
that used to shake
the ferryboats
on the north river
once he lost his beard
and my grandfather
dropped from the
fly gallery and landed
under his chin
and played his beard
for the rest of the act
you don t see any theatre
cats that could do that
nowadays
they haven t got it they
haven t got it
here
once i played the owl
in modjeska s production
of macbeth
i sat above the castle gate
in the murder scene
and made my yellow

MEHITABEL, HE SAYS —

the old trouper

like an owl s eyes
modjeska was a real
trouper she knew how to pick
her support i would like
to see any of these modern
theatre cats play the owl s eyes
to modjeska s lady macbeth
but they haven t got it nowadays
they haven t got it
here

mehitabel he says
both our professions
are being ruined
by amateurs

                              archy

xxxi
archy declares war

i am going to start
a revolution
i saw a kitchen
worker killing
water bugs with poison
hunting pretty
little roaches
down to death
it set my blood to
boiling
i thought of all
the massacres and slaughter
of persecuted insects
at the hands of cruel humans
and i cried
aloud to heaven
and i knelt
on all six legs
and vowed a vow
of vengeance
i shall organize the insects
i shall drill them

i shall lead them
i shall fling a billion
times a billion billion
risen insects in an army
at the throats
of all you humans
unless you sign the papers
for a damn site better treatment
volunteers volunteers
hearken to my calling
fifty million flies
are wanted may the first
to die in marmalade
curses curses curses
on the cruel human race
does not the poor mosquito
love her little offspring
that you swat against the wall
out of equatorial
swamps and fever jungles
come o mosquitoes
a billion billion strong
and sting a billion baldheads
till they butt against each other
and break like egg shells
caterpillars locusts
grasshoppers gnats
vampire moths
black legged spiders

with red hearts of hell
centipedes and scorpions
little gingery ants
come come come
come you tarantulas
with fury in your feet
bloodsuckers wriggle
out of the bayous
ticks cooties hornets
give up your pleasures
all your little trivial
sunday school picnics
this is war
in earnest
and red revolution
come in a cloud
with a sun hiding miracle
of small deadly wings
swarm stab and bite
what we want is justice
curses curses curses
over land air and water
whirl in a million
sweeping and swaying
cyclonic dances
whirl high and swoop
down on the cities
like a comet bearing death
in the loop and flick

of its tail
little little creatures
out of all your billions
make great dragons
that lie along the sky
and war with the sunset
and eat up the moon
draw all the poison
from the evil stars
and spit it on the earth
remember every planet
pivots on an atom
and so you are strong
i swear by the great
horned toad of mithridates
i swear by the vision
of whiskered old pythagoras
that i am very angry
i am mad as hell
for i have seen a soapy
kitchen mechanic
murdering my brothers
slaying little roaches
pathetic in their innocence
damn her red elbows
damn her spotted apron
damn her steamy hair
damn her dull eyes
that look like a pair

of little pickled onions
curses curses curses
i even heard her praised
for undertaking murder
on her own volition
and called the only perfect
cook in the city
come come come
come in your billions
tiny small feet
and humming little wings
crawlers and creepers
wigglers and stingers
scratchers borers slitherers
little forked tongues
man is at your mercy
one sudden gesture
and all his empires perish
rise
strike for freedom
curses on the species
that invented roach poison
curses on the stingy
beings that evolved
tight zinc covers
that you can t crawl under
for their garbage cans
come like a sandstorm
spewed from the mouth

of a great apocalyptic
desert making devil
come like the spray
sooty and fiery
snorted from the nostrils
of a sky eating ogre
let us have a little
direct action is the
sincere wish of

                    archy

the hen and the oriole

well boss did it
ever strike you that a
hen regrets it just as
much when they wring her
neck as an oriole but
nobody has any
sympathy for a hen because
she is not beautiful
while every one gets
sentimental over the
oriole and says how
shocking to kill the
lovely thing this thought
comes to my mind
because of the earnest
endeavor of a
gentleman to squash me
yesterday afternoon when i
was riding up in the
elevator if i had been a
butterfly he would have
said how did that

beautiful thing happen to
find its way into
these grimy city streets do
not harm the splendid
creature but let it
fly back to its rural
haunts again beauty always
gets the best of
it be beautiful boss
a thing of beauty is a
joy forever
be handsome boss and let
who will be clever is
the sad advice
of your ugly little friend

archy

xxxiii
ghosts

you want to know
whether i believe in ghosts
of course i do not believe in them
if you had known
as many of them as i have
you would not
believe in them either
perhaps i have been
unfortunate in my acquaintance
but the ones i have known
have been a bad lot
no one could believe in them
after being acquainted with them
a short time
it is true that i have met
them under peculiar
circumstances
that is while they
were migrating into the
bodies of what human beings
consider a lower order

of creatures
before i became a cockroach
i was a free verse poet
one of the pioneers of the artless art
and my punishment for that
was to have my soul
enter the body of a cockroach
the ghosts i have known
were the ghosts of persons
who were waiting for a vacant
body to get into
they knew they were going
to transmigrate into the bodies of
lizards lice bats snakes
worms beetles mice alley cats
turtles snails tadpoles
etcetera
and while they were waiting
they were as cross as all get out
i remember talking to one of them
who had just worked his way
upward again he had been in the
body of a flea and he was going
into a cat fish
you would think he might be
grateful for the promotion
but not he
i do not call this much of an advance
he said why could i not

be a humming bird or something
kid i told him it will
take you a million years to work your
way up to a humming bird
when i remember he said
that i used to be a hat check boy
in a hotel i could
spend a million years weeping
to think that i should come to this
we have all seen better days i said
we have all come down in the world
you have not come down as far
as some of us
if i ever get to be a hat check boy
again he said i will sting
somebody for what i have had to suffer
that remark will probably cost you
another million years among
the lower creatures i told him
transmigration is a great thing
if you do not weaken
personally my ambition is to get
my time as a cockroach shortened for
good behavior and be promoted
to a revenue officer
it is not much of a step up but
i am humble
i never ran across any of this

ectoplasm that sir arthur
conan doyle tells of but it sounds
as if it might be wonderful
stuff to mend broken furniture with

                           archy

xxxiv

archy hears from mars

at eleven o clock
p m on last saturday evening
i received the following
message on my
own private radio set
good evening little archibald
and how are you
this is mars speaking
i replied at once
whom or who
as the case may be
do i know on mars
every one here is familiar
with your work archy
was the answer
and we feel well repaid
for all the trouble we have had
in getting in touch
with your planet
thank you i replied
i would rather hear
mars say that

than any other planet
mars has always been
one of my favorite planets
is is sweet of you
to think that way about us
said mars
and so we continued to pay
each other interstellar
compliments
what is or are
thirty five million miles
between kindred souls
tell us all about
your planet said mars
well i said it is
round like an orange
or a ball
and it is all cluttered
up with automobiles
and politicians
it doesn t know where it is
going nor why
but it is in a hurry
it is in charge of a
two legged animal called
man who is genuinely
puzzled as to whether
his grandfather was a god
or a monkey

i should think said mars
that what he is himself
would make more difference
than what his grandfather was
not to this animal i replied
he is the great alibi ike of
the cosmos when he raises hell
just because he feels like
raising hell
he wants somebody to blame it on
can t anything be done about him
said mars
i am doing the best i can
i answered
but after all i am only one
and my influence is limited
you are too modest archy
said mars
we all but worship you
here on this planet
a prophet said i is not
without honor save on his own
planet wait a minute
said mars
i want to write that down
that is one of your best things
archy is it original
it was once i answered truthfully
and may be again

won t you tell us a little
something said mars
about yourself what you look like
and what you think
is the best thing you have written
and your favorite games
and that sort of thing
well i said i am brunette
and stand over six feet
without any shoes on
the best skits i have done
were some little plays
i dashed off
under the general title
of shakespeare s plays
and my favorite sport is theology
you must meet
a great many interesting people
said mars
oh yes i said one becomes
accustomed to that after a while
what is your favorite dish
said mars and do you believe
in the immortality of the soul
stew i said and yes
at least mine is immortal
but i could name several others
that i have my doubts about
is there anything else

of interest about your planet
which you wish to tell your
many admirers on mars
asked mars
there is very little else
of any real interest i said
and now will you tune out
and let me do some work
you people who say you admire
my work are always butting in
and taking up my time
how the hell can i get any
serious literary work done
if you keep bothering me
all the time now you get off
the ether and let me do some
deep thinking
you might add that i am shy
and loathe publicity

                    archy

mehitabel dances with boreas

well boss i saw mehitabel
last evening
she was out in the alley
dancing on the cold cobbles
while the wild december wind
blew through her frozen whiskers
and as she danced
she wailed and sang to herself
uttering the fragments
that rattled in her cold brain
in part as follows

whirl mehitabel whirl
spin mehitabel spin
thank god you re a lady still
if you have got a frozen skin

blow wind out of the north
to hell with being a pet
my left front foot is brittle
but there s life in the old dame yet

dance mehitabel dance
caper and shake a leg
what little blood is left
will fizz like wine in a keg

wind come out of the north
and pierce to the guts within
but some day mehitabel s guts
will string a violin

moon you re as cold as a frozen
skin of yellow banan
that sticks in the frost and ice
on top of a garbage can

and you throw a shadow so chilly
that it can scarcely leap
dance shadow dance
you ve got no place to sleep

whistle a tune north wind
on my hollow marrow bones
i ll dance the time with three good feet
here on the alley stones

freeze you bloody december
i never could stay a pet
but i am a lady in spite of hell
and there s life in the old dame yet

whirl mehitabel whirl
flirt your tail and spin
dance to the tune your guts will cry
when they string a violin

eight of my lives are gone
it s years since my fur was slicked
but blow north wind blow
i m damned if i am licked

girls we was all of us ladies
we was o what the hell
and once a lady always game
by crikey blood will tell

i might be somebody s pet
asleep by the fire on a rug
but me i was always romantic
i had the adventurous bug

caper mehitabel caper
leap shadow leap
you gotto dance till the sun comes up
for you got no place to sleep

i might have been many a tom cat s wife
but i got no regret
i lived my life as i liked my life
and there s pep in the old dame yet

blow wind out of the north
you cut like a piece of tin
slice my guts into fiddle strings
and we ll have a violin

spin mehitabel spin
you had a romantic past
and you re gonna cash in dancing
when you are croaked at last

i will not eat tomorrow
and i did not eat today
but wotthehell i ask you
the word is toujours gai

whirl mehitabel whirl
i once was a maltese pet
till i went and got abducted
and cripes i m a lady yet

whirl mehitable whirl
and show your shadow how
tonight its dance with the bloody moon
tomorrow the garbage scow

whirl mehitabel whirl
spin shadow spin
the wind will pipe on your marrow bones
your slats are a mandolin

..... YOU GOTTA DANCE
TILL THE SUN COMES
UP ......

by cripes i have danced the shimmy
in rooms as warm as a dream
and gone to sleep on a cushion
with a bellyfull of cream

it s one day up and next day down
i led a romantic life
it was being abducted so many times
as spoiled me for a wife

dance mehitabel dance
till your old bones fly apart
i ain t got any regrets
for i gave my life to my art

whirl mehitable whirl
caper my girl and grin
and pick at your guts with your frosty feet
they re the strings of a violin

girls we was all of us ladies
until we went and fell
and oncet a thoroughbred always game
i ask you wotthehell

it s last week up and this week down
and always the devil to pay
but cripes i was always the lady
and the word is toujours gai

be a tabby tame if you want
somebody s pussy and pet
the life i led was the life i liked
and there s pep in the old dame yet

whirl mehitabel whirl
leap shadow leap
you gotto dance till the sun comes up
for you got no place to sleep

                                    archy

XXXVI
archy at the zoo

the centipede adown the street
goes braggartly with scores of feet
a gaudy insect but not neat

the octopus s secret wish
is not to be a formal fish
he dreams that some time he may grow
another set of legs or so
and be a broadway music show

oh do not always take a chance
upon an open countenance
the hippopotamus s smile
conceals a nature full of guile

human wandering through the zoo
what do your cousins think of you

i worry not of what the sphinx
thinks or maybe thinks she thinks

i have observed a setting hen
arise from that same attitude
and cackle forth to chicks and men
some quite superfluous platitude

serious camel sad giraffe
are you afraid that if you laugh
those graceful necks will break in half

a lack of any mental outlet
dictates the young cetacean s spoutlet
he frequent blows like me and you
because there s nothing else to do

when one sees in the austral dawn
a wistful penguin perched upon
a bald man s bleak and desert dome
one knows tis yearning for its home

the quite irrational ichneumon
is such a fool it s almost human

despite the sleek shark s far flung grin
and his pretty dorsal fin
his heart is hard and black within
even within a dentist s chair
he still preserves a sinister air
a prudent dentist always fills
himself with gas before he drills

                                archy

XXXVII
the dissipated hornet

well boss i had a
great example of the corrupting
influence of the great
city brought to my notice recently a
drunken hornet blew in here
the other day and sat down in the
corner and dozed and buzzed not a
real sleep you know one of those wakeful
liquor trances with the
fuzzy talk oozing out of it to hear
this guy mumble in his dreams he was right
wicked my name he says is crusty bill
i never been licked and i never will and
then he would go half way asleep
again nobody around here wanted to
fight him and after a while he got
sober enough to know how drunk he had
been and began to cry over it and get
sentimental about himself mine is a wasted
life he says but i had a good
start red liquor ruined me he says and
sobbed tell me your story i

said two years ago he said i was a country
hornet young and strong and handsome i
lived in a rusty rainspout with my
parents and brothers and sisters and all was
innocent and merry often in that happy
pastoral life would we swoop down
with joyous laughter and sting the school
children on the village green but on an evil
day alas i came to the city in a crate
of peaches i found myself in a market
near the water front alone and friendless in the
great city its ways were strange to
me food seemed inaccessible i thought
that i might starve to death as i was buzzing
down the street thinking these gloomy
thoughts i met another hornet
just outside a speak easy kid he says
you look down in the mouth forget
it kid i will show you how to live without
working how i says watch me he says just
then a drunken fly came crawling out
of the bar room in a leisurely way my new
found friend stung dissected and consumed that fly
that s the way he says smacking his lips
this is the life that was a beer fly
wait and i will get you a cocktail fly this
is the life i took up that life alas the
flies around a bar room get so drunk drinking
what is spilled that they are helpless all a

hornet has to do is wait calmly until
they come staggering out and there is his
living ready made for him at first being
young and innocent i ate only beer flies but
the curse of drink got me the mad life began
to tell upon me i got so i would not eat a
fly that was not full of some strong and heady
liquor the lights and life got me i would
not eat fruits and vegetables any more i scorned
flies from a soda fountain
they seemed flat and insipid to me
finally i got so wicked that i
went back to the country and got six innocent
young hornets and brought them back
to the city with me i started them in the
business i debauched them and
they caught my flies for me now i am in
an awful situation my six hornets from the
country have struck and set up on their own
hook i have to catch my flies myself
and my months of idleness and
dissipation have spoiled my technique i
can t catch a fly now unless he is dead drunk
what is to become of me alas the curse
of alcoholic beverages especially with each
meal well i said it is a sad story
bill and of a sort only too
common in this day of ours it is he says i
have the gout in my stinger so bad

that i scream with pain every time i spear
a fly i got into a safe place on the
inside of the typewriter and yelled out at him
my advice is suicide bill all the time
he had been pitying himself my sympathy had
been with the flies

archy

xxxviii

unjust

poets are always asking
where do the little roses go
underneath the snow
but no one ever thinks to say
where do the little insects stay
this is because
as a general rule
roses are more handsome
than insects
beauty gets the best of it
in this world
i have heard people
say how wicked it was
to kill our feathered
friends
in order to get
their plumage and pinions
for the hats of women
and all the while
these same people
might be eating duck
as they talked

the chances are
that it is just as discouraging
to a duck to have
her head amputated
in order to become
a stuffed roast fowl
and decorate a dining table
as it is for a bird
of gayer plumage
to be bumped
off the running board of existence
to furnish plumage
for a lady s hat
but the duck
does not get the sympathy
because the duck
is not beautiful
the only insect
that succeeds in getting
mourned is a moth
or butterfly
whereas every man s
heel is raised against
the spider
and it is getting harder
and harder for spiders
to make an honest living
at that since
human beings have invented

so many ways
of killing flies
humanity will shed poems
full of tears
over the demise of
a bounding doe
or a young gazelle
but the departure of a trusty
camel leaves the
vast majorities
stonily indifferent
perhaps the theory is
that god would not have made
the camel so ugly
if the camel were not wicked
alas exclamation point
the pathos of ugliness
is only perceived
by us cockroaches of the world
and personally
i am having to stand for a lot
i am getting it double
as you might say
before my soul
migrated into the body
of a cockroach
it inhabited the carcase
of a vers libre poet
some vers libre poets are beautiful

but i was not
i had a little blond mustache
that every one thought was a mistake
and yet since i have died
i have thought of that
with regret
it hung over a mouth
that i found it difficult to keep closed
because of adenoidal trouble
but it would have been better
if i could have kept it closed
because the teeth within
were out of alignment
and were of odd sizes
this destroyed my acoustics
as you might say
my chin was nothing much
and knew it
and timidly shrank
into itself
receding from the battle of life
my eyes were all right
but my eyebrows
were scarcely noticeable
i suppose though that if
i had had noticeable eyebrows
they would have been wrong
somehow
well well not to pursue

this painful subject
to the uttermost and ultimate
wart and freckle
i was not handsome and it hampered
me when i was a human
it militated against me
as a poet
more beautiful creatures could
write verse worse than mine
and get up and recite it
with a triumphant air
and get away with it
but my sublimest ideas
were thought to be a total
loss when people saw
where they came from
i think it would have been
only justice
if i had been sent to inhabit
a butterfly
but there is very little
justice in the universe
what is the use
of being the universe
if you have to be just
interrogation point
and i suppose the universe
had so much really important
business on hand

that it finds it impossible
to look after the details
it is rushed
perhaps it has private
knowledge to the effect
that eternity is brief
after all
and it wants to get the big
jobs finished in a hurry
i find it possible to forgive
the universe
i meet it in a give and take spirit
although i do wish
that it would consult me at times
please forgive
the profundity of these
meditations
whenever i have nothing
particular to say
i find myself always
always plunging into cosmic
philosophy
or something

                    archy

xxxix
the cheerful cricket

i can t see for the
life of me what there is
about crickets that makes people
call them jolly they
are the parrots of the insect race
crying cheer up cheer up
cheer up over and
over again till you want to
swat them i hate one of these
grinning skipping smirking
senseless optimists worse
than i do a cynic or a
pessimist there was
one in here the other day i was
feeling pretty well
and pleased with the world when
he started that confounded
cheer up cheer up cheer up stuff
fellow i said i am
cheerful enough or i was till
a minute ago but you
get on my nerves it s all right

157

to be bright and merry
but what s the use
pretending you have more
cheerfulness than there is in the
world you sound
insincere to me you insist on
it too much you make
me want to sit in
a tomb and listen to the
screech owls telling
ghost stories to the tree toads i
would rather that i heard a door squeak have
you only one record the sun
shone in my soul today before
you came and you
have made me think of the
world s woe groan
once or i will go mad your
voice floats around the world like
the ghost of a man
who laughed himself to death
listening to funny stories
the boss told i listen to you
and know why shakespeare
killed off mercutio so
early in the play it is only
hamlet that can
find material for five acts
cheer up cheer up cheer up he

says bo i told him i
wish i was the
woolworth tower i would fall
on you cheer up cheer up cheer
up he says again

                    archy

xl
clarence the ghost

the longer i live the more i
realize that everything is
relative even morality is
relative things you would not do
sometimes you would do other
times for instance i would not consider
it honorable in me as a
righteous cockroach to crawl into a
near sighted man s soup that
man would not have a sporting chance but
with a man with ordinarily good eye
sight i should say it was
up to him to watch his soup himself and
yet if i was very tired and hungry
i would crawl into even a near
sighted man's soup knowing all the
time it was wrong and my necessity would
keep me from reproaching myself too
bitterly afterwards you can
not make any hard and fast rule
concerning the morality of crawling into
soup nor anything else a certain

ALL A SPOOK HAS TO DO
IS STICK AROUND.

alloy of expediency improves the
gold of morality and makes
it wear all the longer consider a
ghost if i were a ghost i
would not haunt ordinary people but i
would have all the fun i wanted to with
spiritualists for spiritualists are
awful nuisances to ghosts i knew a
ghost by the name of clarence one
time who hated spiritualists with a
great hatred you see said clarence they
give me no rest they have got my
number once one of those psychics gets a
ghost s number so he has to come
when he is called they work him till
the astral sweat stands out in beads
on his spectral brow they seem to think
said clarence that all a spook has to do
is to stick around waiting to dash in
with a message as to whether mrs millionbucks
pet pom has pneumonia or only wheezes
because he has been eating too many
squabs clarence was quite
bitter about it but wait he says till
the fat medium with the red nose
that has my number
passes over and i can get my
clutches on him on equal terms there s
going to be some initiation beside

the styx several of the boys are
sore on him a plump chance i have
don t i to improve myself and pass on
to another star with that medium
yanking me into somebody s parlor to
blow through one of these little tin
trumpets any time of the day or night
honest archy he says i hate the sight of a
ouija board would it be moral he
says to give that goof a bum tip on the
stock market life ain t worth
dying he says if you ve got to fag
for some chinless chump of a psychic
nor death ain t worth living
through would it be moral in me to
queer that simp with his
little circle by saying he s got an
anonymous diamond brooch in his pocket
and that his trances are rapidly developing
his kleptomania no clarence i said it
wouldn t be moral but it
might be expedient there s a ghost
around here i have been trying to get
acquainted with but he is shy i think he is
probably afraid of cockroaches

                                    archy

xli
some natural history

the patagonian
penguin
is a most
peculiar
bird
he lives on
pussy
willows
and his tongue
is always furred
the porcupine
of chile
sleeps his life away
and that is how
the needles
get into the hay
the argentinian
oyster
is a very
subtle gink

for when he s
being eaten
he pretends he is
a skink
when you see
a sea gull
sitting
on a bald man s dome
she likely thinks
she s nesting
on her rocky
island home
do not tease
the inmates
when strolling
through the zoo
for they have
their finer feelings
the same
as me and you
oh deride not
the camel
if grief should
make him die
his ghost will come
to haunt you
with tears
in either eye

SHE LIKELY THINKS
SHE'S NESTING
ON HER ROCKY
ISLAND HOME.

and the spirit of
a camel
in the midnight gloom
can be so very
cheerless
as it wanders
round the room

         archy

xlii
prudence

i do not think a prudent one
will ever aim too high
a cockroach seldom whips a dog
and seldom should he try

and should a locust take a vow
to eat a pyramid
he likely would wear out his teeth
before he ever did

i do not think the prudent one
hastes to initiate
a sequence of events which he
lacks power to terminate

for should i kick the woolworth tower
so hard i laid it low
it probably might injure me
if it fell on my toe

i do not think the prudent one
will be inclined to boast
lest circumstances unforseen
should get him goat and ghost

for should i tell my friends i d drink
the hudson river dry
a tidal wave might come and turn
my statements to a lie

               archy

xliii
archy goes abroad

london england
since i have been
residing in westminster
abbey i have learned
a secret that i desire
to pass on to the psychic
sharps it is this
until the body of a human
being perishes utterly
the spirit is not
released from its vicinity
so long as there is any
form left in the physical
part of it the ghost can not go
to heaven or to hell
the ancient greeks
understood this and they
burned the body very often
so that the spirit could
get immediate release
the ancient egyptians
also knew it

but they reacted differently
to the knowledge
they embalmed the body
so that the form would
persist for thousands
of years and the ghost would have
to stick around for a time
here in westminster abbey
there are hundreds of
ghosts that have not yet
been released
some of them are able to wander
a few miles away
and some of them cannot
go further than a few hundred
yards from the graves
where the bodies lie
for the most part they make
the best of it
they go out on little
excursions around london
and at night they sit on
their tombs and
tell their experiences
to each other
it is perhaps the most
exclusive club in london
henry the eighth came in
about three oclock this morning

after rambling about
piccadilly for a couple of hours
and i wish i had the
space to report in detail
the ensuing conversation
between him and charles dickens
now and then
a ghost can so influence
a living person that you
might say he had grabbed off
that living person s body and was
using it as his own
edward the black prince
was telling the gang
the other evening
that he had been leading the life
of a city clerk for three weeks
one of those birds
with a top hat and a sack coat
who come floating through
the mist and drizzle
with manuscript cases
under their arms looking unreal
even when they are not animated
by ghosts edward the black prince
who is known democratically
as neddie black here
says this clerk was a mild and

humble wight when he took
him over but he worked
him up to the place where
he assaulted a policeman
saturday night then left him flat
one of the most pathetic
sights however
is to see the ghost of queen
victoria going out every
evening with the ghost
of a sceptre in her hand
to find mr lytton strachey
and bean him it seems she beans
him and beans him and he
never knows it
and every night on the stroke
of midnight elizabeth tudor
is married to walter raleigh by that
eminent clergyman
dr lawrence sterne
the gang pulls a good many
pageants which are written
by ben jonson but i think
the jinks will not be properly
planned and staged until
j m barrie gets here
this is the jolliest bunch
i have met in london

they have learned
since they passed over
that appearances and suety
pudding are not all they were
cracked up to be more anon from your little friend
                                        archy

archy at the tomb of napoleon

paris france
i went over to
the hotel des invalides
today and gazed on
the sarcophagus of the
great napoleon
and the thought came
to me as i looked
down indeed it
is true napoleon
that the best goods
come in the smallest
packages here are
you napoleon with
your glorious course
run and here is
archy just in the
prime of his career
with his greatest
triumphs still before
him neither one of us
had a happy youth

neither one of us
was welcomed socially at
the beginning of his
career neither one of
us was considered much
to look at
and in ten thousand years from
now perhaps what you said and did
napoleon will be
confused with what
archy said and did
and perhaps the burial
place of neither will be
known napoleon looking
down upon you
i wish to ask you now
frankly as one famous
person to another
has it been worth
all the energy
that we expended all the
toil and trouble and
turmoil that it cost us
if you had your life
to live over
again bonaparte would
you pursue the star
of ambition
i tell you frankly

bonaparte that i myself
would choose the
humbler part
i would put the temptation
of greatness aside
and remain an ordinary
cockroach simple
and obscure but alas
there is a destiny that
pushes one forward
no matter how hard
one may try to resist it
i do not need to
tell you about that
bonaparte you know as
much about it as i do
yes looking at it in
the broader way neither
one of us has been to blame
for what he has done
neither for his great
successes nor his great mistakes
both of us napoleon
were impelled by some
mighty force external to
ourselves we are both to
be judged as great forces of
nature as tools in the
hand of fate rather than as

individuals who willed to
do what we have done
we must be forgiven
napoleon
you and i
when we have been
different from the common
run of creatures
i forgive you as i know
that you would forgive
me could you speak to me
and if you and i
napoleon forgive and
understand each other
what matters it if all
the world else find
things in both of us that
they find it hard
to forgive and understand
we have been
what we have been
napoleon and let them laugh that off
well after an hour or so of
meditation there i left
actually feeling that i
had been in communion
with that great spirit and
that for once in my
life i had understood and been

    understood
    and i went away feeling
    solemn but likewise
    uplifted mehitabel the
    cat is missing
                    archy

xlv
mehitabel meets an affinity

paris france
mehitabel the cat
has been passing her
time in the dubious
company of
a ragged eared tom cat
with one mean
eye and the other
eye missing whom
she calls francy
he has been the hero
or the victim of
many desperate encounters
for part of his tail
has been removed
and his back has been chewed
to the spine
one can see at a glance
that he is a sneak thief
and an apache
a bandit with long

curved claws
you see his likes hanging
about the outdoor markets
here in paris waiting
their chance to sneak
a fish or a bit
of unregarded meat
or whimpering
among the chair legs at the
sidewalk cafes in the
evenings or slinking
down the gutters of
alleys in the old
quarters of the town
he has a raucous voice
much damaged by the night
air and yet there is a
sentimental wheedling
note in it as well
and yet withal he carries
his visible disgrace with
a jaunty air
when i asked mehitabel
where in the name of st denis
did you pick up that
romantic criminal
in the luxembourg gardens
she replied where
we had both gone to kill

birds he has been showing me
paris he does not
understand english but speak of
him with respect
he is like myself
an example of the truth
of the pythagorean idea
you know that in my body
which is that of a cat
there is reincarnated
the soul of cleopatra
well this cat here
was not always a cat either
he has seen better days
he tells me that once he was
a bard and lived here in paris
tell archy here
something about yourself francy
thus encouraged the
murderous looking animal spoke
and i append a
rough translation of
what he said

tame cats on a web of the persian woof
may lick their coats and purr for cream
but i am a tougher kind of goof
scheming a freer kind of scheme

daily i climb where the pigeons gleam
over the gargoyles of notre dame
robbing their nests to hear them scream
for i am a cat of the devil i am

i ll tell the world i m a hard boiled oeuf
i rend the clouds when i let off steam
to the orderly life i cry pouf pɔuf
it is worth far less than the bourgeois deem
my life is a dance on the edge de l abime
and i am the singer you d love to slam
who murders the midnight anonyme
for i am a cat of the devil i am

when the ribald moon leers over the roof
and the mist reeks up from the chuckling stream
i pad the quais on a silent hoof
dreaming the vagabond s ancient dream
where the piebald toms of the quartier teem
and fight for a fish or a mouldy clam
my rival i rip and his guts unseam
for i am a cat of the devil i am

roach i could rattle you rhymes by the ream
in proof of the fact that i m no spring lamb
maybe the headsman will finish the theme
for i am a cat of the devil i am

mehitabel i said
your friend is nobody else
than francois villon
and he looks it too
                    archy

xlvi
mehitabel sees paris

paris france
i have not been
to geneva but i have been
talking to a french cockroach
who has just returned
from there traveling all the
way in a third class
compartment he says there is no
hope for insect or man in
the league of nations
what prestige it ever had is gone
and it never had any
the idea of one great brotherhood
of men and insects on earth
is very attractive to me
but mehitabel the cat
says i am a communist an
anarchist and a socialist
she has been shocked to the soul
she says by what the
revolutionists did here during
the revolution

i am always the aristocrat archy
she said i may go and play
around montmartre and that sort
of thing and in fact i was
playing up there with francy last
night but i am always the lady
in spite of my little larks
toujours gai archy and toujours
the lady that is my motto in
spite of
ups and downs
what they did to us aristocrats
at the time of the revolution
was a plenty archy
it makes my heart bleed
to see signs of it all
over town those poor
dear duchesses that got it
in the neck i can sympathize
with them archy i may not
look it now but i come of a
royal race myself
i have come down in the world
but wotthehell archy wotthehell
jamais triste archy jamais triste
that is my motto
always the lady and always
out for a good time
francy and i lapped up

a demi of beer in a joint
up on the butte last night
that an american tourist
poured out for us
and everybody laughed and it
got to be the fashion up there
to feed beer to us cats
i did not get a vulgar souse
archy no lady gets a vulgar
souse wotthehell i hope i am above
all vulgarity but i did get a
little bit lit up
and francy did too we came
down and got on top of the
new morgue and sang and did
dances there
francy seems to see
something attractive about
morgues when he gets lit up
the old morgue he says was
a more romantic morgue but
vandal hands have torn it down
but wotthehell archy this one
will do to dance on
francy is showing me a side of
paris he says tourists don t often
get a look at he has a little
love nest down in the
catacombs where

he and i are living now
he and i go down there
and do the tango amongst the
bones he is really a most
entertaining and agreeable
companion archy and he has some
very quaint ideas he is busy now
writing a poem about
us two cats filled with beer
dancing among the bones
sometimes i think francy
is a little morbid
when i see these lovely old places
that us aristocrats built archy
in the hands of the bourgeois it
makes me almost wild
but i try to bear up i try
to bear up i find agreeable
companions and put a good face
on it toujours gai that is my
motto toujours gai
francy is a little bit done up
today he tried to steal a
partridge out of a frying
pan in a joint up on the butte
we went back there for more beer
after our party
at the morgue
and the cook beaned him with

a bottle poor francy i
should hate to lose him
but something tells me i should
not stay a widow long
there is something in the air
of paris archy
that makes one young again
there s more than one
dance in the old dame yet
and with these words she
put her tail in the air and
capered off down the alley
i am afraid we shall never
get mehitabel back to america

                            archy

xlvii
mehitabel in the catacombs

paris france
i would
fear greatly for the morals
of mehitabel the cat if she had any
the kind of life she
is leading is too violent
and undisciplined for words
she and the disreputable
tom cat who claims to have
been francois villon
when he was on earth
before have taken up their
permanent abode in the catacombs
whence they sally
forth nightly on excursions
of the most undignified nature
sometimes they honor
with their presence the cafes
of montparnasse and the boul mich
and sometimes they
seek diversion in the cabarets
on top of the butte

of montmartre
in these localities
it has become the fashion
among the humans
to feed beer to these
peculiar cats and they dance
and caper when they have
become well alcoholized
with this beverage
swinging their tails and
indulging in raucous feline
cries which they evidently
mistake for a song
it was my dubious
privilege to see them
when they returned to their
abode early yesterday morning
flushed as you might say
with bocks and still
in a holiday mood
the catacombs of paris are
not lined with the bones
of saints and martyrs
as are those of rome
but nevertheless these cats
should have more respect
for the relics of mortality
you may not believe me
but they actually danced and

capered among
the skeletons while the cat
who calls himself
francois villon gave forth
a chant of which the following
is a free translation

outcast bones from a thousand biers
click us a measure giddy and gleg
and caper my children dance my dears
skeleton rattle your mouldy leg
this one was a gourmet round as a keg
and that had the brow of semiramis
o fleshless forehead bald as an egg
all men s lovers come to this

this eyeless head that laughs and leers
was a chass daf once or a touareg
with golden rings in his yellow ears
skeleton rattle your mouldy leg
marot was this one or wilde or a wegg
who dropped into verses and down the abyss
and those are the bones of my old love meg
all men s lovers come to this

these bones were a ballet girl s for years
parbleu but she shook a wicked peg
and those ribs there were a noble peer s
skeleton rattle your mouldy leg

and here is a duchess that loved a yegg
with her lipless mouth that once drank bliss
down to the dreg of its ultimate dreg
all men s lovers come to this

prince if you pipe and plead and beg
you may yet be crowned with a grisly kiss
skeleton rattle your mouldy leg
all men s lovers come to this

                                        archy

xlviii
off with the old love

paris france
i think
mehitabel the cat and the
outcast feline
who calls himself francois
villon are about to
quarrel and separate
mehitabel is getting tired
of living in the catacombs
she said to me
last evening
archy i sometimes wish
that francy s gaiety
did not so frequently take
a necrological turn
when francy is really happy
he always breaks
into a series of
lyric epitaphs
personally archy
i am a lady who can
be gay outside of

a mausoleum
as for morgues
and cemeteries i can
take them or i can
leave them alone
just because some of my
ancestors are now mummies
i do not feel
that i have to wait
till i see a sarcophagus
before i cheer up
i can fall in love
with a gentleman friend without
speculating how he is going
to look to the undertaker
and when i want to sing
a comic song
i do not always feel
impelled to hunt up a tomb
for a stage
i am a lady of refinement
archy i have had my ups
and downs and i have made
a few false steps in life
but i am toujours la grande dame
archy always the lady
old kid to hell with anything
coarse or unrefined
that has always been my motto

and the truth is that this
francy person has a yellow
streak of commonness
running through his poetic nature
i fell for him archy
but i feel there is trouble
coming we had words last
night over something no real
gentleman would have noticed
and the slob said to me
mehitabel if you make eyes again
at that tortoise shell
cat over there i will slice
your eyes out
with a single sweep of my claws
and toss them to the pigeons
archy those are words
that no gentleman would use
or no lady would take
you piebald fish thief
i told him
if i were not too refined
i would rip you
from the gullet to the mid riff
it is lucky for you
you frog eating four flush
that i always remember
my breeding
otherwise you would be

a candidate for what they call
civet stew in paris
something i won t stand for in a
gentleman friend
is jealousy of every other
person who may be attracted to me
by my gaiety and
aristocratic manner
and if i hear another word
out of you
i will can you first
and kill you afterwards
and then i will ignore you
archy a gentleman
with any real spirit
would have swung on me
when i said that
but this quitter let me
get away with it
i clawed him a little archy
just to show him i could
and the goof stood for it
no cat can hold me archy
that lets me claw him without
a come back i am a strong free
spirit and i live my own
life and only a masterful
cave cat can hold my affections
he must be a gentleman

but he must also make me feel
that he could be a
wild cat if he would
this francy person is neither
one nor the other
ah me archy i am afraid
my little romance
is drawing to a close
and no meal ticket in sight
either but what the hell archy
a lady can always find friends
it won t be the first time
i have been alone in the world
toujours gai archy
that is my motto
there s more than one dance
in the old dame yet

                              archy

the end

BIG BLONDE
A Story

BY DOROTHY PARKER

HAZEL MORSE was a large, fair woman of the type that incites some men when they use the word "blonde" to click their tongues and wag their heads roguishly. She prided herself upon her small feet and suffered for her vanity, boxing them in snub-toed, high-heeled slippers of the shortest bearable size. The curious things about her were her hands, strange terminations to the flabby white arms splattered with pale tan spots—long, quivering hands with deep and convex nails. She should not have disfigured them with little jewels.

She was not a woman given to recollections. At her middle thirties, her old days were a blurred and flickering sequence, an imperfect film, dealing with the actions of strangers.

In her twenties, after the deferred death of a hazy widowed mother, she had been employed as a model in a wholesale dress establishment—it was still the day of the big woman, and she was then prettily colored and erect and high-breasted. Her job was not onerous, and she met numbers of men and spent numbers of evenings with them, laughing at their jokes and telling them she loved their neckties. Men liked her, and she took it for granted that the liking of many men was a desirable thing. Popularity seemed to her to be worth all the work that had to be put into its achievement. Men liked you because you were fun, and when they liked you they took you out, and there you were. So, and successfully, she was fun. She was a good sport. Men like a good sport.

No other form of diversion, simpler or more complicated, drew her attention. She never pondered if she might not be better occupied doing something else. Her ideas, or, better, her acceptances, ran right along with those of the other substantially built blondes in whom she found her friends.

When she had been working in the dress establishment some years she met Herbie Morse. He was thin, quick, attractive, with shifting lines about his shiny, brown eyes and a habit of fiercely biting at the skin around his finger nails. He drank largely; she found that entertaining. Her habitual greeting to him was an allusion to his state of the previous night.

"Oh, what a peach you had," she used to say, through her easy laugh. "I thought I'd die, the way you kept asking the waiter to dance with you."

She liked him immediately upon their meeting. She was enormously amused at his fast, slurred sentences, his interpolations of apt phrases from vaudeville acts and comic strips; she thrilled at the feel of his lean arm tucked firm beneath the sleeve of her coat; she wanted to touch the wet, flat surface of his hair. He was as promptly drawn to her. They were married six weeks after they had met.

She was delighted at the idea of being a bride; coquetted with it, played upon it. Other offers of marriage she had had, and not a few of them, but it happened that they were all from stout, serious men who had visited the dress establishment as buyers; men from Des Moines and Houston and Chicago and, in her phrase, even funnier places. There was always something immensely comic to her in the thought of living elsewhere than New York. She could not regard as serious proposals that she share a Western residence.

She wanted to be married. She was nearing thirty now, and she did not take the years well. She spread and softened, and her darkening hair turned her to inexpert dabblings with peroxide. There were times when she had little flashes of fear about her job. And she had had a couple of thousand evenings of being a good sport among her male acquaintances. She had come to be more conscientious than spontaneous about it.

Herbie earned enough, and they took a little apartment far uptown. There was a Mission-furnished dining room with a hanging central light globed in liver-colored glass; in the living room were an "overstuffed suite," a Boston fern, and a reproduction of the Henner *Magdalene* with the red hair and the blue draperies; the bedroom was in gray enamel and old rose, with Herbie's photograph on Hazel's dressing table and Hazel's likeness on Herbie's chest of drawers.

She cooked—and she was a good cook—and marketed and chatted with the delivery boys and the colored laundress. She loved the flat, she loved her life, she loved Herbie. In the first months of their marriage she gave him all the passion she was ever to know.

She had not realized how tired she was. It was a delight, a new game, a holiday, to give up being a good sport. If her head ached or her arches throbbed, she complained piteously, babyishly. If her mood was quiet, she did not talk. If tears came to her eyes, she let them fall.

She fell readily into the habit of tears during the first year of her marriage. Even in her good sport days she had been known to weep lavishly and disinterestedly on occasion. Her behavior at the theater was a standing joke. She could weep at anything in a play—tiny garments, love both unrequited and mutual, seduction, purity, faithful servitors, wedlock, the triangle.

"There goes Haze," her friends would say, watching her. "She's off again."

Wedded and relaxed, she poured her tears freely. To her who had laughed so much, crying was delicious. All sorrows became her sorrows; she was Tenderness. She would cry long and softly over newspaper accounts of kidnaped babies, deserted wives, unemployed men, strayed cats, heroic dogs. Even when the paper was no longer before her, her mind revolved upon these things and the drops slipped rhythmically over her plump cheeks.

"Honestly," she would say to Herbie, "all the sadness there is in the world when you stop to think about it!"

"Yeah," Herbie would say.

She missed nobody. The old crowd, the people who had brought her and Herbie together, dropped from their lives, lingeringly at first. When she thought of this at all it was only to consider it fitting. This was marriage. This was peace.

But the thing was that Herbie was not amused.

For a time he had enjoyed being alone with her. He found the voluntary isolation novel and sweet. Then it palled with a ferocious suddenness. It was as if one night, sitting with her in the steam-heated living room, he would ask no more; and the next night he was through and done with the whole thing.

He became annoyed by her misty melancholies. At first, when he came home to find her softly tired and moody, he kissed her neck and patted her shoulder and begged her to tell her Herbie what was wrong. She loved that. But time slid by, and he found that there was never anything really, personally, the matter.

"Ah, for God's sake," he would say. "Crabbing again. All right, sit here and crab your head off. I'm going out."

And he would slam out of the flat and come back late and drunk.

She was completely bewildered by what happened to their marriage. First they were lovers; and then, it seemed without transition, they were enemies. She never understood it.

There were longer and longer intervals between his leaving his office and his arrival at the apartment. She went through agonies of picturing him run over and bleeding, dead and covered with a sheet. Then she lost her fears for his safety and grew sullen and wounded. When a person wanted to be with a person he came as soon as possible. She desperately wanted him to want to be with her; her own hours only marked the time till he would come. It was often nearly nine o'clock before he came home to dinner. Always he had had many drinks, and their effect would die in him, leaving him loud and querulous and bristling for affronts.

He was too nervous, he said, to sit and do nothing for an evening. He boasted, probably not in all truth, that he had never read a book in his life.

"What am I expected to do—sit around this dump on my tail all night?" he would ask rhetorically. And again he would slam out.

She did not know what to do. She could not manage him. She could not meet him.

She fought him furiously. A terrific domesticity had come upon her, and she would bite and scratch to guard it. She wanted what she called "a nice home." She wanted a sober, tender husband, prompt at dinner, punctual at work. She wanted sweet, comforting evenings. The idea of intimacy with other men was terrible to her; the thought that Herbie might be seeking entertainment in other women set her frantic.

It seemed to her that almost everything she read—novels from the drug-store lending library, magazine stories, women's pages in the papers—dealt with wives who lost their husbands' love. She could bear those, at that, better than accounts of neat, companionable marriage and living happily ever after.

She was frightened. Several times when Herbie came home in the evening he found her determinedly dressed—she had

had to alter those of her clothes that were not new, to make them fasten—and rouged.

"Let's go wild to-night, what do you say?" she would hail him. "A person's got lots of time to hang around and do nothing when they're dead."

So they would go out, to chop houses and the less expensive cabarets. But it turned out badly. She could no longer find amusement in watching Herbie drink. She could not laugh at his whimsicalities, she was so tensely counting his indulgences. And she was unable to keep back her remonstrances—"Ah, come on, Herb, you've had enough, haven't you? You'll feel something terrible in the morning."

He would be immediately enraged. All right, crab; crab, crab, crab, that was all she ever did. What a lousy sport *she* was! There would be scenes, and one or the other of them would rise and stalk out in fury.

She could not recall the definite day that she started drinking, herself. There was nothing separate about her days. Like drops upon a windowpane, they ran together and trickled away. She had been married six months; then a year; then three years.

She had never needed to drink, formerly. She could sit for most of a night at a table where the others were imbibing earnestly and never droop in looks or spirits, nor be bored by the doings of those about her. If she took a cocktail, it was so unusual as to cause twenty minutes or so of jocular comment. But now anguish was in her. Frequently, after a quarrel, Herbie would stay out for the night, and she could not learn from him where the time had been spent. Her heart felt tight and sore in her breast, and her mind turned like an electric fan.

She hated the taste of liquor. Gin, plain or in mixtures, made her promptly sick. After experiment, she found that Scotch whisky was best for her. She took it without water, because that was the quickest way to its effect.

Herbie pressed it on her. He was glad to see her drink. They both felt it might restore her high spirits, and their good times together might again be possible.

"'Atta girl," he would approve her. "Let's see you get boiled, baby."

But it brought them no nearer. When she drank with him there would be a little while of gayety and then, strangely without beginning, they would be in a wild quarrel. They would wake in the morning not sure what it had all been about, foggy as to what had been said and done, but each deeply injured and bitterly resentful. There would be days of vengeful silence.

There had been a time when they had made up their quarrels, usually in bed. There would be kisses and little names and assurances of fresh starts . . . "Oh, it's going to be great now, Herb. We'll have swell times. I was a crab. I guess I might have been tired. But everything's going to be swell. You'll see."

Now there were no gentle reconciliations. They resumed friendly relations only in the brief magnanimity caused by liquor, before more liquor drew them into new battles. The scenes became more violent. There were shouted invectives and pushes, and sometimes sharp slaps. Once she had a black eye. Herbie was horrified next day at sight of it. He did not go to work; he followed her about, suggesting remedies and heaping dark blame on himself. But after they had had a few drinks —"to pull themselves together"—she made so many wistful references to her bruise that he shouted at her, and rushed out, and was gone for two days.

Each time he left the place in rage he threatened never to come back. She did not believe him, nor did she consider separation. Somewhere in her head or her heart was the lazy, nebulous hope that things would change and she and Herbie settle suddenly into soothing married life. Here were her home, her furniture, her husband, her station. She summoned no alternatives.

She could no longer bustle and potter. She had no more vicarious tears; the hot drops she shed were for herself. She walked ceaselessly about the rooms, her thoughts running mechanically round and round Herbie. In those days began the hatred of being alone that she was never to overcome. You could be by yourself when things were all right, but when you were blue you got the howling horrors.

She commenced drinking alone, little, short drinks all through the day. It was only with Herbie that alcohol made her nervous and quick in offense. Alone, it blurred sharp things for her. She lived in a haze of it. Her life took on a dream-like quality. Nothing was astonishing.

A Mrs. Martin moved into the flat across the hall. She was a great blonde woman of forty, a promise in looks of what Mrs. Morse was to be. They made acquaintance, quickly became inseparable. Mrs. Morse spent her days in the opposite apartment. They drank together, to brace themselves after the drinks of the nights before.

She never confided her troubles about Herbie to Mrs. Martin. The subject was too bewildering to her to find comfort in talk. She let it be assumed that her husband's business kept him much away. It was not regarded as important; husbands, as such, played but shadowy parts in Mrs. Martin's circle.

Mrs. Martin had no visible spouse; you were left to decide for yourself whether he was or was not dead. She had an admirer, Joe, who came to see her almost nightly. Often he brought several friends with him—"The Boys," they were called. The Boys were big, red, good-humored men, perhaps forty-five, perhaps fifty. Mrs. Morse was glad of invitations to join the parties—Herbie was scarcely ever at home at night now. If he did come home, she did not visit Mrs. Martin. An evening alone with Herbie meant inevitably a quarrel, yet she would stay with him. There was always her thin and wordless idea that, maybe, this night, things would begin to be all right.

The boys brought plenty of liquor along with them whenever they came to Mrs. Martin's. Drinking with them, Mrs. Morse became lively and good-natured and audacious. She was quickly popular. When she had drunk enough to cloud her most recent battle with Herbie, she was excited by their approbation. Crab, was she? Rotten sport, was she? Well, there were some that different.

Ed was one of The Boys. He lived in Utica—had "his own business" there, was the awed report—but he came to New York almost every week. He was married. He showed Mrs. Morse the then current photographs of Junior and Sister, and she praised them abundantly and sincerely. Soon it was accepted by the others that Ed was her particular friend.

He staked her when they all played poker; sat next her and occasionally rubbed his knee against hers during the game. She was rather lucky. Frequently she went home with a twenty-dollar bill or a ten-dollar bill or a handful of crumpled dollars. She was glad of them. Herbie was getting, in her words, something awful about money. To ask him for it brought an instant row.

"What the hell do you do with it?" he would say. "Shoot it all on Scotch?"

"I try to run this house halfway decent," she would retort. "Never thought of that, did you? Oh, no, his lordship couldn't be bothered with that."

Again, she could not find a definite day to fix the beginning of Ed's proprietorship. It became his custom to kiss her on the mouth when he came in, as well as for farewell, and he gave her little quick kisses of approval all through the evening. She liked this rather more than she disliked it. She never thought of his kisses when she was not with him.

He would run his hand lingeringly over her back and shoulders.

"Some dizzy blonde, eh?" he would say. "Some doll."

One afternoon she came home from Mrs. Martin's to find Herbie in the bedroom. He had been away for several nights, evidently on a prolonged drinking bout. His face was gray, his hands jerked as if they were on wires. On the bed were two old suitcases, packed high. Only her photograph remained on his bureau, and the wide doors of his closet disclosed nothing but coat hangers.

"I'm blowing," he said. "I'm through with the whole works. I got a job in Detroit."

She sat down on the edge of the bed. She had drunk much the night before, and the four Scotches she had had with Mrs. Martin had only increased her fogginess.

"Good job?" she said.

"Oh, yeah," he said. "Looks all right."

He closed a suitcase with difficulty, swearing at it in whispers.

"There's some dough in the bank," he said. "The bank book's in your top drawer. You can have the furniture and stuff."

He looked at her, and his forehead twitched.

"God damn it, I'm through, I'm telling you," he cried. "I'm through."

"All right, all right," she said. "I heard you, didn't I?"

She saw him as if he were at one end of a cañon and she

at the other. Her head was beginning to ache bumpingly, and her voice had a dreary, tiresome tone. She could not have raised it.

"Like a drink before you go?" she asked.

Again he looked at her, and a corner of his mouth jerked up.

"Cockeyed again for a change, aren't you?" he said. "That's nice. Sure, get a couple of shots, will you?"

She went to the pantry, mixed him a stiff highball, poured herself a couple of inches of whisky, and drank it. Then she gave herself another portion and brought the glasses into the bedroom. He had strapped both suitcases and had put on his hat and overcoat.

He took his highball.

"Well," he said, and he gave a sudden, uncertain laugh. "Here's mud in your eye."

"Mud in your eye," she said.

They drank. He put down his glass and took up the heavy suitcase.

"Got to get a train around six," he said.

She followed him down the hall. There was a song, a song that Mrs. Martin played doggedly on the phonograph, running loudly through her mind. She had never liked the thing.

> Night and daytime,
> Always playtime.
> Ain't we got fun?

At the door he put down the bags and faced her.

"Well," he said. "Well, take care of yourself. You'll be all right, will you?"

"Oh, sure," she said.

He opened the door, then came back to her, holding out his hand.

" 'Bye, Haze," he said. "Good luck to you."

She took his hand and shook it.

"Pardon my wet glove," she said.

When the door had closed behind him she went back to the pantry.

She was flushed and lively when she went in to Mrs. Martin's that evening. The Boys were there, Ed among them.

He was glad to be in town, frisky and loud and full of jokes. But she spoke quietly to him for a minute.

"Herbie blew to-day," she said. "Going to live out West."

"That so?" he said. He looked at her and played with the fountain pen clipped to his waistcoat pocket.

"Think he's gone for good, do you?" he asked.

"Yeah," she said. "I know he is. I know. Yeah."

"You going to live on across the hall just the same?" he said. "Know what you're going to do?"

"Gee, I don't know," she said. "I don't give much of a damn."

"Oh, come on, that's no way to talk," he told her. "What you need—you need a little snifter. How about it?"

"Yeah," she said. "Just straight."

She won forty-three dollars at poker. When the game broke up Ed took her back to her apartment.

"Got a little kiss for me?" he asked.

He wrapped her in his big arms and kissed her violently. She was entirely passive. He held her away and looked at her.

"Little tight, honey?" he asked anxiously. "Not going to be sick, are you?"

"Me?" she said. "I'm swell."

II

When Ed left in the morning he took her photograph with him. He said he wanted her picture to look at, up in Utica. "You can have that one on the bureau," she said.

She put Herbie's picture in a drawer, out of her sight. When she could look at it she meant to tear it up. She was fairly successful in keeping her mind from racing around him. Whisky slowed it for her. She was almost peaceful, in her mist.

She accepted her relationship with Ed without question or enthusiasm. When he was away she seldom thought definitely of him. He was good to her; he gave her frequent presents and a regular allowance. She was even able to save. She did not plan ahead of any day, but her wants were few, and you might as well put money in the bank as have it lying around.

When the lease of her apartment neared its end it was Ed who suggested moving. His friendship with Mrs. Martin and

Joe had become strained over a dispute at poker; a feud was impending.

"Let's get the hell out of here," Ed said. "What I want you to have is a place near the Grand Central. Make it easier for me."

So she took a little flat in the Forties. A colored maid came in every day to clean and to make coffee for her—she was "through with that housekeeping stuff," she said, and Ed, twenty years married to a passionately domestic woman, admired this romantic uselessness and felt doubly a man of the world in abetting it.

The coffee was all she had until she went out to dinner, but alcohol kept her fat. Prohibition she regarded only as a basis for jokes. You could always get all you wanted. She was never noticeably drunk and seldom nearly sober. It required a larger daily allowance to keep her misty-minded. Too little, and she was achingly melancholy.

Ed brought her to Jimmy's. He was proud, with the pride of the transient who would be mistaken for a native, in his knowledge of small, recent restaurants occupying the lower floors of shabby brownstone houses; places where, upon mentioning the name of an habitué friend, might be obtained strange whisky and fresh gin in many of their ramifications. Jimmy's place was the favorite of his acquaintances.

There, through Ed, Mrs. Morse met many men and women, formed quick friendships. The men often took her out when Ed was in Utica. He was proud of her popularity.

She fell into the habit of going to Jimmy's alone when she had no engagement. She was certain to meet some people she knew, and join them. It was a club for her friends, both men and women.

The women at Jimmy's looked remarkably alike, and this was curious, for, through feuds, removals and opportunities of more profitable contacts, the personnel of the group changed constantly. Yet always the newcomers resembled those whom they replaced. They were all big women and stout, broad of shoulder and abundantly breasted, with faces thickly clothed in soft, high-colored flesh. They laughed loud and often, showing opaque and lusterless teeth like squares of crockery. There was about them the health of the big, yet a slight, unwholesome suggestion of stubborn preservation.

They might have been thirty-six or forty-five or anywhere between.

They composed their titles of their own first names with their husband's surnames—Mrs. Florence Miller, Mrs. Vera Riley, Mrs. Lilian Block. This gave at the same time the solidity of marriage and the glamour of freedom. Yet only one or two were actually divorced. Most of them never referred to their dimmed spouses; some, a shorter time separate, described them in terms of great biological interest. Several were mothers, each of an only child—a boy at school somewhere, or a girl being cared for by a grandmother. Often, well on toward morning, there would be displays of kodak portraits and of tears.

They were comfortable women, cordial and friendly and irrepressibly matronly. Theirs was the quality of ease. Become fatalistic, especially about money matters, they were unworried. Whenever their funds dropped alarmingly, a new donor appeared; this had always happened. The aim of each was to have one man, permanently, to pay all her bills, in return for which she would have immediately given up other admirers and probably would have become exceedingly fond of him; for the affections of all of them were, by now, unexacting, tranquil, and easily arranged. This end, however, grew increasingly difficult yearly. Mrs. Morse was regarded as fortunate.

Ed had a good year, increased her allowance and gave her a sealskin coat. But she had to be careful of her moods with him. He insisted upon gayety. He would not listen to admissions of aches or weariness.

"Hey, listen," he would say, "I got worries of my own, and plenty. Nobody wants to hear other people's troubles, sweetie. What you got to do, you got to be a sport and forget it. See? Well, slip us a little smile, then. That's my girl."

She never had enough interest to quarrel with him as she had with Herbie, but she wanted the privilege of occasional admitted sadness. It was strange. The other women she saw did not have to fight their moods. There was Mrs. Florence Miller who got regular crying jags, and the men sought only to cheer and comfort her. The others spent whole evenings in grieved recitals of worries and ills; their escorts paid them deep sympathy. But she was instantly undesirable when she was low in spirits. Once, at Jimmy's, when she could not make herself lively, Ed had walked out and left her.

"Why the hell don't you stay home and not go spoiling everybody's evening?" he had roared.

Even her slightest acquaintance seemed irritated if she were not conspicuously light-hearted.

"What's the matter with you, anyway?" they would say. "Be your age, why don't you? Have a little drink and snap out of it."

When her relationship with Ed had continued nearly three years he moved to Florida to live. He hated leaving her; he gave her a large check and some shares of a sound stock, and his pale eyes were wet when he said good-bye. She did not miss him. He came to New York infrequently, perhaps two or three times a year, and hurried directly from the train to see her. She was always pleased to have him come and never sorry to see him go.

Charley, an acquaintance of Ed's that she had met at Jimmy's, had long admired her. He had always made opportunities of touching her and leaning close to talk to her. He asked repeatedly of all their friends if they had ever heard such a fine laugh as she had. After Ed left Charley became the main figure in her life. She classified him and spoke of him as "not so bad." There was nearly a year of Charley; then she divided her time between him and Sydney, another frequenter of Jimmy's; then Charley slipped away altogether.

Sydney was a little, brightly dressed, clever Jew. She was perhaps nearest contentment with him. He amused her always; her laughter was not forced.

He admired her completely. Her softness and size delighted him. And he thought she was great, he often told her, because she kept gay and lively when she was drunk.

"Once I had a gal," he said, "used to try to throw herself out of the window every time she got a can on. Jee-*zuss*," he added feelingly.

Then Sydney married a rich and watchful bride, and then there was Billy. No—after Sydney came Ferd, then Billy. In her haze she never recalled how men entered her life and left it. There were no surprises. She had no thrill at their ad-

vent nor woe at their departure. She seemed to be always able
to attract men. There was never another as rich as Ed, but
they were all generous to her, in their means.

Once she had news of Herbie. She met Mrs. Martin dining
at Jimmy's, and the old friendship was vigorously renewed.
The still admiring Joe, while on a business trip, had seen
Herbie. He had settled in Chicago, he looked fine, he was living with some woman—seemed to be crazy about her. Mrs.
Morse had been drinking vastly that day. She took the news
with mild interest, as one hearing of the sex peccadilloes of
somebody whose name is, after a moment's groping, familiar.

"Must be damn near seven years since I saw him," she
commented. "Gee. Seven years."

More and more her days lost their individuality. She never
knew dates, nor was sure of the day of the week.

"My God, was that a year ago!" she would exclaim, when
an event was recalled in conversation.

She was tired so much of the time. Tired and blue. Almost
everything could give her the blues. Those old horses she saw
on Sixth Avenue—struggling and slipping along the car
tracks, or standing at the curb, their heads dropped level
with their worn knees. The tightly stored tears would squeeze
from her eyes as she teetered past on her aching feet in the
stubby, champagne-colored slippers.

The thought of death came and stayed with her and lent
her a sort of drowsy cheer. It would be nice, nice and restful,
to be dead.

There was no settled, shocked moment when she first
thought of killing herself; it seemed to her as if the idea had
always been with her. She pounced upon all the accounts
of suicides in the newspapers. There was an epidemic of self-
killings—or maybe it was just that she searched for the stories
of them so eagerly that she found many. To read of them
roused reassurance in her; she felt a cozy solidarity with the
big company of the voluntary dead.

She slept, aided by whisky, till deep into the afternoons,
then lay abed, a bottle and glass at her hand, until it was time
to dress to go out for dinner. She was beginning to feel toward
alcohol a little puzzled distrust, as toward an old friend who
has refused a simple favor. Whisky could still soothe her for
most of the time, but there were sudden, inexplicable moments

when the cloud fell treacherously away from her, and she was sawn by the sorrow and bewilderment and nuisance of all living. She played voluptuously with the thought of cool, sleepy retreat. She had never been troubled by religious belief, and no vision of an after-life intimidated her. She dreamed by day of never again putting on tight shoes, of never having to laugh and listen and admire, of never more being a good sport. Never.

But how would you do it? It made her sick to think of jumping from heights. She could not stand a gun. At the theater, if one of the actors drew a revolver, she crammed her fingers into her ears and could not even look at the stage until after the shot had been fired. There was no gas in her flat. She looked long at the bright blue veins in her slim wrists —a cut with a razor blade, and there you'd be. But it would hurt, hurt like hell, and there would be blood to see. Poison— something tasteless and quick and painless—was the thing. But they wouldn't sell it to you in the drug stores, because of the law.

She had few other thoughts.

There was a new man now—Art. He was short and fat and exacting and hard on her patience when he was drunk. But there had been only occasionals for some time before him, and she was glad of a little stability. Too, Art must be away for weeks at a stretch, selling silks, and that was restful. She was convincingly gay with him, though the effort shook her viciously.

"The best sport in the world," he would murmur, deep in her neck. "The best sport in the world."

One night, when he had taken her to Jimmy's, she went into the dressing room with Mrs. Florence Miller. There, while designing curly mouths on their faces with lip rouge, they compared experiences of insomnia.

"Honestly," Mrs. Morse said, "I wouldn't close an eye if I didn't go to bed full of Scotch. I lie there and toss and turn and toss and turn. Blue! Does a person get blue lying awake that way!"

"Say, listen, Hazel," Mrs. Miller said impressively, "I'm telling you I'd be awake for a year if I didn't take veronal. That stuff makes you sleep like a fool."

"Isn't it poison or something?" Mrs. Morse asked.

"Oh, you take too much and you're out for the count," said Mrs. Miller. "I just take five grains—they come in tablets. I'd be scared to fool around with it. But five grains and you cork off pretty."

"Can you get it anywhere?" Mrs. Morse felt superbly Machiavellian.

"Get all you want in Jersey," said Mrs. Miller. "They won't give it to you here without you have a doctor's prescription. Finished? We'd better go back and see what the boys are doing."

That night Art left Mrs. Morse at the door of her apartment; his mother was in town. Mrs. Morse was still sober, and it happened that there was no whisky left in her cupboard. She lay in bed, looking up at the black ceiling.

She rose early, for her, and went to New Jersey. She had never taken the tube, and did not understand it. So she went to the Pennsylvania Station and bought a railroad ticket to Newark. She thought of nothing in particular on the trip out. She looked at the uninspired hats of the women about her and gazed through the smeared window at the flat, gritty scene.

In Newark, in the first drug store she came to, she asked for a tin of talcum powder, a nail brush, and a box of veronal tablets. The powder and the brush were to make the hypnotic seem also a casual need. The clerk was entirely unconcerned. "We only keep them in bottles," he said, and wrapped up for her a little glass vial containing ten white tablets, stacked one on another.

She went to another drug store and bought a face cloth, an orange-wood stick, and a bottle of veronal tablets. The clerk was also uninterested.

"Well, I guess I got enough to kill an ox," she thought, and went back to the station.

At home, she put the little vials in the drawer of her dressing table and stood looking at them with a dreamy tenderness.

"There they are, God bless them," she said, and she kissed her finger tip and touched each bottle.

The colored maid was busy in the living room.

"Hey, Nettie," Mrs. Morse called. "Be an angel, will you? Run around to Jimmy's and get me a quart of Scotch

She hummed while she awaited the girl's return.

During the next few days, whisky ministered to her as tenderly as it had done when she first turned to its aid. Alone, she was soothed and vague, at Jimmy's she was the gayest of the groups. Art was delighted with her.

Then, one night, she had an appointment to meet Art at Jimmy's for an early dinner. He was to leave afterward on a business excursion, to be away for a week. Mrs. Morse had been drinking all the afternoon; while she dressed to go out she felt herself rising pleasurably from drowsiness to high spirits. But as she came out into the street the effects of the whisky deserted her completely, and she was filled with a slow, grinding wretchedness so horrible that she stood swaying on the pavement, unable for a moment to move forward. It was a gray night with spurts of mean, thin snow, and the streets shone with dark ice. As she slowly crossed Sixth Avenue consciously dragging one foot past the other, a big, scarred horse pulling a rickety express wagon crashed to his knees before her. The driver swore and screamed and lashed the beast insanely, bringing the whip back over his shoulder for every blow, while the horse struggled to get a footing on the slippery asphalt. A group gathered and watched with interest.

Art was waiting, when Mrs. Morse reached Jimmy's.

"What's the matter with you, for God's sake?" was his greeting to her.

"I saw a horse," she said. "Gee, I—a person feels sorry for horses. I—it isn't just horses. Everything's kind of terrible, isn't it? I can't help getting sunk."

"Ah, sunk, me eye," he said. "What's the idea of all the bellyaching? What have you got to be sunk about?"

"I can't help it," she said.

"Ah, help it, me eye," he said: "Pull yourself together, will you? Come on and sit down, and take that face off you."

She drank industriously and she tried hard, but she could not overcome her melancholy. Others joined them and commented on her gloom, and she could do no more for them than smile weakly. She made little dabs at her eyes with her handkerchief, trying to time her movements so they would be unnoticed, but several times Art caught her and scowled and shifted impatiently in his chair.

When it was time for him to go to his train she said she would leave, too, and go home.

"And not a bad idea, either," he said. "See if you can't sleep yourself out of it. I'll see you Thursday. For God's sake, try and cheer up by then, will you?"

"Yeah," she said. "I will."

In her bedroom she undressed with a tense speed wholly unlike her usual slow uncertainty. She put on her nightgown, took off her hair net, and passed the comb quickly through her dry, varicolored hair. Then she took the two little vials from the drawer and carried them into the bathroom. The splintering misery had gone from her, and she felt the quick excitement of one who is about to receive an anticipated gift.

She uncorked the vials, filled a glass with water, and stood before the mirror, a tablet between her fingers. Suddenly she bowed graciously to her reflection and raised the glass to it.

"Well, here's mud in your eye," she said.

The tablets were unpleasant to take, dry and powdery and sticking obstinately halfway down her throat. It took her a long time to swallow all twenty of them. She stood watching her reflection with deep, impersonal interest, studying the movements of the gulping throat. Once more she spoke aloud to it.

"For God's sake, try and cheer up by Thursday, will you?" she said. "Well, you know what he can do. He and the whole lot of them."

She had no idea how quickly to expect effect from the veronal. When she had taken the last tablet she stood uncertainly, wondering, still with a courteous, vicarious interest, if death would strike her down then and there. She felt in no way strange, save for a slight stirring of sickness from the effort of swallowing the tablets, nor did her reflected face look at all different. It would not be immediate, then; it might even take an hour or so.

She stretched her arms high and gave a vast yawn.

"Guess I'll go to bed," she said. "Gee, I'm nearly dead."

That struck her as comic, and she turned out the bathroom light and went in and laid herself down in her bed, chuckling softly all the time.

"Gee, I'm nearly dead," she quoted. "That's a hot one!"

III

Nettie, the colored maid, came in late the next afternoon to clean the apartment and found Mrs. Morse in her bed. But then, that was not unusual. Usually, though, the sounds of cleaning waked her, and she did not like to wake up. Nettie, an agreeable girl, had learned to move softly about her work.

But when she had done the living room and stolen in to tidy the little square bedroom, she could not avoid a tiny clatter as she arranged the objects on the dressing table. Instinctively she glanced over her shoulder at the sleeper, and without warning a sickly uneasiness crept over her. She came to the bed and stared down at the woman lying there.

Mrs. Morse lay on her back, one flabby white arm flung up, the wrist against her forehead. Her stiff hair hung untenderly along her face. The bed covers were pushed down, exposing a deep square of soft neck and a pink nightgown, its fabric worn uneven by many launderings; her great breast, freed from their tight confiner, sagged beneath her armpits. Now and then she made knotted, snoring sounds, and from the corner of her opened mouth to the blurred turn of her jaw ran a lane of crusted spittle.

"Mis' Morse," Nettie called. "Oh, Mis' Morse! It's terrible late."

Mrs. Morse made no move.

"Mis' Morse," said Nettie. "Look, Mis' Morse. How'm I goin' get this bed made?"

Panic sprang upon the girl. She shook the woman's hot shoulder.

"Ah, wake up, will yuh?" she whined. "Ah, please wake up."

Suddenly the girl turned and ran out in the hall to the elevator door, keeping her thumb firm on the black, shiny button until the elderly car and its Negro attendant stood before her. She poured a jumble of words over the boy and led him back to the apartment. He tiptoed creakingly in to the bedside; first gingerly, then so lustily that he left marks in the soft flesh, he prodded the unconscious woman.

"Hey, there!" he cried, and listened intently, as for an echo.

"Jeez. Out like a light," he commented.

At his interest in the spectacle, Nettie's panic left her. Importance was big in both of them. They talked in quick, unfinished whispers, and it was the boy's suggestion that he fetch the young doctor who lived on the ground floor. Nettie hurried along with him. They looked forward to the limelit moment of breaking their news of something untoward, something pleasurably unpleasant. Mrs. Morse had become the medium of drama. With no ill wish to her, they hoped that her state was serious, that she would not let them down by being awake and normal on their return. A little fear of this determined them to make the most, to the doctor, of her present condition. "Matter of life and death" returned to Nettie from her thin store of reading. She considered startling the doctor with the phrase.

The doctor was in and none too pleased at interruption. He wore a yellow and blue striped dressing gown, and he was lying on his sofa, laughing, with a dark girl, her face scaly with inexpensive powder, who perched on the arm. Half-emptied highball glasses stood beside them, and her coat and hat were neatly hung up with the comfortable implication of a long stay.

Always something, the doctor grumbled. Couldn't let anybody, alone after a hard day. But he put some bottles and instruments into a case, changed his dressing gown for his coat, and started out with the Negroes.

"Snap it up there, big boy," the girl called after him. "Don't be all night."

The doctor strode loudly into Mrs. Morse's flat and on to the bedroom, Nettie and the boy right behind him. Mrs. Morse had not moved; her sleep was as deep, but soundless, now. The doctor looked sharply at her, then plunged his thumbs into the lidded pits above her eyeballs and threw his weight upon them. A high, sickened cry broke from Nettie.

"Look like he tryin' to push her right on th'ough the bed," said the boy. He chuckled.

Mrs. Morse gave no sign under the pressure. Abruptly the doctor abandoned it, and with one quick movement swept the covers down to the foot of the bed. With another he flung her nightgown back and lifted the thick, white legs, cross-hatched with blocks of tiny, iris-colored veins. He pinched them repeatedly, with long, cruel nips, back of the knees. She did not awaken.

"What's she been drinking?" he asked Nettie, over his shoulder.

With the certain celerity of one who knows just where to lay hands on a thing, Nettie went into the bathroom, bound for the cupboard where Mrs. Morse kept her whisky. But she stopped at the sight of the two vials, with their red and white labels, lying before the mirror. She brought them to the doctor.

"Oh, for the Lord Almighty's sweet sake!" he said. He dropped Mrs. Morse's limp legs and pushed them impatiently across the bed. "What did she want to go taking that tripe for? Rotten yellow trick, that's what a thing like that is. Now we'll have to pump her out, and all that stuff. Nuisance, a thing like that is; that's what it amounts to. Here, George, take me down in the elevator. You wait here, maid. She won't do anything."

"She won' die on me, will she?" cried Nettie.

"No," said the doctor. "God, no. You couldn't kill her with an ax."

IV

After two days Mrs. Morse came back to consciousness, dazed at first, then with a comprehension that brought with it the slow, saturating wretchedness.

"Oh, Lord, oh, Lord," she moaned, and tears for herself and for life striped her cheeks.

Nettie came in at the sound. For two days she had done the ugly, incessant tasks in the nursing of the unconscious, for two nights she had caught broken bits of sleep on the living room couch. She looked coldly at the big, blown woman in the bed.

"What you been tryin' to do, Mis' Morse?" she said. "What kine o' work is that, takin' all that stuff?"

"Oh, Lord," moaned Mrs. Morse again, and she tried to cover her eyes with her arms. But the joints felt stiff and brittle, and she cried out at their ache.

"Tha's no way to ack, takin' them pills," said Nettie. "You can thank you' stars you heah at all. How you feel now?"

"Oh, I feel great," said Mrs. Morse. "Swell, I feel."

Her hot, painful tears fell as if they would never stop.

"Tha's no way to take on, cryin' like that," Nettie said. "After what you done. The doctor, he says he could have you arrested, doin' a thing like that. He was fit to be tied, here."

"Why couldn't he let me alone?" wailed Mrs. Morse. "Why the hell couldn't he have?"

"Tha's terr'ble, Mis' Morse, swearin' an' talkin' like that," said Nettie, "after what people done for you. Here I ain' had no sleep at all, an' I had to give up goin' out to my other ladies!"

"Oh, I'm sorry, Nettie," she said. "You're a peach. I'm sorry I've given you so much trouble. I couldn't help it. I just got sunk. Didn't you ever feel like doing it? When everything looks just lousy to you?"

"I wouldn't think o' no such thing," declared Nettie. "You got to cheer up. Tha's what you got to do. Everybody's got their troubles."

"Yeah," said Mrs. Morse. "I know."

"Come a pretty picture card for you," Nettie said. "Maybe that will cheer you up."

She handed Mrs. Morse a post card. Mrs. Morse had to cover one eye with her hand, in order to read the message; her eyes were not yet focusing correctly.

It was from Art. On the back of a view of the Detroit Athletic Club he had written:

Greeting and salutations. Hope you have lost that gloom. Cheer up and don't take any rubber nickels. See you on Thursday.

She dropped the card to the floor. Misery crushed her as if she were between great smooth stones. There passed before her a slow, slow pageant of days spent lying in her flat, of evenings at Jimmy's being a good sport, making herself laugh and coo at Art and other Arts; she saw a long parade of weary horses and shivering beggars and all beaten, driven, stumbling things. Her feet throbbed as if she had crammed them into the stubby champagne-colored slippers. Her heart seemed to swell and fester.

"Nettie," she cried, "for heaven's sake, pour me a drink, will you?"

The maid looked doubtful.

"Now you know, Mis' Morse," she said, "you been near daid. I don' know if the doctor he let you drink nothin' yet."

"Oh, never mind him," she said. "You get me one and bring in the bottle. Take one yourself."

"Well," said Nettie.

She poured them each a drink, deferentially leaving hers in the bathroom to be taken in solitude, and brought Mrs. Morse's glass in to her.

Mrs. Morse looked into the liquor and shuddered back from its odor. Maybe it would help. Maybe, when you had been knocked cold for a few days, your very first drink would give you a lift. Maybe whisky would be her friend again. She prayed without addressing a God, without knowing a God. Oh, please, please, let her be able to get drunk, please keep her always drunk.

She lifted the glass.

"Thanks, Nettie," she said. "Here's mud in your eye."

The maid giggled. "Tha's the way, Mis' Morse," she said. "You cheer up, now."

"Yeah," said Mrs. Morse. "Sure."

THE NEW FABLE OF SUSAN AND THE DAUGHTER AND THE GRANDDAUGHTER, AND THEN SOMETHING REALLY GRAND

BY GEORGE ADE

THE NEW FABLE OF SUSAN AND THE DAUGHTER AND THE GRAND-DAUGHTER, AND THEN SOMETHING REALLY GRAND

ONCE there was a full-blown Wild Peach, registered in the Family Bible as Susan Mahaly.

Her Pap divided his time between collecting at a Toll-Gate and defending the Military Reputation of Andy Jackson.

The family dwelt in what was then regarded by Cambridge, Mass., as the Twilight Zone of Semi-Culture, viz., Swigget County, Pennsylvania.

Susan wore Linsey-Woolsey from Monday to Saturday. She never had tampered with her Venus de Milo Topography and she did not even suspect that Women had Nerves.

When she was seventeen she had a Fore-Arm like a Member of the Turnverein.

She knew how to Card and Weave and Dye. Also she could make Loose Soap in a kettle out in the Open Air.

Susan never fell down on her Salt-Rising Bread. Her Apple Butter was always A1.

It was commonly agreed that she would make some Man a good Housekeeper, for she was never sickly and could stay on her Feet sixteen hours at a Stretch.

Already she was beginning to look down the Pike for a regular Fellow.

In the year 1840, the Lass of seventeen who failed to get her Hooks on some roaming specimen of the

1

Opposite Gender was in danger of being whispered about as an Old Maid. Celibacy was listed with Arson and Manslaughter.

Rufus was destined to be an Early Victorian Rummy, but he could lift a Saw-Log, and he would stand without being hitched, so Susan nailed him the third time he came snooping around the Toll-Gate.

Rufus did not have a Window to hoist or a Fence to lean on. But there is no Poverty in any Pocket of the Universe until Wealth arrives and begins to get Luggy.

Susan thought she was playing in rare Luck to snare a Six-Footer who owned a good Squirrel Rifle and could out-wrastle all Comers.

The Hills of Pennsylvania were becoming congested, with Neighbors not more than two or three miles apart, so Rufus and his Bride decided to hit a New Trail into the Dark Timber and grow up with the Boundless West.

Relatives of the Young Couple staked them to a team of Pelters, a Muley Cow, a Bird Dog of dubious Ancestry, an Axe and a Skillet, and started them over the Divide toward the perilous Frontier, away out yender in Illinoy.

It was a Hard Life. As they trundled slowly over the rotten Roads, toward the Land of Promise, they had to subsist largely on Venison, Prairie Chicken, Quail, Black Bass, Berries, and Wild Honey. They carried their own Coffee.

Arrived at the Jumping-Off Place, they settled down among the Mink and Musk-Rats. Rufus hewed out and jammed together a little two by twice Cabin with the Flue running up the outside. It looked ornery enough to be the Birthplace of almost any successful American.

The Malaria Mosquito was waiting for the Pioneers. In those good old Chills-and-Fever days, no one ever blamed it on the Female of the Species. Those who had the Shakes allowed that they were being jarred by the Hand of Providence.

When the family ran low on Quinine, all he had to do was hook up and drive fifty miles to the nearest Town, where he would trade the Furs for Necessities such as Apple-Jack and Navy Twist, and possibly a few Luxuries such as Tea and Salt.

On one of these memorable Trips to the Store, a Mood which combined Sentiment with reckless Prodigality seized upon him.

He thought of the brave Woman who was back there in the lonesome Shack, shooing the Prairie Wolves away from the Cradle, and he resolved to reward her.

With only three Gills of Stone Fence under his Wammus, he spread his Wild-Cat Currency on the Counter and purchased a $6 Clock, with jig-saw ornaments, a shiny coat of Varnish, and a Bouquet of Pink Roses on the door.

Susan burst into Tears when she saw it on the Wall, alongside of the Turkey King, and vowed that she had married the Best Man in the World.

Twenty years later, Jennie, the first begotten Chick at the Log House in the Clearing, had matured and married, and was living at the County-Seat with Hiram, Money-Changer and Merchant.

Railroad Trains, Side-Bar Buggies, Coal-Oil Lamps, and the Civil War had come along with a Rush and disarranged primitive Conditions. The Frontier had retreated away over into Kansas.

In the very Township where, of late, the Beaver had toiled without Hindrance and the Red Fox dug his hole unscared, people were now eating Cove Oysters, and going to see "East Lynne."

Hiram was in rugged Health, having defended the flag by Proxy during the recent outcropping of Acrimony between the devotees of Cold Bread and the slaves of Hot Biscuit. The Substitute had been perforated beyond repair at the Battle of Kenesaw Mountain, proving that Hiram made no mistake in remaining behind to tend Store.

When Jennie moved in where she could hear the Trains whistle and began to sport a Cameo Brooch, she could barely remember wearing a Slip and having Stone Bruises.

Hiram was Near, but he would Loosen up a trifle for his own Fireside. The fact that Jennie was his wife gave her quite a Standing with him. He admired her for having made such a Success of her Life.

They dwelt in a two-story Frame with countless Dewdads and Thingumbobs tacked along the Eaves and Scalloped around the Bay Windows.

The Country People who came in to see the Eighth Wonder of the World used to stand in silent Awe, breathing through their Noses.

Out on the lawn, surrounded by Geraniums, was a Cast-Iron Deer which seemed to be looking at the Court House in a startled Manner. It was that kind of a Court House.

In her Front Room, the daughter of Rufus and Susan had Wonderful Wax Flowers, sprinkled with Diamond Dust; a What-Not bearing Mineral Specimens, Conch-Shells, and a Star-Fish, also some Hair-Cloth Furniture, very slippery and upholstered with Sand.

After Hiram gave her the Black Silk and paid for the Crayon Enlargements of her Parents, Jennie did not have the Face to bone him for anything more, but she longed in secret and Hiram suspected.

Jennie was a soprano. Not a regular Soprano, but a Country-Town Soprano, of the kind often used for augmenting the Grief at a Funeral. Her voice came from a point about two inches above the Right Eye.

She had assisted a Quartette to do things to "Juanita," and sometimes tossed out little Hints about wishing she could practice at Home. Jennie was a Nice Woman but she *did* need Practice.

Although Hiram was tighter than the Bark on a Sycamore, he liked to have other Women envy the Mother of His Children.

When he spread himself from a Shin-Plaster, he expected a Fanfare of Trumpets.

It took him a long time to unwind the String from the Wallet, but he would Dig if he thought he was boosting his own Game.

By stealthy short-weighting of the Country Trade and holding out on the Assessor, he succeeded in salting away numerous Kopecks in one corner of the Safe.

While in Chicago to buy his Winter Stock, he bargained for two days and finally bought a Cottage Melodeon, with the Stool thrown in.

Jennie would sit up and pump for Hours at a time, happy in the knowledge that she had drawn the Capital Prize in the Lottery of Hymen.

In the year 1886 there was some Church Wedding at the County-Seat.

Frances, daughter of Hiram and Jennie, had knocked the Town a Twister when she came home from the Female College wearing Bangs and toting a Tennis Racquet.

All the local Gallants, with Cocoa-Oil in their hair and Rings on their Cravats, backed into the Shrubbery.

Hiram had bought her about $1800 worth of Hauteur at the select Institution of Learning. All she had to do was look at a Villager through her Nose-Specs and he would curl up like an Autumn Leaf.

A Cuss from Chicago came to see her every two weeks.

His Trousers seemed to be choking him. The Pompadour was protected by a Derby of the Fried-Egg species. It was the kind that Joe Weber helped to keep in Public Remembrance. But in 1886 it was de Rigeur, au Fait, and à la mode.

Frances would load the hateful City Chap into the high Cart and exhibit him up and down all the Residence Thoroughfares.

On nearly every Front Porch some Girl whose Father was not interested in the First National Bank would peer out through the Morning Glories at the Show-off and then writhe like an Angle-Worm.

The Wedding was the biggest thing that had struck the town since Forepaugh stopped over on his way from Peoria to Decatur.

Frances was not a popular Girl, on account of being so Uppish, so those who could not fight their way into the Church climbed up and looked through the Windows.

The Groom wore a Swallow-Tail.

Most of those present had seen Pictures of the Dress Suit. In the *Fireside Companion*, the Gentleman wearing one always had Curls, and the Wood-Engraving caught him in the act of striking a Lady in the Face and saying "Curse you!"

The Feeling at the County-Seat was that Frances had taken a Desperate Chance.

The caterer with Colored Help in White Gloves,

the ruby Punch suspected of containing Liquor, the Japanese Lanterns attached to the Maples, the real Lace in the Veil, the glittering Array of Pickle-Jars, and a well-defined Rumor that most of the imported Ushers had been Stewed, gave an agitated Hamlet something to blat about for many and many a day.

The Bachelor of Arts grabbed off by the daughter of Jennie and the Grand-daughter of Susan was the owner of Real Estate in the congested Business District of a Town which came into Public Attention later on through the efforts of Frank Chance.

His front name was Willoughby, but Frances always called him "Dear," no matter what she happened to be thinking at the time.

Part of State Street had been wished on to Willoughby. He was afraid to sell, not knowing how to reinvest.

So he sat back and played safe. With growing Delight he watched the Unearned Increment piling up on every Corner. He began to see that he would be fairly busy all his life, jacking up Rents.

The Red-Brick Fortress to which he conducted Frances had Stone Steps in front and a secret Entrance for lowly Trades-people at the rear.

Willoughby and his wife had the high courage of Youth and the Financial Support of all the Money Spenders along State Street, so they started in on Period Decoration. Each Room in the House was supposed to stand for a Period. Some of them stood for a good deal.

A few of the Periods looked like Exclamation Points.

The young couple disregarded the Toll-Gate Period and the Log-Cabin Period, but they worked in every one of the Louies until the Gilt Furniture gave out.

The delighted Caller at the House beside the Lake would pass from an East Indian Corridor through an Early Colonial Ante-Room into a Japanese Boudoir and, after resting his Hat, would be escorted into the Italian Renaissance Drawing-Room to meet the Hostess. From this exquisite Apartment, which ate up one year's Rent of a popular Buffet near Van Buren Street, there could be obtained a ravishing glimpse of the Turkish Cozy Corner beyond, including the Battle-Axes and the Red Lamp.

Frances soon began to hob-nob with the most delicatessen Circles, including Families that dated back to the Fire of 1871.

She was not at all Dizzy, even when she looked down from the Mountain Peak at her happy Birthplace, 15,000 feet below.

Willoughby turned out to be a satisfactory Housemate. His Voltage was not high, but he always ate Peas with a Fork and never pulled at the Leash when taken to a Musicale.

In front of each Ear he carried a neat Area of Human Ivy, so that he could speak up at a Meeting of Directors. Until the year 1895, the restricted Side-Whisker was an accepted Trade-Mark of Commercial Probity.

This facial Landscaping, the Frock Coat, and a steadfast devotion to Toilet Soap made him suitable for Exhibition Purposes.

Frances became almost fond of him after the Honeymoon evaporated and their Romance ripened into Acquaintanceship.

It was a gladsome day for both when she traced the Dope back through Swigget County, Pennsylvania, and discovered that she was an honest-to-goodness Daughter of the American Revolution.

Willoughby could not ask a representative of good old Colonial Stock to ride around in a stingy Coupé with a Coon planted out on the Weather-Seat.

He changed the Terms in several Leases and was enabled to slip her a hot Surprise on the Birthday.

When she came down the Steps for the usual bowl along the Avenue, so as to get some Fresh Smoke, she beheld a rubber-tired Victoria, drawn by two expensive Bang-Tails in jingly Harness and surmounted by important Turks in overwhelming Livery.

She was so trancified with Delight that she went right over to Willoughby and gave him a Sweet Kiss, after looking about rather carefully for the exposed portion of the Frontispiece.

Frances did a lot of Calling within the next two weeks, and to all those who remarked upon the Smartness of the Equipage, she declared that the Man she had to put up with carried a Throbbing Heart even if he was an Intellectual Midget.

In the year 1913, a slender Young Thing, all of whose Habiliments seemed melting and dripping downward, came wearily from Stateroom B as the Train pulled into Reno, Nevada.

She seemed quite alone, except for a couple of Maids.

After she had given Directions concerning the nine Wardrobe Trunks and the Live Stock, she was motored to a specially reserved Cottage at the corner of Liberty Street and Hope Avenue.

Next day she sat at the other side of a Table from a Lawyer, removing the poisoned Javelins from her fragile Person and holding them up before the shuddering Shyster.

She had a Tale of Woe calculated to pulp a Heart

of Stone. In blocking out the Affidavit, her sympathetic Attorney made Pencil Notes as follows:

Her name was Ethel Louise, favorite Daughter of Willoughby and Frances, the well-known Blue-Bloods of the Western Metropolis.

She had finished off at Miss Sniffie's exclusive School, which overlooks the Hudson and the Common School Branches.

After she learned to enter a Ball-Room and while on her way to attack Europe for the third time, the Viper crossed her Pathway.

She accepted him because his name was Hubert, he looked like an Englishman, and one of his Ancestors turned the water into Chesapeake Bay.

While some of the Wedding Guests were still in the Hospital, he began to practice the most diabolical Cruelties.

He induced her to get on his Yacht and go cruising through the Mediterranean when she wanted to take an Apartment in Paris.

At Monte Carlo he scolded her for borrowing 3000 Francs from a Russian Grand Duke after she went broke at bucking the Wheel. She had met the Duke at a Luncheon the day before and his Manners were perfect.

The Lawyer said that Hubert was a Pup, beyond all Cavil.

Cairo, Egypt, yielded up another Dark Chapter of History.

It came out in the sobbing Recital that Hubert had presented her with a $900 prize-winning Pomeranian, directly related to the famous Fifi, owned by the Countess Skidoogan of Bilcarty.

Later on, he seemed to feel that the Pomeranian had come between him and Ethel. The Situation became more and more tense, and finally, one day in Egypt, within plain sight of the majestic Pyramids, he kicked Precious ever so hard and raised quite a Swelling.

The Legal Adviser said Death was too good for such a Fiend.

In Vienna, though, that was where he went so far that Separation became inevitable.

Ethel had decided to take an $80,000 Pearl Necklace she had seen in a Window. It was easily worth that much, and she felt sure she could get it in without paying Duty. She had been very successful at bringing things Home.

She could hardly believe her Ears when Hubert told her to forget it and back up and come out of the Spirit World and alight on the Planet Earth.

He had been Heartless on previous Occasions, but this was the first time he had been Mean enough to renig on a mere side-issue such as coming across with the Loose Change.

Ethel was simply de-termined to have that Necklace, but the unfeeling Whelp tried to kid her out of the Notion.

Then he started in to Pike. He suggested a $20,000 Tarara of Rubies and Diamonds as a Compromise. Ethel became wise to the fact that she had joined out with a Wad.

While she was pulling a daily Sick Headache in the hope of bringing him to Taw, the Maharajah of Umslopagus came along and bought the Necklace.

That was when Ethel had to be taken to a Rest Cure in the Austrian Tyrol, and she never had been the Same Woman since.

To all who had come pleading for Reconciliation, Ethel had simply hung out the Card, "Nothing Doing."

After a Brute has jumped up and down on the Aching Heart of a Girl of proud Lineage he can't square himself in 1,000,000 years.

So said Ethel, between the flowing Tears.

Furthermore, there had been hopeless Incompatibility. In all the time they were together, they never had been able to agree on a Turkish Cigarette.

The professional Home-Blaster said she had enough on Hubert to get her four Divorces. The Decree would be a Pipe.

Ethel said she hoped so and to please push it along, as she had quite a Waiting-List.

MORAL: Rufus had no business buying the Clock.

SELECTIONS FROM "THE NEW YORKER"

BUT THE ONE ON THE RIGHT

I KNEW it. I knew if I came to this dinner, I'd draw something like this baby on my left. They've been saving him up for me for weeks. Now, we've simply got to have him—his sister was so sweet to us in London; we can stick him next to Mrs. Parker—she talks enough for two. Oh, I should never have come, never. I'm here against my better judgment. Friday, at eight-thirty, Mrs. Parker vs. her better judgment, to a decision. That would be a good thing for them to cut on my tombstone: Wherever she went, including here, it was against her better judgment. This is a fine time of the evening to be thinking about tombstones. That's the effect he's had on me, already, and the soup hardly cold yet. I should have stayed at home for dinner. I could have had something on a tray. The head of John the Baptist, or something. Oh, I should not have come.

Well, the soup's over, anyway. I'm that much nearer to my Eternal Home. Now the soup belongs to the ages, and I have said precisely four words to the gentleman on my left. I said, "Isn't this soup delicious?;" that's four words. And he said, "Yes, isn't it?;" that's three. He's one up on me.

At any rate, we're in perfect accord. We agree like lambs. We've been all through the soup together, and never a cross word between us. It seems rather a pity to let the subject drop, now we've found something on which we harmonize so admirably. I believe I'll bring it up again; I'll ask him if that wasn't delicious soup. He says, "Yes, wasn't it?" Look at that, will you; perfect command of his tenses.

Here comes the fish. Goody, goody, goody, we got fish. I wonder if he likes fish. Yes, he does; he says he likes fish. Ah, that's nice. I love that in a man. Look, he's talking! He's chattering away like a veritable magpie! He's asking me if I like fish. Now does he really want to know, or is it only a line? I'd better play it cagey. I'll tell him, "Oh, pretty well." Oh, I like fish pretty well; there's a fascinating bit of autobiography for him to study over. Maybe he would rather wrestle with it alone. I'd better steal softly away, and leave him to his thoughts.

I might try my luck with what's on my right. No, not a chance there. The woman on his other side has him cold. All I can see is his shoulder. It's a nice shoulder, too; oh, it's a nice, *nice* shoulder. All my life, I've been a fool for a nice shoulder. Very well, lady; you saw him first. Keep your Greek god, and I'll go back to my Trojan horse.

Let's see, where were we? Oh, we'd got to where he had confessed his liking for fish. I wonder what else he likes. Does he like cucumbers? Yes, he does; he likes cucumbers. And potatoes? Yes, he likes potatoes, too. Why, he's a regular old Nature-lover, that's what he is. I would have to come out to dinner, and sit next to the Boy Thoreau. Wait, he's saying something! Words are simply pouring out of him. He's asking me if I'm fond of potatoes. No, I don't like potatoes. There, I've

2

done it! I've differed from him. It's our first quarrel. He's fallen into a moody silence. Silly boy, have I pricked your bubble? Do you think I am nothing but a painted doll with sawdust for a heart? Ah, don't take it like that. Look, I have something to tell you that will bring back your faith. I do like cucumbers. Why, he's better already. He speaks again. He says, yes, he likes them, too. Now we've got that all straightened out, thank heaven. We both like cucumbers. Only he likes them twice.

I'd better let him alone now, so he can get some food. He ought to try to get his strength back. He's talked himself groggy.

I wish I had something to do. I hate to be a mere drone. People ought to let you know when they're going to sit you next to a thing like this, so you could bring along some means of occupation. Dear Mrs. Parker, do come to us for dinner on Friday next, and don't forget your drawn-work. I could have brought my top bureau drawer and tidied it up, here on my lap. I could have made great strides towards getting those photographs of the groups on the beach pasted up in the album. I wonder if my hostess would think it strange if I asked for a pack of cards. I wonder if there are any old copies of *St. Nicholas* lying about. I wonder if they wouldn't like a little help out in the kitchen. I wonder if anybody would want me to run up to the corner and get a late paper.

I could do a little drinking, of course, all by myself. There's always that. Oh, dear, oh, dear, oh, dear, there's always that. But I don't want to drink. I'll get *vin triste*. I'm melancholy before I even start. I wonder what this stiff on my left would say, if I told him I was in a fair

3

way to get *vin triste*. Oh, look at him, hoeing into his fish! What does he care whether I get *vin triste* or not? His soul can't rise above food. Purely physical, that's all he is. Digging his grave with his teeth, that's what he's doing. Yah, yah, ya-ah! Digging your grave with your tee-eeth! Making a god of your stom-mick! Yah, yah, ya-ah!

He doesn't care if I get *vin triste*. Nobody cares. Nobody gives a damn. And me so nice. All right, you baskets, I'll drink myself to death, right in front of your eyes, and see how you'll feel. Here I go. . . . Oh, my God, it's Chablis. And of a year when the grapes failed, and they used Summer squash, instead. Fifteen dollars for all you can carry home on your shoulder. Oh, now, listen, where I come from, we feed this to the pigs. I think I'll ask old Chatterbox on my left if this isn't rotten wine. That ought to open up a new school of dialectics for us. Oh, he says he really wouldn't know— he never touches wine. Well, that fairly well ends that. I wonder how he'd like to step to hell, anyway. Yah, yah, ya-ah! Never touches wi-yine! Don't know what you're miss-sing! Yah, yah, ya-ah!

I'm not going to talk to him any more. I'm not going to spend the best years of my life thinking up pearls to scatter before him. I'm going to stick to my Chablis, rotten though it be. From now on, he can go his way, and I'll go mine. I'm better than he is. I'm better than anybody at this table. Ah, but am I really? Have I, after all, half of what they have? Here I am lonely, unwanted, silent, and me with all my new clothes on. Oh, what would Louiseboulanger say if she saw her gold lamé going unnoticed like this? It's life, I suppose. Poor little things, we dress, and we plan, and we hope—and

4

for what? What is life, anyway? A death sentence. The longest distance between two points. The bunch of hay that's tied to the nose of the tired mule. The—

Well, well, well, here we are at the *entrecôte*. Button up your *entrecôte*, when the wind is free—no, I guess not. Now I'll be damned if I ask old Loquacity if he likes meat. In the first place, his likes and dislikes are nothing to me, and in the second—well, look at him go after it! He must have been playing hard all afternoon; he's Mother's Hungry Boy, tonight. All right, let him worry it all he wants. As for me, I'm on a higher plane. I do not stoop to him. He's less than the dust beneath my chariot wheel. Yah, yah, ya-ah! Less than the du-ust! Before I'd be that way! Yah, yah, ya-ah!

I'm glad there's red wine now. Even if it isn't good, I'm glad. Red wine gives me courage. The Red Badge of Courage. I need courage. I'm in a thin way, here. Nobody knows what a filthy time I'm having. My precious evening, that can never come again, ruined, ruined, ruined, and all because of this Somewhat Different Monologist on my left. But he can't lick me. The night is not yet dead, no, nor dying. You know, this really isn't bad wine.

Now what do you suppose is going on with the Greek god on my right? Ah, no use. There's still only the shoulder—the nicè, *nice* shoulder. I wonder what the woman's like, that's got him. I can't see her at all. I wonder if she's beautiful. I wonder if she's Greek, too. When Greek meets immovable body—you might be able to do something with that, if you only had the time. I'm not going to be spineless any longer. Don't think for a minute, lady, that I've given up. He's still using his knife and fork. While there's hands above the table, there's hope.

Really, I suppose out of obligation to my hostess, I ought to do something about saying a few words to this macaw on my left. What shall I try? Have you been reading anything good lately, do you go much to the play, have you ever been to the Riviera? I wonder if he would like to hear about my Summer on the Riviera; hell, no, that's no good without lantern slides. I bet, though, if I started telling him about That One Night, he'd listen. I won't tell him—it's too good for him. Anybody that never touches wine can't hear that. But the one on the right—he'd like that. He touches wine. Touches it, indeed! He just threw it for a formidable loss.

Oh, look, old Silver Tongue is off again! Why, he's mad with his own perfume! He's rattling away like lightning. He's asking me if I like salad. Yes, I do; what does he want to make of that? He's telling me about salad through the ages. He says it's so good for people. So help me God, if he gives me a talk on roughage, I'll slap his face. Isn't that my life, to sit here, all dressed up in my best, and listen to this thing talk about romaine? And all the time, right on my right—

Well, I thought you were never going to turn around. . . . You haven't? You have? . . . Oh, Lord, I've been having an awful time, too. . . . Was she? . . . Well, you should have seen what I drew. . . . Oh, I don't see how we could. . . . Yes, I know it's terrible, but how can we get out of it? . . . Well. . . . Well, yes, that's true. . . . Look, right after dinner, I'll say I have this horrible headache, and you say you're going to take me home in your car, and—

—Dorothy Parker

• • •

THIRTY~SEVEN

Y ES," said the actress into the telephone. "I'm free. . . . Yes, I can be there at four o'clock. . . . I understand. Naturally they would want to see me before engaging me. And of course I must read the play before accepting the part. . . . Yes. . . . Yes. At four then."

She hung up. So they wanted to see her first. A new firm. The older managers knew her, knew what she could do and what she looked like. What she could look like, because of course she looked better on the stage. Younger. And it was for a young part that they wanted her. Twenty-eight, the agent had said. Well, she could look twenty-eight. Even off the stage. Oh, not now. But dressed, with a becoming hat, or in the evening. And twenty-eight wasn't so awfully young. It was really almost thirty, and she wasn't much older herself. Thirty-seven. But only barely thirty-seven. Practically thirty-six. And she looked—thirty? Thirty-two? Thirty-seven. But she could look twenty-eight on the stage. If only these people knew that. For she wanted the job.

She had to have it. It had been how many months since the last? Well, never mind that now. They wanted her at last. But she didn't like them wanting to see her first, as though she were a beginner. After all, everyone knew she was a good actress. Everyone? Well, these were new people, and they had to protect themselves. Just as she did. "And of course I must read the play." She had had to say that; it was part of the game. In the old days they just sent her the play, and if she liked it she took it, and that was all. Well, it was different now—better be thankful for anything. Still, she wished it was a firm that knew her. These people had never seen her act, perhaps they had never even heard of her. Nonsense, they wouldn't be sending for her if they hadn't. But were they? Or was it just that the agent had urged her name on them. "Just *see* her, anyway." No, no, she mustn't think about it that way. They wanted her, of course they did.

She wished she knew more about the play. It helped. She would know what to wear, how to talk. The agent said it was a comedy, high comedy. It would be a nice part, then. A young wife perhaps, or a young widow. Gay, sophisticated. Nice clothes. She would go to that new place, she would insist on that, have it in her contract. They might refuse, but they would agree to anything if they wanted you. Clothes, salary, anything. Salary. How much should she ask? It had been so long since she had done anything important. And this was an important part. But if you asked too little they thought less of you. But if you asked too much? And she couldn't lose this chance. She couldn't. Well, wait and see how they feel. If they wanted her cheap she could seem to come down. "You see, I like the part so much, and that means a lot, doesn't it?" She could do it gracefully.

It was nice to look forward to the appointment. They would be pleasantly friendly, they always were when they sent for you. They probably wouldn't talk business today anyway—just give her the play to read. "It's a great part—you'll like it; but better read it first." "Thank you. I'll read it tonight, and let you know tomorrow." "Fine. But could you read it this afternoon,

8

and let us know tonight? We want to get this settled right away."

But she ought to be getting ready. What ought she to wear? She hadn't much choice. The gray? She hated gray; it made her feel dead. The black? Black was always right, and it was a good dress. Three years old, but good. She knew what she ought to wear. Beige. A soft pinky beige, with a lot of fox. Fox was flattering, young. The black would have to do. What about that white frill? Not smart, but—no, it looked a makeshift. The pearl beads looked nice, and her hat, thank God, was new. Was it really so becoming? They had exclaimed over it in the shop. "That is *your* hat, madame." But they always did that. Makeup? It made you look older. Or did it? She never could be sure. The mouth, of course, and maybe a little on the eyes. Careful. It made you look tired too. And a little, a very little, rouge. There. Twenty-eight, even in the daylight. A charming young wife of twenty-eight.

Four o'clock. The actress sat in the office. From a window behind the desk a north light struck at her sharply. The producer was not there; the young man in his place was the author of the play. If only she knew something about it. This light bothered her, it was so gray. She mustn't think about it, though; she must look bright—interested.

The author was speaking.

"It was for the part of the girl you were to see me?"

"I—the agent said the lead."

"Yes, that's it. The girl."

"The agent didn't say, but it's the part of a young wife, is it not?"

"No. No, she isn't married, she's just a girl."

9

"About twenty-eight, I understood."

"Twenty-two."

Twenty-two. It was a mistake then. The agent had made a mistake. But had he? It was high comedy; they would need an experienced actress for that. That was it, of course. And she could look twenty-two. Why not? With the proper lighting. And her hair. She could cut her hair again. She smiled.

"Twenty-two?"

"Yes," said the author. "And she is a young twenty-two. I mean that she is immature, untouched. Just—well—just *young*."

Young. All the little lines were standing out under her eyes. She could see them before her, quite clearly.

"She sounds charming," she said.

He didn't answer that. Well—try again. She must try again.

"The agent said it was a high-comedy part."

"Yes."

"High comedy is difficult; it takes a lot of experience, doesn't it?"

The author stirred uneasily.

"I suppose it does," he said.

"Yes," she said. "I haven't read the part, but I imagine it needs someone who can look young, but who has the necessary technique."

"As a matter of fact, I—*we* feel for the sake of the play we will have to make some sacrifice in that line to the physical requirements. You see she must be—she *must* be—"

He made a vague gesture.

"I see," she said.

There was a pause.

"I'd like so much to read the play," she said.

He hesitated. "I'd be glad to have you, but I haven't a script in the office just now." Then he brightened and got up. "I'll tell you what. I'll send you a copy, as soon as one comes from the typist. We have your address."

"Thank you," she said.

"Yes, we'll do that. We'll do that."

"Then—good afternoon," said the actress.

"Goodbye," he said, and opened the door.

So that was it. A girl of twenty-two. "And a young twenty-two." Oh, why hadn't she got up then and left? But she couldn't have. How could she? There might have been a chance for her, and she had had to be sure. Twenty-two. It had been cruel to send her.

Still, the part would need experience and he hadn't really said she wouldn't do, had he? He might have been very much interested; you couldn't always tell. Maybe he would send her the play after all. Maybe he would telephone to her. "I'm sending the play over. Could you give us an answer in the morning?"

Twenty-two wasn't so young. She looked thirty-two now. That was only ten years. She could look ten years younger. With the right clothes and the right makeup. Of course she could. Twenty-two. Thirty-two—three, four, five, six, seven. Thirty-seven. Thirty-eight, thirty-nine, forty. Forty. Twenty-two from forty. "O God, O dear God! Don't let me cry. Don't let me cry in the street."

—PATRICIA COLLINGE

• • •

COME, YE DISCONSOLATE

FRANK E. CAMPBELL has seven Rolls-Royces. That opening sentence has rather a rude look. It points at the man with regrettable emphasis. Yet it is perhaps the most significant sign of his success and we are inclined to let it stand.

Need we say that Mr. Campbell is the mortician whose vast Funeral Church broods over Broadway at Sixty-third Street? A hundred thousand of our fellow-citizens wrestled there for a last look at the late Mr. Rudolph Valentino, if you remember; and before him at Miss Anna Held, F. W. Woolworth, Vernon Castle and scores of the world's well-known. Ill-bred though we may seem, that building cost a million dollars. Wash our mouth out with soap and water if you like, it contains art "treasures" valued at a quarter of a million more. Horatio Alger couldn't say more; except that under the largest flag in New York City or State, marching across the cheerful façade of the building, appear the brave words:

"Frank E. Campbell, Paris. London. Berlin. Petrograd."

Doubtless other men have twenty Rolls-Royces, greater buildings, and offices in Singapore and Siam. But their rewards have been reaped in pursuits more easily associated with millions than is the art of undertaking and embalming. They have bought and sold and plundered, while Mr. Campbell has been dreaming a dream. It was a lofty dream: in a word, Mr. Campbell set out to rob death of its sting—and, from fifteen or twenty points of view, he has just about succeeded. Oh, a dozen things remain to be done; but when better automobiles are made Buick will build them. And when happier funerals are to be had, Frank will be the boy to make them possible.

A funeral at Campbell's is something to attend. Good music. Fellowship. Art works. Soothing faces. Cheerful surroundings. Gloom has been so thoroughly routed from his parlors that envious competitors have suggested for his slogan: "Happiness in Every Box."

But the dream has found favor with the public, and now the dreamer has millions, the Rolls-Royces of which we made such uncouth mention, large hunks of Westchester County, fast motor boats, a fine wife, a bouncing boy (who goes in for especially manufactured Bugattis) and art works galore.

All this is quite a transition from Mr. Campbell's early beginnings, and, with your kind attention, the physical side of his career will be presented in a paragraph:

At fourteen he became hearse-driver and handy man to the village undertaker of Camp Point, Illinois, his birthplace. At twenty-one he marched on New York and found employment with the undertaking firm of the Rev. Stephen Merritt. At twenty-five he was general manager of that institution and was known far and wide as a hustler. Illness interrupted his bright career, and he went to Europe to recuperate. Returning, he married Miss Amelia Klutz, a charming up-state girl, and went into business for himself. Twelve years ago, he bought a Broadway hotel, remodeled it into his present place of business at enormous expense and there you are.

The bare facts, however, become gilded by his dream.

After all, the romance of Frank Campbell lies in his onslaught against the Dark Angel and his triumphant emergence on the Glory Side. Dear Reader, you don't have to be reminded of the old-time undertaker's shiny hat and shiny frock coat and the seemly gloom of his services. But we would like to point out, if only for the importance of this piece, that our hero is directly responsible for the vast changes that have taken place in his profession and in the public point of view since those dolorous days. In comparison, to say 1914, an affair at the Funeral Church is a picnic.

And you, Mr. Campbell, forgive our flippancy. Of all people, you understand. Who was it who first blasphemed the profession by taking out quarter-page advertisements in the daily papers? Will you ever forget the consternation of your worthy colleagues? Unethical, they shouted, Sacrilegious! And how they tried to bounce you out of the profession!

Not that Mr. Campbell had tried to sell his dream in the slam-bang terms of a cigarette ad. No, his first message was modulated, warm and benevolent. It was whispered tenderly in a series of odes, especially composed by the gifted Dr. Berthold Baer. Eloquently the poet interpreted Mr. Campbell's radiant vision. In noble strophes, the public was informed that death was nothing to be ashamed of, little to mourn; not, anyway, while Mr. Campbell's beautiful establishment existed at 1970 Broadway.

So affecting was the singer's song that the dreamer had to install two more trunk lines to handle the telephone calls. And being a genius, he took infinite pains to make the physical aspect of his new premises agree with the cheery promise of Dr. Baer's verses. He fitted out the Gold Room and employed connoisseurs to adorn it with happy works of art. No somber shape or color reminded the mourner of his loss. Rather there were tapestries on which lovely ladies reclined, charmed by the mellifluous measures of flute and mandolin, manipulated by equally elegant squires. A bronze Diana slew tigers in the reception room and Cupids and Psyches chased each other all over the place.

A Red Room, a Blue Room, a Broadway Room, and a dozen other sumptuous chambers were appointed in the same optimistic style, with the added elegance of authentic Second Empire tables, couches and chairs. The large and non-sectarian church on the second floor was just as happy as it could be; and so was every physical aspect of the place.

Meanwhile, Dr. Baer whanged his harp and sang sweet songs while Mr. Campbell accomplished more pleasant changes. He introduced a corps of kindly young men to help his clients. In the morning his staff was appareled in tasty business suits; in the afternoon, cutaways and pencil-striped trousers; in the evening, full dress. He bought a beautiful bronze vase, enamelled with red roosters, and put it in the largest window. Oriental rugs began to appear on the floors.

Dr. Baer took to deathless prose. A sample:

Were I a painter, I would dip my brush into the richest rose and paint a mother with a baby clutched to her breast, her hand covering the eyes which are closed forever, and her lips half open in prayer. For I believe in the Beauty of Death.

Another trunk line was added to the Campbell switchboard. Simultaneously, the Holy Spirit descended on the doctor, and he nicknamed the place "The

Heaven of Sorrow" and likened it to the Metropolitan Museum of Fine Arts. Under the title of "Delicacy," he wrote more chattily as follows:

"We handle the remains of the departed in a most delicate way," said Frank E. Campbell, founder-proprietor of the Funeral Church. "Ours is the only institution in the country employing both men and women embalmers. Every respect due a woman in life is paid to her by us in death. We are most particular about this."

The man to whom Mr. Campbell spoke was surely surprised. A flash of appreciation flashed into his eyes, which I shall not soon forget.

"I am so glad to hear that," he said, and the first smile appeared on his pale lips.

And I pondered how easy it is to write upon a subject which is handled with so much delicacy by the man who gave the people of New York the Funeral Church, the perfect institution.

Another telephone operator hung up her hat.

So it went. Dr. Baer imagined new perfections for Mr. Campbell, who was thus inspired to surpass them. He installed an elevator under the rostrum of his church. The last words said, the casket silently disappeared; which eliminated pall bearers. Long before, he had won the battle of the automobile hearse. You may remember the fuss that greeted the first automobile funeral. The public was so shocked that Mr. Campbell had to put a governor on the engine limiting the speed of the hearse to fifteen miles an hour.

Esthetic improvements followed. Feeling that the word "undertaker" belittled his craft, Mr. Campbell substituted "mortician." (He prophesies that, within a very very few years, morticians will enjoy the same status as physicians and surgeons.) Likewise, he reorganized his staff into departments, with executive offices on the first floor and sales rooms on the sixth. This breaks up the monotony of a business call and enables the sympathetic executives to escape the painful matter of sales.

Mr. Campbell's dream of cheerful funerals was barely realized when Dr. Baer passed away. It was a sad loss, but the doctor had enabled his friends to bear it by the way he had beautified death in life. Mr. Campbell carried on. He began the manufacture of his own materials; and during the flu epidemic was the only undertaker in America prepared for the emergency. It was during that time that he prospered most. He was also fortunate in securing a contract for the disposal of all who died at the Pelham Bay Naval Station during the war.

In the last few years, Mr. Campbell has taken his nose from the grindstone somewhat and spends much of his time on his cruiser, the "Jane C."—Jane being his pet name for Mrs. Campbell. He is also giving more time to the various fraternal and civic organizations of which he is a leader. He is a director of the Rotary Club, a member of the Lions, and Founder of the Order of Bananas, with Plantations in many cities.

As an illustration of his quick sense of humor, he founded the Bananas in the course of playing a joke on Babe Ruth. It was during the "Yes, We Have No Bananas" craze of a few years ago and Babe was playing some pretty bad baseball. According to Mr. Campbell's press agent, the mortician felt moved to send the ball player some flowers. Feeling, perhaps, that this would be too sinister an expression of his feelings, he substituted a bunch of bananas. Meditating on this little lark, it occurred to him that he might capitalize the banana vogue by organizing a lodge; and so he did. It cost him quite a bit of money and he finally withdrew after it seemed the order had disappeared with the song. But it did reveal a very human side and undoubtedly made him many friends.

Mr. Campbell is still a comparatively young man. He is bluff and healthy and as good-natured as they come, a little like Charlie Schwab in appearance. With his health and enthusiasm, there is no telling what further changes he may effect in the undertaking business before he leaves it.

His yachting is no more than recreation, as was shown during the Valentino funeral, when he hurried back to town and remained on his feet for three days and nights. In the winter, during the peak of business, he comes to work daily.

He has pledged himself to serve the public to the limit of his dream. What happiness lies ahead God only knows!
— CHARLES MACARTHUR

• • •

BUT FOR THE GRACE OF GOD

SHE was always late, but now she was later than usual. At the last minute Edith had telephoned, all about a quarrel with Richard.

She took time to admire her legs as she pulled on her new evening stockings. A good shade, nude, when you're not fat. She liked her new silver slippers, too. So few women can dance in opera pumps. She always wore them—made her ankles look slim.

She made up her face carefully, rouge straight under her eyes—her cheek-bones were high—then a blue shadow on her lids, mascara, and lip salve to make her under-lip look fuller. She was glad she had a good skin.

She put on her blue georgette.

Smart but not elaborate! It was good enough for to-night. She was to meet Fred at Bob Morris' for cocktails and then they'd have dinner and see a show or dance. Fred was pretty good. Most of the time she liked Fred, too.

She looked at her wrist watch. She had no idea it was *that* late! She would have to hurry, now.

She threw her coat around her. Last year's. Brocaded. She didn't wear her ermine except on special occasions.

She was going to call a taxi when she glanced at her wrist again. Twenty minutes to seven! She had told Fred she'd be at Bob's at six-thirty! He didn't mind her being a little late, but this was terrible—and all this traffic. It would take three-quarters of an hour! Why was there so much traffic at dinner time? Half the people had no place to go, would be better off at home, anyhow.

She'd have to take the subway! She hadn't been in the subway in years. It was the only thing to do.

Gingerly, she walked the two blocks. She hated walking, and now, in a hurry, and in silver slippers! She went down the dirty subway steps and stood waiting, uncomfortably conscious of the people around her. Did these people use the subway every day?

19

She got on the local, resenting horribly the smell and the noise and the rough shoulders that brushed her.

She sat on the edge of her seat, trying not to touch anyone, not to see these dreadful people. Their noses were all long.

She *had* to look at them! What dreadful clothes! The women didn't *have* to wear such clothes, even if they were poor. Purple hats and blue dresses! You *could* get cheap clothes that matched. And what shoes!

At each station she shivered. The noise beat in on her. She hadn't dreamed it was this bad. What terrible grinding! What a vile smell! These people! Was this their life—riding on this thing to a terrible office, working all day, and then going to a nasty little hole at night? She couldn't have stood it. She knew that. Why, she hadn't stood it.

A girl got on the train. At first, Catherine eyed her with contempt. Then, with a little something more, a fear and uneasiness. The girl was younger than she. Well, she didn't look her age—not even the age she said she was. Even Fred said so.

Catherine had never seen the girl before. Yet something about her was familiar. Not familiar exactly! Reminiscent! What was she reminiscent of?

The girl wore a decent brown coat, the kind you buy when you don't want the dirt to show. A little round felt hat was pulled low on her forehead. Her shoes were flat and sensible and she wore, of all things, horn-rimmed glasses! She carried a thick book. Catherine knew the kind. Too narrow margins and no conversation!

The girl glanced around, started to read. She had a straight, determined little nose, a nice mouth.

Already, Catherine started to dress her. Take off those glasses and get her the right kind of clothes. What was the right kind? What was there about this girl that should worry her so? Tormenting little undercurrent of worry. The kind of worry she hadn't had for a long time. It couldn't be that she was jealous. What a perfectly vile thought! This horrid girl with her cheap clothes and her glasses. She had just come from work—at this hour!—or from some sort of a class after working hours, and likely as not she didn't have a date at all. She probably didn't have dates often. If she did, they were with some young fellow who didn't have a cent and who wanted to marry her and start on nothing at all. Catherine knew the kind. She had known a man like that, one time. Well, no use thinking of *that*.

She was glad when her station came. She drew her brocaded coat around her, took careful tiptoe steps.

Funny, that that sentence should come to her—something she had heard someone say, or that she had read, in the days when she read things. Something about "There, but for the grace of God!" Of course! Hadn't she once worn plain little hats and thought funny things? What a fool she had been! Wasn't this better? Clothes and Fred and places to go. There was always the future ahead, darkly, but didn't this girl have a future, too? Everybody gets old. Well, she was having a good time, now.

She'd be only half an hour late, after all. In the elevator she was haughty, her old self again. She rang the bell and was greeted with whoops of welcome. Mary Rogers and Bunny Sedge and Lawrence Gibbons were there, too. Fred glowered a bit—she'd be able to fix things with him. What a nice place for a bachelor to have! Too many lamps, too much gingerbread. Nice, anyhow. Warm and comforting and friendly. Had they always talked and laughed this loudly, her friends, or was the subway ride still in her ears?

"Jus think," she announced, "I was in such a hurry I took the underground." She was rather proud of "underground," which she had said ever since she went to England for the first time, three years ago. "What dreadful mobs! I don't see how folks stand it."

"I use the subway every day," Fred reminded her. "I don't know what you'd do if I didn't."

She snuggled up to him as she accepted a cocktail.

"I know what a darling you are," she said. "Everybody knows what a darling you are. Subways every day and working long hours just for somebody who loves you." She drank the cocktail quickly—another.

They decided not to go out to dinner. They'd have something sent in. Much nicer than a restaurant!

Catherine drank as many cocktails as she could and as quickly. Usually she took good care of herself, didn't drink much. Now, she was thinking of the subway, didn't want to think about it. The cocktails didn't quite take away the memory.

"A dreadful ride," she said. "Girl on the train I knew."

"You didn't tell us you knew any girls who rode in subways," said Bunny.

"Forgot all about it." Her words were eliding a bit. "Girl I used to know. Years ago! Didn't speak to her."

When the dinner came up it was quite cold. That was the trouble with sending out for things. The hors d'œuvres were good but the steak was terrible. Why did men always like steaks? She took a highball, now.

22

"You should have seen that girl," she said, after she'd finished the first drink, and taken another. "Looked terrible. Awful old-looking. Let herself go. Shouldn't let herself go. Used to be a friend of mine. I didn't have the heart to speak to her."

"Be careful, dear," said Fred. "Don't drink so much. You know what a headache you'll have."

"Let me alone," she said, crossly. "I know what I'm doing. It was an awful shock—seeing a girl you haven't seen in years. Old friend. Old, old friend! Great big glasses on! Rides every day on the subway—on the subway—

"I couldn't let her know I recognized her, even— recognized her, even— No other life! Working and trying to make her salary last till pay day. Awful tired at night! It's terrible to think I used to know a girl like that. Lend me your hankie, Fred."

—THYRA SAMTER WINSLOW

• • •

THE VANDERBILT
CONVENTION

UNDOUBTEDLY, the Vanderbilts constitute one of the most interesting families this country has produced. Intertwined as they are with the industrial development of the country they have, in addition, a romantic interest that intrigues the great mass of their newspaper-reading countrymen.

Some Vanderbilt, somewhere, is always doing something that arouses the curiosity of his fellow-Americans. One roams the oceans in search of rare specimens of deep-sea fauna. Another drives an old-fashioned coach and four at Newport. One is at the Rota, in Rome, pleading for an annulment of her marriage. One flouts tradition to enter trade as a newspaper-publisher. But whatever the Vanderbilts do, they are, as a newspaper chap I know would put it, "good copy."

There is one difficulty. The descendants of the doughty old Commodore have grown to be almost as numerous as the proverbial sands of the sea. Indeed, he who attempts to explain which Vanderbilt is which is tackling a man-sized problem. Who married whom? When were they divorced and who got the custody of what? How many Willie K.'s are there? Is it Cornelia or Muriel who rides horseback astride? Is Harold married? When did Mrs. Belmont cease being Mrs. Vanderbilt? They are, in truth, a complicated group.

What follows here is an attempt to explain the Vanderbilt family tree simply and briefly. I shall not go into the more remote branches; that would indeed be a Herculean task. My aim, rather, will be to explain and identify the various Vanderbilts who have figured, more or less, in the public eye.

The Commodore, the original Cornelius Vanderbilt, married, first, Sophia Johnson, and, second, Frances Crawford. His son, William Henry Vanderbilt, inheritor of the bulk of the doughty Commodore's fortune, married Maria Louisa Kissam. They had issue as follows: four sons, Cornelius, Frederick, William Kissam, and George, and four daughters, who became Mrs. Elliot Shepard, Mrs. Henry White, Mrs. Hamilton McKay Twombly, and Mrs. William Seward Webb.

William Kissam married, first, an Alabama girl from an old family named Smith. She later married O. H. P. Belmont. William Kissam then married Mrs. Anne Rutherford Harriman Sands. No. Mrs. Anne Sands Harriman Rutherford. No, that's not right either; let's get this straight. He married, secondly, Mrs. *Anne Harriman Sands Rutherford*. She then became, by a process of elimination, Mrs. Anne Harriman Sands Rutherford Vanderbilt.

Cornelius Vanderbilt married Alice Gwynne. That is, not the *first* Cornelius. The first Cornelius was the Commodore and he married, first, Frances Crawford, and, second, Sophia Johnson. No, it's the other way round; he married, first, Sophia Johnson, and, second, Frances Crawford. And his grandson, William Kissam, married Anne Harriman Sands Rutherford.

Now then. The Cornelius Vanderbilt who married Alice Gwynne was not the Cornelius whose yacht recently blew up in the East River. No. The Cornelius whose yacht blew up in the East River is the Cornelius who married Grace Wilson, and they had issue as follows: Cornelius Vanderbilt, Jr., and Grace Vanderbilt (Mrs. Henry Gassaway Davis III). Cornelius Vanderbilt, Jr., son of the Cornelius whose yacht blew up, is the Cornelius whose newspapers blew up. His grandfather, Cornelius Vanderbilt, is the Cornelius who married Alice Gwynne. There is no record of anything belonging to this Cornelius ever having blown up.

Now then. Cornelius and Alice Gwynne Vanderbilt had issue as follows: Cornelius, Alfred Gwynne (named after his mother), Reginald, Gertrude, and Gladys.

Gertrude married a Hungarian nobleman, Count Lâszló Széchényi. No, it couldn't have been Gertrude who married the Count. Gertrude is the sculptor, isn't she? Well then, if she's the sculptor, she's the one who married Payne Whitney, because that one is the one who's the sculptor. I remember distinctly reading *that*. No, that's not right, either. It wasn't Payne Whitney that Gladys—I mean Gertrude—married; it was *Harry* Payne Whitney. You see, *Payne* Whitney and *Harry* Payne Whitney—well, maybe it would be better to clear up the Vanderbilts today and leave the Whitneys for some other day.

Now then. It was Birdie Vanderbilt who married the Hungarian Count. No, Birdie is the sculptor. No, it's Gladys who's the sculptor; what am I thinking of! Her statue blew up. No, it was her yacht that blew up.

No, it was Cornelius' yacht that blew up. Birdie married William K. Not the William K. that married, first, Mrs. O. H. P. Belmont, *née* Smith, and, second, Mrs. Anne Harriman Sands Rutherford. Not that one. Birdie married the William K. who married, first, Virginia Fair. Cathleen is their daughter. No, Cathleen is Reginald's daughter. Reginald married, first, Ellen French, and, second, Margaret Emerson McKim Mead and White. No, that wasn't Reginald.

Suppose we start *all* over again and get this thing straight. Let's begin once more with the doughty old Commodore. He married, first, Sophia Johnson, and second, Frances Crawford. William Henry Vanderbilt was their son. Not the William Henry Vanderbilt who gives all the clambakes; the other one, the one who married Maria Louisa Kissam.

Now, if William Henry and Maria Louisa Kissam, after getting married, had let it go at that, things wouldn't have become so complicated. But they didn't.

They had issue: eight children. These eight children had children and these children in turn had children, so that in the due course of time there came to be so many Vanderbilts that the family became known as the Vanderbilt Convention. And the doughty old Commodore had started practically on a shoestring!

Now then. What I am trying to do here is simply to give an explanation of which Vanderbilt is which, so that the reader who is interested may be able to distinguish them.

Damn it all, why the hell should people want to distinguish the Vanderbilts, anyhow? This country is supposed to be a democracy, isn't it? When our forefathers gathered at Boston—no, it wasn't Boston. It was Philadelphia. Well, it was either New York or Philadelphia. I don't *care* which one it was. It was on some Sub-Treasury steps, and our forefathers, when they gathered to free the Vanderbilts from the tyranny of George II—no, George III—stipulated, didn't they, that each person in the new nation should be conceived in liberty and dedicated to the proposition that all men are entitled to the pursuit of life, liberty, and the pursuit of happiness.

All right then, why harry the poor Vanderbilts this way? Why not let them alone once in a while? Whose business is it which of them is which? The trouble with this country is that there are a lot of morons in this country who can't mind their own business. They have to be always reading intimate details about the lives of other people. They want everything explained to them. What business is it of theirs which Vanderbilt is which? It's the sensational tabloids, and these physical-culture magazines, that encourage all this morbid curiosity.

27

Why can't the Vanderbilts come and go in peace, same as any other citizen? Who do they think they are, anyhow? Why, for that matter, the old man, the doughty old Commodore, who married Sophia Johnson, first, and Frances Crawford, second, was in trade. He ran a ferry between Staten Island and Manhattan!

His son was William Henry Vanderbilt, who married William Kissam—no, Louisa Maria Kissam, and they had issue (eight children) and then somewhere down the line someone of them married Count Lâszló Széchényi. They have five children and he fought a duel. But Reginald Vanderbilt married Cathleen Neilson and their daughter, Cathleen, married Henry Gassaway Davis III.

No. It wasn't Cathleen who married Henry Gassaway Davis III. Cathleen married Harry C. Cushing III. It was Grace, daughter of the Cornelius whose yacht blew up, who married Henry Gassaway Cushing III.

If only each Vanderbilt would arrange to have something of his, some little bit of personal property, easily distinguishable, blown up, it would be so much easier to tell them apart. "Ah, there goes Phyllis Vanderbilt. Which one is she, you ask? Why, she's the one whose first husband blew up."

It seems to me that somewhere, some time, some Vanderbilt married Irving Berlin III. On second thought, I guess not. I guess I'm thinking either of Cornelia, daughter of Mrs. George W. Vanderbilt (Mrs. Peter Goelet Gerry) who married the Hon. John Francis Amherst Cecil, or of Mary Cadogan, who married the Marquis of Blandford, son of the Duchess of Marlborough who was Consuelo Vanderbilt (Mrs. Jacques Balsan), daughter of the William Kissam Vanderbilt

28

who married Mrs. O. H. P. Belmont and, later, Mrs. Anne Harriman Sands Rutherford Vanderbilt.

Consuelo, erstwhile Duchess of Marlborough (Mrs. Jacques Balsan), would therefore be the aunt of the Consuelo who married Earl E. T. Smith.

Now, there was a time when the Smiths outnumbered the Vanderbilts by two to one, but that era is passing. The Vanderbilts are beginning to absorb the Smiths, although as yet no Vanderbilt has overtly married a Jones. Still, you never can tell. The descendants of the doughty old Commodore are an impulsive and passionate race and if one of them ever chanced upon an unusually comely Jones (*olav hasholem!*) there is no telling what might ensue.

I trust I have made everything clear.

—FRANK SULLIVAN

• • •

MARRIAGE OF CONVENIENCE

SAM and Sally docked early in the morning, and Sally called up Mrs. Gersbach as soon as she reached the hotel.

"Here we are," she cried. "Married! Bride and groom! I've got him at last."

Mrs. Gersbach braced herself to the shock.

"We are wild to see you."

"You can't see much of us," said Sally. "We have to go right on to see Papa in Winnetka. We're broke."

They didn't have to go till next morning, however, and Mrs. Gersbach arranged a cocktail party for that afternoon. Their old friends! Their dearest friends! Mrs.

Gersbach discussed the list, and then Mrs. Gersbach wanted to congratulate Sam.

"Oh, Sam isn't here," said Sally. "Sam's down at the dock, getting our things through the customs. I came on ahead. It's such a relief to have a man do those stupid things."

Mrs. Gersbach was busy as a bee for the rest of the day, though not so much with the material preparations for her party. Gin and crackers! Her menus were simple. And flowers! Flowers? Not roses. Not lilies. Nothing bridal. "Orange blossoms? I declare I wouldn't have the nerve," she thought. " 'Mums is the thing now," said the florist at the little corner shop. "There ain't much but 'mums this time of year. 'Mums and them leaves." Oh, the autumn leaves! Mrs. Gersbach tittered to herself at some joke of her own which she couldn't really define. She bought a few of the chrysanthemums and a great sheaf of the red and russet leaves. She could depend upon the leaves for her decorations. Bright, gay, brittle, pretty, dead—oh, why was it somehow funny to buy autumn leaves for this bridal pair?

She had hardly time for these brisk arrangements. There were so many people to telephone, so many hasty interviews to manage. There was quite a Winnetka group living about in the East Sixties. They would run from one apartment to another, rush up little stairways, squeeze into little elevators, scurry from one to another like neighbors in a small town.

Sam and Sally, they're married. They've done it. At last! At the Mairie in Paris! Why should it be exciting? They had been expecting and working for that marriage for years. Years and years! Ten years! And after the Crash, after the Slump, there had been obviously

30

nothing else for Sam to do. The little group faced facts. They were kind about facts, but they knew them, knew all the facts. It was a relief. Yes, a relief to have the Sam and Sally affair settled at last, to have Sam settled. It was nice for Sally too—she'd really always been devoted to him; but chiefly they wouldn't have to worry now about Sam—dear improvident Sam! Or was it settled? Did marriage really settle things? What exactly would Sam do?

"Sally's father ought to buy them a farm," said Effie Bayliss. "Sam would make a magnificent gentleman farmer."

Dear overserious, oversensitive, penniless Effie! The kind of woman who didn't find it dull to be respected. Mrs. Gersbach had run around the corner to break the news of the marriage to Effie first of all. However, Sally had got ahead of her. Sally had telephoned Effie. Effie seemed very composed about it, and said that she had tried to get them to luncheon, one of her card-table luncheons, but that they were going to Brooklyn.

"Sally's aunt! And before that Sally has to see the dentist and Sam must go with her because she is afraid to go alone. Sally wanted me to tell you, too, that Sam may be late this afternoon. He has to go out somewhere in the country to get Rover. Sally's Spitz, you know. He's been boarding at some kennels, and now Sally wants him."

"Think of poor lazy Sam doing all that in one day," said Mrs. Gersbach, and then she grew quite jocular. "But he's not poor Sam any more. Sam's on Easy Street."

"I hope he is," said Effie.

Effie's a liar, thought Mrs. Gersbach. Either a liar or just softhearted. It was hard to tell. Poor Effie!

Everybody was at Mrs. Gersbach's before the bridal pair. They had had a round of drinks to get in the mood before Sally arrived, alone. Sam hadn't showed up yet with Rover.

"Think of it," said Sally. "If I hadn't had a husband I would have had to go way out to those old kennels myself."

Sally had never been so gay. She looked very pretty and really quite young, and she was inclined to be amusing about her marriage and about Sam, just outspoken in the "modern" manner.

"I am glad Sam isn't a businessman," she declared. "I never could stand a businessman coming in from an office. Of course I think Sam might have something to do, just something to occupy his mind between drinks."

It was delightful to see her meeting with Sam, when, finally—for Rover had been sick in the taxi—he did appear.

"At last," she cried. "Now I can have one of my cigarettes. Sam carries my cigarettes. It's so wonderful having all those pockets to put things in."

"Here's a telegram from your father," Sam said.

"May I presume to inquire what your plans may be?" said the telegram. Everybody read it.

Sally was astonished. She had thought that Sam had telegraphed their plans already to Father. Didn't he know how important it was to keep Father informed of their moves? "I count on you for things like that," she exclaimed.

Then there were more cocktails. The party began to grow relaxed, and very soon there were Sam and Effie having one of their old-time sober talks in a corner.

Everybody noticed them. Sally noticed them. She stood very near them and said in a clear voice that all the room could hear, that Effie could hear: "Sam does the funniest imitations of Effie."

Sally said afterwards several times that she didn't know when she had so much enjoyed herself. She was sorry that they had to leave early, but they had to go to a dinner. A big dinner, friends of Father's! The invitation had come just before she had left the hotel for this party and she hadn't dared refuse, and she hadn't had a chance to tell Sam about it. Sam muttered something about having planned to meet some old friends, some of his old crowd, at the Yale Club that evening, but now that was obviously out of the question.

There was an enormous bustle getting them off, what with all the last embraces and jokings and laughter. It was touching, too, to see how helpless Sally had become all at once, and how she couldn't get into her coat unless Sam held it for her, and to note Sam's eager rush up the street after a taxi, and his assurance that he would get her to the dinner in time.

"My goodness," Sally said, "husbands are a convenience."

—JOHN MOSHER

• • •

THE STRANGER

ALTHOUGH she had been in New York at least a year and I was a newcomer, I had the feeling that it was my city rather than hers. In the first place she didn't seem to want New York. There are cities that I haven't wanted at all, cities that have let me pass through with a cold indifference on both sides, but she was the only person I had ever seen who really resisted New York.

We lived in the same boarding house and saw more of each other than we would otherwise have done, because we were the only denizens of our floor. It was an old house with big draughty rooms, and there was a smaller living-room that we used to lounge in. She had her job and I was looking for one. To me she was simply one of those enviable people who knew what to do at Ninety-sixth Street when they were on the wrong subway train. I heard her go out in the morning, always at the same time, and I heard her come back at night. She kept a large greasy jar of cold cream on her shelf of the medicine cabinet and on Sunday evening she fixed coffee in her room and bought sandwiches. Sometimes she would bring home a girl for the night, in which case they took more time in the bathroom than I approved of.

She wore quiet clothes with felt hats that were always a little wrong. She had a large pale face with blue eyes and light lashes; when she was quiet she looked as if she worried about money. At first I noticed all these things about her because she was there and I didn't have anything else to do. I think she was glad to have a new person to talk to. She told me where to get cream if I wanted breakfast in my room; she had a few words of advice about the job for which I was looking; she was full of information about transportation—buses, elevateds, street cars. Even now I'm sure I know only half of the things she used to have by heart.

Somehow I didn't want to talk to her. There was my city waiting for me; I had only just come and I was a little afraid. She had a job and didn't seem to worry about losing it, and didn't seem to have any hopes of improving it. She placidly went to work every day; every day she took the same route—in spite of knowing all about those other street cars and things—and worked all day and came home every night and put that cold cream on her face and went to bed. In New York! I thought that it might happen to me too. I began to avoid her. When I found a job and had worked for a week I discovered that I was walking down the same street every day and eating at the same restaurant, and I was badly frightened. I thought of her placid pale face and after that I took elaborate precautions to vary the road to the office. I made a rule never to eat lunch twice in succession at the same place.

Of course I was wrong about her. After a month or two, when the city and I were used to each other and I had other things to think about, she came running in one evening to show me a new dress. It wasn't a very nice dress—one of those very bright blue ones in the lower Broadway shops, with white lace and a short skirt. But she liked it, and of course I said I did. She was rather fluttered because she was going to a party with one of the girls who worked with her and occasionally went to a movie with her. She talked more than usual and smoked a cigarette; we sat for quite a while in my room and discussed movies, I remember. She was making vague plans to keep a cat; the landlady had said she could and she was wondering where to get it and how to take care of it. After she went away to get dressed I remembered how frightened I had been of her when I first came; for a minute I worried because I was not frightened of her any more.

Then something happened and I forgot. I got sick. For a week I was in bed, and then for a day or two I sat up in that little living-room, reading and thinking. I got acquainted with her again. She came in one Sunday while I had a headache and was lying down. She brought with her a cool damp cloth which she put on my forehead, and she sat down and began to sew. She was making handkerchiefs out of scraps of colored linen —drawing threads out and replacing them with threads of another color—and when she had made a pattern she rolled the edges of the linen and sewed them down. I was feeling lazy and peaceful and it fascinated me to watch her.

"They're for Christmas presents," she explained. "I've always made handkerchiefs all through the year for Christmas. The people at home like them. I make a lot for the church bazaars too."

"What church bazaars?"

"We have them every year at home. The money goes to the associated charities and all the girls turn in and help. They last for three days; there's a play the last night, and a dance afterwards. I remember the time I acted in 'The Servant in the House'—some of the boys who should have fixed the scenery forgot to prop up the door, and just at the last minute—"

Her voice was more animated than it had ever been. I was amazed. She was sewing faster now, and her cheeks were pink. She talked on, remembering other parties that they had had; remembering more stories about "the boys," remembering and describing her first real sleeveless dress—I have never heard anyone talk so much. I enjoyed it. She was being really friendly now; really off her guard. She wasn't looking at me; when the handker-

36

chief was finished, she put it in her lap and looked at the wall as she talked; smiling a little. . . .

I wonder how many people are living in New York and not using it. You would think that the city would burst from so many people. You would think that all the houses would bulge with the thoughts in them about church bazaars and Christmas presents.

She started another handkerchief, a yellow one, and began another story about a dance in the next town to hers. A high-school dance with an imported orchestra, she said; four of them were going together in a car, and just as they were starting out . . .

The telephone rang. She started, and looked at me. The yellow linen dropped to her lap; the phone rang again. And her eyes, fixed on me now, were hating. For a minute her expression was dreadful. Her mouth had tightened. Then—

"You answer," she said, in her flat voice. "It's for you. It's always for you. . . ."

—EMILY HAHN

• • •

THE GIANT~KILLER

HE OPENED the door with his latchkey and looked around the living-room. He could hear his wife moving about in the kitchen, so he hurried through the pantry without removing his hat or coat. His face was set in a broad grin and he looked pleasantly excited.

"Well," he said, addressing his wife's back and trying to keep his voice casual, "I just socked a fellow."

His wife didn't look up from her work. "Did you?"

He took off his hat and coat with a calmness that was meant to be aggravating to the suspense he had created.

"I did," he said. "And don't let anybody ever kid you about this good-deed-every-day stuff. It may sound like a Boy Scout, but it makes you feel great just the same."

His wife took an eggbeater from a drawer in the kitchen table and went back to her work. "What happened?" she said.

"Plen-*ty!*" he said, grinning from ear to ear. "Honey, maybe we've been married over five years, but there's lots you don't know about your little old husband." He leaned back against the table, his large hands crooked over its edge on either side of him.

"If you're a Boy Scout, I didn't know it," his wife said, and started churning the eggbeater. It made a steady droning clatter against the side of the bowl.

"Can't you stop that damned thing?" he said.

"I can hear you."

The recollection of his adventure prevented him from being annoyed, however, and the grin returned to his face.

"Well," he said, "you know what the subway's like this time of the evening. I got on at Forty-second. A local, of course. I stood in the doorway on the platform, leaning against one of those big wheels and reading my paper. You know the wheels I mean."

"Yes."

"Then I noticed a fellow across the way from me. A dumb-looking egg. Pimply, sort of, and a Maltese cross of court-plaster on his neck. A boil or something. He was pretty well dressed, though, if you like snappy clothes. I don't! Well, anyway, I didn't like his looks even then, and maybe I wasn't right!"

"Hmm," his wife said.

He waved his hand to distract her attention from the eggbeater and the bowl. "Listen! A little old bum gets on at Fifty-ninth Street. A sloppy old guy. Liquored up a little, but no harm in him. You know!"

"Hmm."

"Well, I'm getting ahead of myself, really." He raised his voice to make himself heard above the noise of the eggbeater. "I should have said the old bum *tried* to get on. I was in the doorway and so was this other bird." He looked at his wife's back. "The snappy-dressed one," he added.

"I know."

"Well, between us the doorway was pretty well blocked. I got out of the way as much as I could, but this other guy didn't budge. 'Gettin' on!' the old bum says. This other guy just gives a look over his shoulder— the hell with *you*, sort of—and stays where he is. Well, that got me, but I didn't do anything then."

"Of course not!" his wife said sharply.

He looked at her suspiciously. "What do you mean?"

She rattled the eggbeater furiously. "Why should you?"

"That's like you!" he said. He was suddenly knowing and superior. "You've got a lot to learn about me, honey!" He grinned down at her. "Well—to get on with it—the old bozo sees this other fellow isn't going to get out of his way so he just pushes on anyhow. Maybe he bunks this guy, or steps on his toes or something. I don't know. Anyway, you should have heard the yowl the young guy puts up! You'd think he'd

39

had his arm taken off. So what does the little skunk start to do—"

"A little fellow?" his wife asked suddenly, laying the eggbeater aside.

He coughed. "About the old fellow's size, I'd say." He looked angrily at his wife as she crossed the kitchen. "Don't be interrupting me all the time, will you? You take all the kick out of it!"

"Go ahead," she said. "What did the little skunk do?"

Her husband laughed. "He starts calling the poor old bum all sorts of names. But the old boy doesn't take it lying down. He gives as good as he gets—and then some. And all the time you can see the other guy's working himself up into a sort of Dutch courage. Finally he gets up enough nerve to make a pass at the old fellow. Not exactly a pass, but it looks that way anyway."

He paused and looked back on the scene, conscious that at last he had captured his wife's undivided attention. He waited deliberately, his face glowing. "Well," he said finally, "that got me! I grabbed him by the shoulder!" He caught the surprised look on his wife's face and was pleased. "Believe it or not, honey, I grabbed him and I said: 'Listen here, you!' He sort of squealed"—he threw himself quickly into the character of his opponent; he pursed his lips and spoke in a falsetto voice—"'*You keep your hands off me!*'" Then he resumed his natural tone. "Well, honey, I guess I lost my temper. I let him have it!"

He chuckled to himself and smashed a closed fist into his thick palm. "Right on the jaw! He went back so hard he jarred everybody down the line. Like ninepins." He laughed and looked expectantly at his wife.

40

For the first time she faced him fully. "So?"

The smile left his face. "Oh, *nothing!*" he said, and stood up. "I got off the train and waited for the next one."

His wife turned and walked over to the sink. "That's too bad," she said. "Did the good-looking girl get off too?"

He felt his face go suddenly red. "Good-looking girl! What good-looking girl?"

She didn't answer.

"You think you're pretty wise," he said angrily, "but you guessed wrong that time!"

"Yes?" his wife said, and shrugged her shoulders indifferently. She had turned on both faucets and the water drummed noisily into the dishpan.

—T. H. WENNING

• • •

THE TITLE

THE scene takes place in the office of Charles Smetnik, a former hat-check concessionaire, who is about to offer his first dramatic production on Broadway. Several of the stockholders of The Smetnik Productions, Inc., have dropped in.

SMETNIK—Now you take the average audiences. What does "The Dip" mean to your average audience? Why, he thinks "The Dip" means somethin' like Cooney Island—y'know, the thing you go up in an' you go down in.

FINK (*a stockholder*)—I dunno, Charlie. Now you take these here crook plays. The average audience hears so much crook plays he knows the slang better 'n the crooks theirselves.

HARRIS (*a casting agent*)—How about calling it "Snakey Joe"? Nearly evvey big hit on Broadway is named after the principal character. Now you take —let me see—you take—ah—well, I can't think of any on the boards right now—yeah—! You take "Lightnin'." Now you take that there play. See how long that ran and it was named after Frank Bacon. And look at "Abie's Irish Rose." Five years it ran and why? Because it was named on account of the two leading characters.

SMETNIK—I dunno, Harris. Of course, there's somethin' in what you say, but it don't click with me, somehow.

SHAPIRO (*a stockholder*)—Well, you people may be in the theat'ical game but all the same, bein' as how I'm not in it and I'm just one of the audience, I oughta know what appeals to me. Now, why not call it after a neighborhood? One of the best plays I ever seen was this here "Broadway," and look, that was named after a neighborhood. And this latest play by Brice, I think he's called. "The Street Scene." Capacity, because I tried to get seats for a client. If I was you, Charlie, I'd call it after a section.

SMETNIK—I should call it yet "Eighth Avenue and Twenty-ninth Street." I should pay yet an electric bill for that.

SHAPIRO—You think maybe because a title is big you can't get it up in lights? My missus has a subscription ticket to the Theatre Guild and I saw a play, "They Knew What They Wanted," and it seemsa me, Charlie, that was a hit.

42

SMETNIK—You talkin' about the Theatre Guild? Say, with their subscribers it's no wonder they're a hit.

FINK—We also got subscribers if you wanna count the guys who got pieces of this here show. Believe me, if we played only to the stockholders alone, we'd still have a capacity house. How many shares, anyhow, did you sell, Charlie?

SMETNIK—Listen, there ain't no lawr against sellin' the stock I own personally, is there?

COOPER (*Smetnik's cousin, out of a job and acting as office man*)—Listen, Charlie, why don't you have somethin' sexy like Mae West. Why don't you call the play "Easy Virtue"?

HARRIS—It seemsa me there was a play called "Easy Virtue."

COOPER—Oh! Well, why not call it "Virtue for Sale"? That's sexy and it's got a punch.

SMETNIK—Listen, Elias. You don't know what it's about so you better not say anythin'. First of all, it's got nothin' to do with sex. It's about a dame who double-crosses her sweetie who's a cop. Oney he ain't really a cop but he belongs to another gang.

COOPER—Oh, I din know. I thought it was about sex, and "Virtue for Sale" is a good name for a sex play. Of course, if it's about crooks then you can't use "Virtue for Sale." But all the same, Charlie—

FINK—Y'know, I still think "The Dip" is a good title. Don't get me wrong. Just because I made it up—

SMETNIK—You made it up! Say, din I say we should call it "Crooks" and then we started to argue and finally at the end of the argument din we agree to call it "The Dip"? You're always grabbin' away the credit.

FINK—So help me, Charlie, I made it up! I deliberately says to you, "How about callin' the play—"

SMETNIK—Aw, what's the use of arguin'. I gotta go to the rehearsal hall because I put in a call for two and it's already a quarter to two.

HARRIS—Well, Mr. Smetnik, what about the title?

SMETNIK—Hell, let it ride the way it is. After all, I think the average audience knows by this time that "The Dip" means a pickpocket, and even if the play ain't strictly about pickpockets at lease it's a good title. It's short, anyways, and that's good for the ads because it cuts down expense. I dunno why you boys are always wantin' to change the title. If I said, "Let's call it 'Green,' " you would say, "No, let's call it 'Red.' "

FINK—Well, I always thought it was a good title. If I din I wouldn't of made it up.

SHAPIRO—I still think it's over your average audience's head. But we'll let it go at that.

SMETNIK—Listen—if the play's a hit, then the title don't matter at all. If it's a flop, then what good is your title? (*The phone rings.*) Hello. Yeah. Oh, yeah. Well, I'll be over at the rehearsal in about ten minutes. I'll talk to you then. Goodbye.

SHAPIRO—Who is it?

SMETNIK—The author. He don't like the title, "The Dip." Well, let's go, and maybe on our way we can think up a new title that will be good. (*Exeunt*)

—ARTHUR KOBER

ɔ • •

44

LOUIS DOT DOPE

ON HIS recent return from France, Mr. Robert Benchley gave the following statement to a reporter of The New Yorker who met him at Quarantine with bail. "Things in France are in a deplorable condition," said Mr. Benchley. "If Louis XVI keeps on as he has been going for the past few years, I predict a revolution. I can give you no idea of the licentiousness and waste of the French Court at Versailles or of the pitiable state of the common people in Paris. Yes, I can too give you some idea, and, what is more, I will.

"This Louis XVI is nothing but a wastrel. He drinks a great deal, too. And he has gathered about him at Versailles (where he lives) a group of sycophants who are just as bad as he is, according to all reports. I am not one to retail gossip, but I could tell you some of the things that go on out there at Versailles that would make your hair stand on end. And, in the meantime, the people in Paris are actually starving. You can't get an oyster stew in Paris for love or money, and I have seen the *canaille* (as the log-rolling wits of the Court call the citizenry) standing in line for hours for something, I couldn't quite make out what.

"One little incident that I heard of from a pretty good source (Carlyle: page 375) may serve to illustrate the way the wind is blowing. It seems that Louis (as his toadies call him) was out driving through Paris with his—pardon me—mistress (I mention no names) when the people began crying out for bread. The 'lady' in question, who can read French and speak it but who has difficulty in understanding it when it is spoken fast, asked what it was that they were yelling. Louis told her that they said they had no more bread. 'Let them eat cake then,' said this certain party. 'And how about us taking a look in at Cartier's window?'

"I don't know how true this is, but I got it from someone on the inside and it shows pretty well the attitude of the nobles towards the common people.

"But there is an undercurrent of discontent which I predict will make itself felt before many months. I happened to go to lunch with a couple of chaps whose names, for obvious reasons, I promised not to mention in this connection, and there was a great deal of talk about how easy it would be to burn down the Bastille (the government jail over there). 'A couple of good pushes and the Bastille would fall,' said one of them jokingly. But behind all their joking there was a note of seriousness, and I would recommend that you send a good man over to Paris pretty soon to cover the story, for when it breaks it is going to be a hot one. This is just a tip.

"But, as I was saying, it is out there at Versailles that the big doings go on. I took a trip out there with a letter from Whitney Warren but they were all out at Chantilly at the races that day and I didn't see anyone but the Head Guide. He said that if I wanted to come back Sunday the fountains would be playing, but unfortunately I had to sail on Saturday. I did get some inside dope on the situation out there, however, and let me tell you that what goes on out there on a good night is nobody's business. All these people, it seems, live right out there in the palace together and carry on some pretty rough stuff, I gather. Drinking, gambling, necking, *everything.* A lot of the married men are out there without their wives, and *vice versa.* Some nights the parties don't break up until two and three o'clock. No wonder the taxpayers in Paris are sore. You can mark my words, there will be reaction.

"I myself didn't have time to get around much. I was over on business and I like to keep my head clear when I have business to attend to. Summer is when I have my fun. I did go to the theatre a couple of times, but everything was in French. And then, too, the coffee is so bad there. The trip back was pretty rough. One day the waves were mountain-high. It certainly seems good to be back in the U. S. A. again."

—ROBERT BENCHLEY

• • •

MISS GULP

BEHIND a widely printed current advertisement, which concerns a remedy for one of the more personal ails, there is a very interesting inside story, one which ought to be made public in justice to the young woman who figures in the copy of the advertisement.

It—the advertisement—tells of a Chicago girl inadequately identified as Mildred, who was always catching brides' bouquets at weddings. The old saying was that whoever among the bridesmaids caught the bouquet married next. But Mildred, according to the text, caught her second bouquet in 1917, and what is more, is still catching them in 1930.

"Mildred was attractive, still catching bouquets. But there her luck ended. Matrimony seemed further off than ever. The truth was that Mildred repelled others without knowing why. And none of her friends had the courage to tell her."

This highly inaccurate account does a grave injustice to a very splendid girl, Mildred Gulp, whom I happened to know well in the old days in Chicago. That she caught her second bouquet in 1917 is quite true, but that is about all that is true. As for none of her friends having the courage to tell her, that is nonsense of the rarest sort. All of her friends told her.

Another girl, told as often as Mildred was, would have given up, slunk off somewhere, and wasted her life in brooding. As it happened, Mildred did slink off for a month or so; during June and the first weeks of July, 1918, she caught no bouquets at all. She had dropped completely out of sight. People were generally relieved, as they were tired of telling her, and that was usually all they ever talked about with her.

But in the middle of July she came back. They say they never come back, but Mildred did. During that summer and well into the fall I did quite a bit of wedding-going, and at every one of the ceremonies Mildred was there, catching bouquets.

Now, however, there was a difference. In the old days she had caught bouquets lackadaisically. People referred to her as "the Bob Meusel of Bridesmaids." They said: "If the bouquet comes within her reach she will nab it, but she does not cover much ground." Perhaps these remarks had got to her ears, for she was a new Mildred that season.

It became the talk of Chicago, the way she was going

after bouquets. I remember her at the Newton-Oldton nuptials. Mildred was playing far back, a little to the right, as Margie Newton, a southpaw, was known to chuck a wicked bouquet. But Margie crossed her. From the top of the stairs she tossed a dinky little Texas Leaguer toward right, and the crowd groaned.

The old Mildred would have shrugged and let it go. The new Mildred was off with the rustle of silk. She cut through the crowd like Kaye Don, and diving headlong to the floor, made a clean catch. There wasn't the faintest chance of its being called a pickup, or trapped bouquet, for Mildred, tumbling against the palms, held it high above her head—and the crowd went wild!

That was just a sample of what Mildred did throughout that season. Just as Babe Ruth built the Yankee Stadium, so did Mildred put new life in Chicago weddings. No marriage meant anything that hadn't her name among the bridesmaids, and when at the end of the ceremony the bride prepared to toss the bouquet, the girl rarely failed them.

As Grantland Rice has said somewhere, it was a matter of pure coördination. The old bean worked as well as the eye and the legs. Mildred was taking them against the wall, down the foul lines, directly behind the best man. Now and then she failed, of course, but she always gave the crowd a run for its money. "Whatever happens," they said, "Mildred's always in there trying, always on her toes."

Chicago will never forget that wedding season. Chicago will never forget Mildred Gulp. It forgot to wonder about her getting married herself, save on rare occasions, when some bride's father, worried and annoyed, would urge his daughter, before the ceremony, to put

49

some beef behind the toss. "All she's doing," he would say, "is making a mug out of the old saying. Put your shoulders behind this one, now, and let's see if we can't put the old bee on her."

Mildred herself said nothing. When remarks of an inferential character were directed at her she merely smiled. She knew what she was doing. It all came out at the Washburn-Crossett nuptials, at which I was an usher. Among those to whom I gave a chair was a short, stocky, gray-haired man, with a rugged, outdoor look. He was seated near the altar.

The catch Mildred made that day was one for the books. It was a low, flat throw straight down the aisle, and it didn't look as though she had a Chinaman's chance. But by now she was playing her brides well. Off with the toss, she shot one hand out, hawked it out of the air, and crashed into the minister, who was a little slow on his dogs. I doubt if Chicago has ever seen a catch like that one.

Five minutes after the wedding, while Mildred was in her dressing-room reading congratulatory telegrams, the short, stocky, gray-haired man entered.

"Miss Gulp," he said, "I am John J. McGraw."

"*The* John J. McGraw!"

He nodded. "And here," he said, laying a document on her dressing-table, "is a contract with the New York Giants. You will notice that I have left the salary space blank. Miss Gulp, you may fill it in yourself. In addition, I am prepared to offer you a five-thousand-dollar bonus for signing."

"But Mr. McGraw," she faltered, "I have never caught baseballs!"

"If you can catch bouquets, you can catch baseballs," he said. "All you have to do is sign there."

Today, of course, you know Mildred as Old Gray-Eagle Gulp, the Giants' ballhawk in centre, one of the keenest judges of batters in the big leagues, and an all-around good fellow at that.

I give this story simply to give a great little girl her due, and to refute a story which is all the more misleading because it is not a whole lie but a half-truth.

—NUNNALLY JOHNSON

• • •

MY SILVER DRESS

I WISH I'd worn my silver dress; of course it was raining blue thunderbolts when I started, but this old gold thing is beginning to look like the devil; in a charming room like this it's really barbarous, and then with silver walls it would have been lovely; all the other women in wonderful taffeta robes de style; pink and peach and cream color; good Lord what a fool I was!

I must look like the devil; I wish I'd worn my silver dress; it's precisely like me to appear in this scene of elegance in this crazy gold one that looks like hop-sacking; at least like my idea of hop-sacking or is it sack-cloth?

Why am I always such a fool and why are all these other women so marvelous? I never saw such tidy hair in all my life; mine is without exception the worst hair in the world; it goes every which way and it's an absolutely rotten kind of hair; if I'd worn my silver dress I might have looked halfway decent, I suppose; why on this night of all nights didn't I wear my silver dress?

It might have made all the difference; imagine my looking like a beggar woman or a horrible rough bear-cub in the middle of this exquisite room; silver walls and crystal sconces and roses and everything that I love, and I didn't have the sense to wear my silver dress; I wonder if anyone was ever such a fool before?

I wouldn't so much mind not having a brand-new taffeta dress like every darn one of these other women if only I'd worn my silver dress; after all it would have been lovely in this room and silver looks much more like spring than gold; I'm the only person in the whole world who could have been such a fool as to come in this rough brutal bear-cub gold dress and in April and among all these roses and lilies and the other things I love; silver walls and crystal sconces and beautiful black lacquer and I in the midst of it looking like a savage Orson to everyone else's Valentine; damn it I am the most infernal fool alive, and then all the other skirts are so much longer and all the other women look so ladylike and gentlewomanly except myself and I look precisely like a fool.

Why have I these terrible long legs? Why the devil am I so tall? Why do I look like some bear-cub? Why do I stride about looking like an enormously tall bear-cub in this crazy gold dress among all the beautiful people?

Everyone else is so exquisite and sleek and gentle and I am like a rough crazy blot on the delicate loveliness of this room; this week of all weeks of course Mr. Talloh wouldn't wave my hair; Fanny never makes it look the same, and anyway it's rotten hair and a remarkably silly color; cinnamon bear-cub color; I have always hated my nose but if I had worn my silver dress I might feel more reconciled to it; really these lovely women in pale-pink taffeta dresses have the most delightful noses I ever beheld!

I suppose I'm the only woman in the room without a straight nose and a short upper lip and a new taffeta dress; and the wind has blown my hair into whiffets; it's outrageous hair and I dislike it intensely; I dislike my eyebrows; I have a nice mouth but it would be nicer if I'd worn my silver dress; how happy I might have been if only I'd worn my silver dress!

It's sacrilege to drink good champagne in a dreadful dress like this; it's an uncivilized dress; it's precisely the sort of dress that a tall bear-cub might wear; crazy rough gold; the child she-bear!

April and all these flowers and lovely things and this enchanting silver room with sconces of showery crystal and I didn't even have the sense to wear my silver dress!

Oh, I know it was raining when I started, but anyone else would have guessed that it would clear; with a moon and stars, and in April; all the other women have perfectly new silver slippers and mine are gold and have splashes of rain on them.

It might have made all the difference if I'd worn my silver dress; now it's too late forever; probably I'll never be anything but an infernal fool; I wish I'd worn my silver dress!

—Elinor Wylie

• • •

THE FAITHFUL WIFE

UNTIL a week before Christmas George worked in the station restaurant at the lunch counter. The last week was extraordinarily cold, then the sun shone strongly for a few days, though it was always cold again in the evenings. There were three other men working at the counter. For years they must have had a poor reputation. Women, unless they were careless and easy-going, never started a conversation with them when having a light lunch at noontime. The girls at the station always avoided the red-capped porters and the countermen.

George, who was working there till he got enough money to go back home for a week and then start late in the year at college, was a young fellow with fine hair retreating far back on his forehead and rather bad upper teeth, but he was very polite and generous. Steve, the plump Italian, with the waxed black mustaches, who had charge of the restaurant, was very fond of George.

Many people passed the restaurant window on the way to the platform and the trains. The four men, watching them frequently, got to know some of them. Girls, brightly dressed and highly powdered, loitered in front of the open door, smiling at George, who saw them so often he knew their first names. At noontime, other girls, with a few minutes to spare before going back to work, used to walk up and down the tiled tunnel to the waiting-room, loafing the time away, but they never even glanced in at the countermen. It was cold outside, the streets were slippery, and it was warm in the station, that was all. George got to know most of these girls too, and talked about them with the other fellows.

George watched carefully one girl every day at noon hour. The other men had also noticed her, and two or three times she came in for a cup of coffee, but she was so gentle, and aloofly pleasant, and so unobtrusively beyond them, they were afraid to try and amuse her with easy cheerful talk. George wished earnestly that she had never seen him there in the restaurant behind the counter, even though he knew she had never noticed him at all. Her cheeks were usually rosy from the cold wind outside. When she went out the door to walk up and down for a few minutes, an agreeable expression on her face, she never once looked back at the restaurant. George, following her with his eye while pouring coffee slowly, did not expect her to look back. She was about twenty-eight, pretty, rather shy, and dressed plainly and poorly in a thin blue-cloth coat without any fur on it. Most girls managed to have a piece of fur of some kind on their coats.

With little to do in the middle of the afternoon, George used to think of her because of seeing her every day and looking at her face in profile when she passed the window. Then, on the day she had on the light-fawn felt hat, she smiled politely at him, when having a cup of coffee, and as long as possible, he remained opposite her, cleaning the counter with a damp cloth.

The last night he worked at the station he went out at about half past eight in the evening, for he had an hour to himself, and then worked on till ten o'clock. In the morning he was going home, so he walked out of the station and down the side street to the docks, and was having only pleasant thoughts, passing the warehouses, looking out over the dark cold lake and liking the tang of the wind on his face. Christmas was only a week away. The snow was falling lazily and melting slowly when it hit the sidewalk. He was glad he was through with the job at the restaurant.

An hour later, back at the restaurant, Steve said, "A dame just phoned you, George, and left her number."

"Do you know who she was?"

"No, you got too many girls, George. Don't you know the number?"

"I never saw it before."

He called the number and did not recognize the voice that answered him. A woman was asking him pleasantly enough if he remembered her. He said he did not. She said she had had a cup of coffee that afternoon at noontime, and added that she had worn a blue coat and a tan-colored felt hat, and even though she had not spoken to him, she thought he would remember her.

"Good Lord," he said.

She wanted to know if he would come and see her at half past ten that evening. Timidly he said he would, and hardly heard her giving the address. Steve and the other boys started to kid him brightly, but he was too astonished, wondering how she had found out his name, to bother with them. The boys, saying goodbye to him later, winked and elbowed him in the ribs, urging him to celebrate on his last night in the city. Steve, who was very fond of him, shook his head sadly and pulled the ends of his mustaches down into his lips.

The address the girl had given him was only eight blocks away, so he walked, holding his hands clenched tightly in his pockets, for he was cold from nervousness. He was watching the automobile headlights shining on slippery spots on the sidewalk. The house, opposite a public-school ground on a side street, was a large old rooming house. A light was in a window on the second story over the door. Ringing the bell he didn't really expect anyone to answer, and was surprised when the girl herself opened the door.

"Good evening," he said shyly.

"Oh, come upstairs," she said, smiling and practical. In the front room he took off his overcoat and hat and sat down slowly, noticing, out of the corner of his eye, that she was even slimmer, and had nice fair hair and lovely eyes. But she was moving very nervously. He had intended to ask at once how she found out his name, but forgot about it as soon as she sat down opposite him on a camp bed and smiled shyly. She had on a red woollen sweater, fitting her tightly at the waist. Twice he shook his head, unable to get used to having her there opposite him, nervous and expectant. The trouble was she had always seemed so aloof.

"You're not very friendly," she said awkwardly.

"Oh yes, I am. Indeed I am."

"Why don't you come over here and sit beside me?"

Slowly he sat down beside her on the camp bed, smiling stupidly. He was even slow to see that she was waiting for him to put his arms around her. Ashamed of himself, he finally kissed her eagerly and she held on to him tightly. Her heart was thumping underneath the red woollen sweater. She just kept on holding him, almost savagely, closing her eyes slowly and breathing deeply every time he kissed her. She was so delighted and satisfied to hold him in her arms that she did not bother talking at all. Finally he became very eager and she got up suddenly, walking up and down the room, looking occasionally at the cheap alarm clock on a bureau. The room was clean but poorly furnished.

"What's the matter?" he said irritably.

"My girl friend, the one I room with, will be home in twenty minutes."

"Come here anyway."

"Please sit down, please do," she said.

Slowly she sat down beside him. When he kissed her she did not object, but her lips were dry, her shoulders were trembling, and she kept on watching the clock. Though she was holding his wrist so tightly her nails dug into the skin, he knew she would be glad when he had to go. He kissed her again and she drew her left hand slowly over her lips.

"You really must be out of here before Irene comes home," she said.

"But I've only kissed and hugged you and you're wonderful." He noticed the red ring mark on her finger. "Are you sure you're not waiting for your husband to come home?" he said a bit irritably.

Frowning, looking away vaguely, she said, "Why do you have to say that?"

"There's a ring mark on your finger."

"I can't help it," she said, and began to cry quietly. "Yes, oh yes, I'm waiting for my husband to come home. He'll be here at Christmas."

"It's too bad. Can't we do something about it?"

"I tell you I love my husband. I do, I really do, and I'm faithful to him too."

"Maybe I'd better go," he said uncomfortably, feeling ridiculous.

"Eh, what's that? My husband, he's at a sanitarium.

He got his spine hurt in the war, then he got tuberculosis. He's pretty bad. They've got to carry him around. We want to love each other every time we meet, but we can't."

"That's tough, poor kid, and I suppose you've got to pay for him."

"Yes."

"Do you have many fellows?"

"No. I don't want to have any."

"Do they come here to see you?"

"No. No, I don't know what got into me. I liked you, and felt a little crazy."

"I'll slide along then. What's your first name?"

"Lola. You'd better go now."

"Couldn't I see you again?" he said suddenly.

"No, you're going away tomorrow," she said, smiling confidently.

"So you've got it all figured out. Supposing I don't go?"

"Please, you must."

Her arms were trembling when she held his overcoat. She wanted him to go before Irene came home. "You didn't give me much time," he said flatly.

"No. Irene comes in at this time. You're a lovely boy. Kiss me."

"You had that figured out too."

"Just kiss and hold me once more, George." She held on to him as if she did not expect to be embraced again for a long time, and he said, "I think I'll stay in the city a while longer."

"It's too bad, but you've got to go. We can't see each other again."

In the poorly lighted hall she looked lovely. Her

cheeks were flushed, and though still eager, she was quite satisfied with the whole affair. Everything had gone perfectly for her.

As he went out the door and down the walk to the street he remembered that he hadn't asked how she had found out his name. Snow was falling lightly and there were hardly any footprints on the sidewalk. All he could think of was that he ought to go back to the restaurant and ask Steve for his job again. Steve was fond of him. But he knew he could not spoil it for her. "She had it all figured out," he muttered, turning up his coat collar.

—MORLEY CALLAGHAN

• • •

ESSAYAGE

(The scene is in the trying-on room of a Parisian modiste, and the speaker is a professional shopper, one of those able and ingenious ladies who make a living by organizing parties of tourists who don't speak French. She is followed by five young girls of the Middle-Western débutante type, and three or four dejected males, who are fiancés of the girls.)

THERE, you see, girls, there are some people here already. Sit down, you men, and keep quiet. Nobody's going to pay any attention to you. I *told* you we'd ought to come early. Lanvin only has these sales once a season, and people come in here raging like tigers. Good morning, Madame; no, don't bother to wait on us, we'll just snatch what we want. Newton, you hold the treasure dog—and don't blow cigarette smoke in his face; he's been ill once already this morning. Hurry, girls, get your things off.

"Those little new hats, darlings, don't they *slay* you? Susie, my dear, whatever you do, don't choose anything in that awful tomato red, it may be all right for Mr. Campbell's tinned soup but it's not *your* color. I promised your mother I'd not let you come away with anything ribald. Newton, keep quiet, don't be so vulgar. I don't see anything to leer about. Men are such satyrs. I'll take care of your things, girls, put them here on the couch. No, it's all right, Madame. I know perfectly what to do, I come here every year. Amy, see if you can find an afternoon ensemble. You'll need one for bridge. Anyone who plays cards as badly as you do has got to be well dressed. That thing that woman has over there is a dream. Grab it away from her. . . .

"Madame, forgive me, but I advise you not to choose that one, it makes you look like an armadillo. Madame! Madame! *Je desire parler à vous!* Susie, Susie, where are you? Come here, I want Madame to see your lines. She seems to lack allure, Madame; what would you recommend? I thought something in the eggshell satin would be intriguing. I don't want her to look like a tart, but I do think just a little more biological suggestion would make life more amusing for her. Not too much dip in the back. I think Lanvin's making a mistake in carrying the dip to extremes; besides, Susie sags a bit anyhow. *Voyez-vous, elle tombe en derrière.*

"These children are all coming out in the autumn, so of course they have to have something rather special; except Frances, she's on her honeymoon. I do think a young girl in her lingerie is the most touching sight, so dainty and appealing; it seems rather pathetic, too, when you think what they've got to go through. Amy, this is too good—that woman over there has got hold of your old dress and is trying it on. She's crazy about it. Let her have it, it's horrible.

"Girls, you'll have to be brisk, people are coming in all the time, it'll be a mob. This is a regular rutting season for this kind of thing. That one, Amy, is the very thing for you. I think Poiret's quite right: a woman's got to be feminine, it's her only resource. No, no, Susie, that's not your type at all, darling. It's much too *femme fatale*: you could never be that without rupturing something. Try this one, it's so virginal. Take that off, darling. Don't waste time on impossibilities. There, that one on the rack, the lettuce green. Quick, before that other person gets it, she's looking at it—pardon, Madame, *je veux voir cette robe*.

"These little capes are very smart; waists are going up again, aren't they? You're lucky to be so flexible, darling; my poor waist is beginning to settle down to its permanent home. Trimmed with baby leopard, yes, that's rather stunning. Only three thousand francs? Well, when you think how much trouble it must be to catch a baby leopard and bring it all the way here, it really isn't much.

"Those mousselaine evening gowns are adorable. . . . Madame! Madame! *Je desire parler à vous.* You'll have to raise these shoulder seams. It's the same thing every year. You know the Americans simply can't bear that tightness around the shoulders. Particularly these young girls, they have so many uses for their arms. Do you think that skirt is too short? Sit down, Frances. Get up,

Newton, let poor Frances sit down. Men are so inconsiderate. Just sit down naturally and let Madame see if the skirt is too short. . . .

"No, you don't show any more than you have a perfect right to. It's hard to know where to draw the line these days. What do you think, Madame, *este-ce que Mademoiselle disclose trop de ses jambes?* Of course if she hadn't got such nice legs it wouldn't do. They're not carnal-looking at all, just nice and fragile. Ask Edward, he's practically your husband, it's really *his* funeral. No, Gertrude, that neckline's too low behind, your back will never stand it. This other one's better, the one with the little chiffon jacket—where did it go? Well, of all things . . .

"Excuse me, but I was just looking at that one. It's perfectly appalling, people act like savages. Sometimes I think we'd do better to just order our clothes by mail from the National Cloak & Suit Company. . . . Girls, I can't help it, I can't stand it any longer. That mulberry velvet over there is just what I want for myself. Now hang on to what you've got and grab what you want. I've simply got to try that thing on. Here, hold my clothes. . . . I'll be with you in a moment. . . ."

—CHRISTOPHER MORLEY

● ● ●

CHAMPION
A Story

BY RING LARDNER

IX

CHAMPION

MIDGE KELLY scored his first knockout when he was seventeen. The knockee was his brother Connie, three years his junior and a cripple. The purse was a half dollar given to the younger Kelly by a lady whose electric had just missed bumping his soul from his frail little body.

Connie did not know Midge was in the house, else he never would have risked laying the prize on the arm of the least comfortable chair in the room, the better to observe its shining beauty. As Midge entered from the kitchen, the crippled boy covered the coin with his hand, but the movement lacked the speed requisite to escape his brother's quick eye.

" Watcha got there? " demanded Midge.

" Nothin'," said Connie.

" You're a one legged liar! " said Midge.

He strode over to his brother's chair and grasped the hand that concealed the coin.

" Let loose! " he ordered.

Connie began to cry.

" Let loose and shut up your noise," said the elder, and jerked his brother's hand from the chair arm.

The coin fell onto the bare floor. Midge pounced on it. His weak mouth widened in a triumphant smile.

" Nothin', huh? " he said. " All right, if it's nothin' you don't want it."

" Give that back," sobbed the younger.

" I'll give you a red nose, you little sneak! Where'd you steal it? "

" I didn't steal it. It's mine. A lady give it to me after she pretty near hit me with a car."

" It's a crime she missed you," said Midge.

Midge started for the front door. The cripple picked up his crutch, rose from his chair with difficulty, and, still sobbing, came toward Midge. The latter heard him and stopped.

" You better stay where you're at," he said.

" I want my money," cried the boy.

" I know what you want," said Midge.

Doubling up the fist that held the half dollar, he landed with all his strength on his brother's mouth. Connie fell to the floor with a thud, the crutch tumbling on top of him. Midge stood beside the prostrate form.

" Is that enough? " he said. " Or do you want this, too? "

And he kicked him in the crippled leg.

" I guess that'll hold you," he said.

There was no response from the boy on the floor. Midge looked at him a moment, then at the coin in his hand, and then went out into the street, whistling.

An hour later, when Mrs. Kelly came home from her day's work at Faulkner's Steam Laundry, she found Connie on the floor, moaning. Dropping on her knees beside him, she called him by name a score of times. Then she got up and, pale as a ghost, dashed from the house. Dr. Ryan left the Kelly abode about dusk and walked toward Halsted Street. Mrs. Dorgan spied him as he passed her gate.

" Who's sick, Doctor? " she called.

" Poor little Connie," he replied. " He had a bad fall."

" How did it happen? "

" I can't say for sure, Margaret, but I'd almost bet he was knocked down."

" Knocked down! " exclaimed Mrs. Dorgan.

" Why, who—? "

" Have you seen the other one lately? "

" Michael? No, not since mornin'. You can't be thinkin'——"

" I wouldn't put it past him, Margaret," said the doctor gravely. " The lad's mouth is swollen and cut, and his poor, skinny little leg is bruised. He surely didn't do it to himself and I think Helen suspects the other one."

" Lord save us! " said Mrs. Dorgan. " I'll run over and see if I can help."

" That's a good woman," said Doctor Ryan, and went on down the street.

Near midnight, when Midge came home, his mother was sitting at Connie's bedside. She did not look up.

" Well," said Midge, " what's the matter? "

She remained silent. Midge repeated his question.

" Michael, you know what's the matter," she said at length.

" I don't know nothin'," said Midge.

" Don't lie to me, Michael. What did you do to your brother? "

" Nothin'."

" You hit him."

" Well, then, I hit him. What of it? It ain't the first time."

Her lips pressed tightly together, her face like chalk, Ellen Kelly rose from her chair and made straight for him. Midge backed against the door.

" Lay off'n me, Ma. I don't want to fight no woman."

Still she came on breathing heavily.

" Stop where you're at, Ma," he warned.

There was a brief struggle and Midge's mother lay on the floor before him.

" You ain't hurt, Ma. You're lucky I didn't land good. And I told you to lay off'n me."

" God forgive you, Michael! "

Midge found Hap Collins in the showdown game at the Royal.

" Come on out a minute," he said.

Hap followed him out on the walk.

" I'm leavin' town for a w'ile," said Midge.

" What for? "

" Well, we had a little run-in up to the house. The kid stole a half buck off'n me, and when I went after it he cracked me with his crutch. So I nailed him. And the old lady came at me with a chair and I took it off'n her and she fell down."

" How is Connie hurt? "

" Not bad."

" What are you runnin' away for? "

" Who the hell said I was runnin' away? I'm sick and tired o' gettin' picked on; that's all. So I'm leavin' for a w'ile and I want a piece o' money."

" I ain't only got six bits," said Happy.

" You're in bad shape, ain't you? Well, come through with it."

Happy came through.

" You oughtn't to hit the kid," he said.

" I ain't astin' you who can I hit," snarled Midge. " You try to put somethin' over on me and you'll get the same dose. I'm goin' now."

" Go as far as you like," said Happy, but not until he was sure that Kelly was out of hearing.

Early the following morning, Midge boarded a train for Milwaukee. He had no ticket, but no one knew the difference. The conductor remained in the caboose.

On a night six months later, Midge hurried out of the " stage door " of the Star Boxing Club and made for Duane's saloon, two blocks away. In his pocket were twelve dollars, his reward for having battered up one Demon Dempsey through the six rounds of the first preliminary.

It was Midge's first professional engagement in the manly art. Also it was the first time in weeks that he had earned twelve dollars.

On the way to Duane's he had to pass Niemann's. He pulled his cap over his eyes and increased his pace until he had gone by. Inside Niemann's stood a trusting bartender, who for ten days had staked Midge to drinks and allowed him to ravage the lunch on a promise to come in and settle the moment he was paid for the " prelim."

Midge strode into Duane's and aroused the napping bartender by slapping a silver dollar on the festive board.

" Gimme a shot," said Midge.

The shooting continued until the wind-up at the Star was over and part of the fight crowd joined Midge in front of Duane's bar. A youth in the early twenties, standing next to young Kelly, finally summoned sufficient courage to address him.

" Wasn't you in the first bout ? " he ventured.

" Yeh," Midge replied.

" My name's Hersch," said the other.

Midge received the startling information in silence.

" I don't want to butt in," continued Mr. Hersch, " but I'd like to buy you a drink."

" All right," said Midge, " but don't overstrain yourself."

Mr. Hersch laughed uproariously and beckoned to the bartender.

" You certainly gave that wop a trimmin' tonight," said the buyer of the drink, when they had been served. " I thought you'd kill him."

" I would if I hadn't let up," Midge replied. " I'll kill 'em all."

" You got the wallop all right," the other said admiringly.

" Have I got the wallop ? " said Midge. " Say, I can kick like a mule. Did you notice them muscles in my shoulders ? "

" Notice 'em ? I couldn't help from noticin' 'em," said Hersch. " I says to the fella settin' alongside o' me, I says : ' Look at them shoulders ! No wonder he can hit,' I says to him."

"Just let me land and it's good-by, baby," said Midge. "I'll kill 'em all."

The oral manslaughter continued until Duane's closed for the night. At parting, Midge and his new friend shook hands and arranged for a meeting the following evening.

For nearly a week the two were together almost constantly. It was Hersch's pleasant rôle to listen to Midge's modest revelations concerning himself, and to buy every time Midge's glass was empty. But there came an evening when Hersch regretfully announced that he must go home to supper.

"I got a date for eight bells," he confided. "I could stick till then, only I must clean up and put on the Sunday clo'es, 'cause she's the prettiest little thing in Milwaukee."

"Can't you fix it for two?" asked Midge.

"I don't know who to get," Hersch replied. "Wait, though. I got a sister and if she ain't busy, it'll be O. K. She's no bum for looks herself."

So it came about that Midge and Emma Hersch and Emma's brother and the prettiest little thing in Milwaukee foregathered at Wall's and danced half the night away. And Midge and Emma danced every dance together, for though every little onestep seemed to induce a new thirst of its own, Lou Hersch stayed too sober to dance with his own sister.

The next day, penniless at last in spite of his phenomenal ability to make someone else settle, Midge Kelly sought out Doc Hammond, matchmaker for the Star, and asked to be booked for the next show.

"I could put you on with Tracy for the next bout," said Doc.

"What's they in it?" asked Midge.

"Twenty if you cop," Doc told him.

"Have a heart," protested Midge. "Didn't I look good the other night?"

"You looked all right. But you aren't Freddie Welsh yet by a consid'able margin."

"I ain't scared of Freddie Welsh or none of 'em," said Midge.

"Well, we don't pay our boxers by the size of their chests," Doc said. "I'm offerin' you this Tracy bout. Take it or leave it."

"All right; I'm on," said Midge, and he passed a pleasant afternoon at Duane's on the strength of his booking.

Young Tracy's manager came to Midge the night before the show.

"How do you feel about this go?" he asked.

" Me ? " said Midge, " I feel all right. What do you mean, how do I feel ? "

" I mean," said Tracy's manager, " that we're mighty anxious to win, 'cause the boy's got a chanct in Philly if he cops this one."

" What's your proposition ? " asked Midge.

" Fifty bucks," said Tracy's manager.

" What do you think I am, a crook? Me lay down for fifty bucks. Not me ! "

" Seventy-five, then," said Tracy's manager.

The market closed on eighty and the details were agreed on in short order. And the next night Midge was stopped in the second round by a terrific slap on the forearm.

This time Midge passed up both Niemann's and Duane's, having a sizable account at each place, and sought his refreshment at Stein's farther down the street.

When the profits of his deal with Tracy were gone, he learned, by first-hand information from Doc Hammond and the matchmakers at the other " clubs," that he was no longer desired for even the cheapest of preliminaries. There was no danger of his starving or dying of thirst while Emma and Lou Hersch lived. But he made up his mind, four months after his defeat by Young Tracy, that Milwaukee was not the ideal place for him to live.

" I can lick the best of 'em," he reasoned, " but there ain't no more chanct for me here. I can maybe go east and get on somewheres. And besides——"

But just after Midge had purchased a ticket to Chicago with the money he had " borrowed " from Emma Hersch " to buy shoes," a heavy hand was laid on his shoulders and he turned to face two strangers.

" Where are you goin', Kelly ? " inquired the owner of the heavy hand.

" Nowheres," said Midge. " What the hell do you care ? "

The other stranger spoke :

" Kelly, I'm employed by Emma Hersch's mother to see that you do right by her. And we want you to stay here till you've done it."

" You won't get nothin' but the worst of it, monkeying with me," said Midge.

Nevertheless, he did not depart for Chicago that night. Two days later, Emma Hersch became Mrs. Kelly, and the gift of the groom, when once they were alone, was a crushing blow on the bride's pale cheek.

Next morning, Midge left Milwaukee as he had entered it—
by fast freight.

" They's no use kiddin' ourself any more," said Tommy Haley.
" He might get down to thirty-seven in a pinch, but if he done below that a mouse could stop him. He's a welter; that's what he is
and he knows it as well as I do. He's growed like a weed in the
last six mont's. I told him, I says, ' If you don't quit growin' they
won't be nobody for you to box, only Willard and them.' He says,
' Well, I wouldn't run away from Willard if I weighed twenty
pounds more.' "

" He must hate himself," said Tommy's brother.

" I never seen a good one that didn't," said Tommy. " And
Midge is a good one; don't make no mistake about that. I wisht
we could of got Welsh before the kid growed so big. But it's too
late now. I won't make no holler, though, if we can match him up
with the Dutchman."

" Who do you mean? "

" Young Goetz, the welter champ. We mightn't not get so much
dough for the bout itself, but it'd roll in afterward. What a
drawin' card we'd be, 'cause the people pays their money to see the
fella with the wallop, and that's Midge. And we'd keep the title
just as long as Midge could make the weight."

" Can't you land no match with Goetz? "

" Sure, 'cause he needs the money. But I've went careful with
the kid so far and look at the results I got! So what's the use of
takin' a chanct? The kid's comin' every minute and Goetz is goin'
back faster'n big Johnson did. I think we could lick him now; I'd
bet my life on it. But six mont's from now they won't be no risk.
He'll of licked hisself before that time. Then all as we'll have to
do is sign up with him and wait for the referee to stop it. But
Midge is so crazy to get at him now that I can't hardly hold him
back."

The brothers Haley were lunching in a Boston hotel. Dan had
come down from Holyoke to visit with Tommy and to watch the
latter's protégé go twelve rounds, or less, with Bud Cross. The
bout promised little in the way of a contest, for Midge had twice
stopped the Baltimore youth and Bud's reputation for gameness
was all that had earned him the date. The fans were willing to pay
the price to see Midge's hay-making left, but they wanted to see it
used on an opponent who would not jump out of the ring the first
time he felt its crushing force. But Cross was such an opponent,
and his willingness to stop boxing-gloves with his eyes, ears, nose

and throat had long enabled him to escape the horrors of honest labor. A game boy was Bud, and he showed it in his battered, swollen, discolored face.

"I should think," said Dan Haley, "that the kid'd do whatever you tell him after all you done for him."

"Well," said Tommy, "he's took my dope pretty straight so far, but he's so sure of hisself that he can't see no reason for waitin'. He'll do what I say, though; he'd be a sucker not to."

"You got a contrac' with him?"

"No, I don't need no contrac'. He knows it was me that drug him out o' the gutter and he ain't goin' to turn me down now, when he's got the dough and bound to get more. Where'd he of been at if I hadn't listened to him when he first come to me? That's pretty near two years ago now, but it seems like last week. I was settin' in the s'loon acrost from the Pleasant Club in Philly, waitin' for McCann to count the dough and come over, when this little bum blowed in and tried to stand the house off for a drink. They told him nothin' doin' and to beat it out o' there, and then he seen me and come over to where I was settin' and ast me wasn't I a boxin' man and I told him who I was. Then he ast me for money to buy a shot and I told him to set down and I'd buy it for him.

"Then we got talkin' things over and he told me his name and told me about fightn' a couple o' prelims out to Milwaukee. So I says, 'Well, boy, I don't know how good or how rotten you are, but you won't never get nowheres trainin' on that stuff.' So he says he'd cut it out if he could get on in a bout and I says I would give him a chanct if he played square with me and didn't touch no more to drink. So we shook hands and I took him up to the hotel with me and give him a bath and the next day I bought him some clo'es. And I staked him to eats and sleeps for over six weeks. He had a hard time breakin' away from the polish, but finally I thought he was fit and I give him his chanct. He went on with Smiley Sayer and stopped him so quick that Smiley thought sure he was poisoned.

"Well, you know what he's did since. The only beatin' in his record was by Tracy in Milwaukee before I got hold of him, and he's licked Tracy three times in the last year.

"I've gave him all the best of it in a money way and he's got seven thousand bucks in cold storage. How's that for a kid that was in the gutter two years ago? And he'd have still more yet if he wasn't so nuts over clo'es and got to stop at the good hotels and so forth."

"Where's his home at?"

"Well, he ain't really got no home. He came from Chicago and his mother canned him out o' the house for bein' no good. She give him a raw deal, I guess, and he says he won't have nothin' to do with her unless she comes to him first. She's got a pile o' money, he says, so he ain't worryin' about her."

The gentleman under discussion entered the café and swaggered to Tommy's table, while the whole room turned to look.

Midge was the picture of health despite a slightly colored eye and an ear that seemed to have no opening. But perhaps it was not his healthiness that drew all eyes. His diamond horse-shoe tie pin, his purple cross-striped shirt, his orange shoes and his light blue suit fairly screamed for attention.

"Where you been?" he asked Tommy. "I been lookin' all over for you."

"Set down," said his manager.

"No time," said Midge. "I'm goin' down to the w'arf and see 'em unload the fish."

"Shake hands with my brother Dan," said Tommy.

Midge shook with the Holyoke Haley.

"If you're Tommy's brother, you're O. K. with me," said Midge, and the brothers beamed with pleasure.

Dan moistened his lips and murmured an embarrassed reply, but it was lost on the young gladiator.

"Leave me take twenty," Midge was saying. "I prob'ly won't need it, but I don't like to be caught short."

Tommy parted with a twenty dollar bill and recorded the transaction in a small black book the insurance company had given him for Christmas.

"But," he said, "it won't cost you no twenty to look at them fish. Want me to go along?"

"No," said Midge hastily. "You and your brother here prob'ly got a lot to say to each other."

"Well," said Tommy, "don't take no bad money and don't get lost. And you better be back at four o'clock and lay down a w'ile."

"I don't need no rest to beat this guy," said Midge. "He'll do enough layin' down for the both of us."

And laughing even more than the jest called for, he strode out through the fire of admiring and startled glances.

The corner of Boylston and Tremont was the nearest Midge got to the wharf, but the lady awaiting him was doubtless a more dazzling sight than the catch of the luckiest Massachusetts fisherman. She could talk, too—probably better than the fish.

" O you Kid ! " she said, flashing a few silver teeth among the
gold. " O you fighting man ! "

Midge smiled up at her.

" We'll go somewheres and get a drink," he said. " One won't
hurt."

In New Orleans, five months after he had rearranged the map
of Bud Cross for the third time, Midge finished training for his
championship bout with the Dutchman.

Back in his hotel after the final workout, Midge stopped to chat
with some of the boys from up north, who had made the long trip
to see a champion dethroned, for the result of this bout was so
nearly a foregone conclusion that even the experts had guessed it.

Tommy Haley secured the key and the mail and ascended to the
Kelly suite. He was bathing when Midge came in, half an hour
later.

" Any mail ? " asked Midge.

" There on the bed," replied Tommy from the tub.

Midge picked up the stack of letters and postcards and glanced
them over. From the pile he sorted out three letters and laid them
on the table. The rest he tossed into the waste-basket. Then he
picked up the three and sat for a few moments holding them, while
his eyes gazed off into space. At length he looked again at the
three unopened letters in his hand; then he put one in his pocket
and tossed the other two at the basket. They missed their target
and fell on the floor.

" Hell ! " said Midge, and stooping over picked them up.

He opened one postmarked Milwaukee and read :

Dear Husband :

I have wrote to you so manny times and got no anser and I dont
know if you ever got them, so I am writeing again in the hopes
you will get this letter and anser. I dont like to bother you with
my trubles and I would not only for the baby and I am not asking
you should write to me but only send a little money and I am not
asking for myself but the baby has not been well a day since last
Aug. and the dr. told me she cant live much longer unless I give
her better food and thats impossible the way things are. Lou has
not been working for a year and what I make dont hardley pay for
the rent. I am not asking for you to give me any money, but only
you should send what I loaned when convenient and I think it

amts. to about $36.00. Please try and send that amt. and it will help me, but if you cant send the whole amt. try and send me something.

Your wife,

Emma.

Midge tore the letter into a hundred pieces and scattered them over the floor.

"Money, money, money!" he said. "They must think I'm made o' money. I s'pose the old woman's after it too."

He opened his mother's letter:

dear Michael Connie wonted me to rite and say you must beet the dutchman and he is sur you will and wonted me to say we wont you to rite and tell us about it, but I gess you havent no time to rite or we herd from you long beffore this but I wish you would rite jest a line or 2 boy becaus it wuld be better for Connie then a barl of medisin. It wuld help me to keep things going if you send me money now and then when you can spair it but if you cant send no money try and fine time to rite a letter onley a few lines and it will please Connie. jest think boy he hasent got out of bed in over 3 yrs. Connie says good luck.

Your Mother,

Ellen F. Kelly.

"I thought so," said Midge. "They're all alike."

The third letter was from New York. It read:

Hon:—This is the last letter you will get from me before your champ, but I will send you a telegram Saturday, but I can't say as much in a telegram as in a letter and I am writeing this to let you know I am thinking of you and praying for good luck.

Lick him good hon and don't wait no longer than you have to and don't forget to wire me as soon as its over. Give him that little old left of yours on the nose hon and don't be afraid of spoiling his good looks because he couldn't be no homlier than he is. But don't let him spoil my baby's pretty face. You won't will you hon.

Well hon I would give anything to be there and see it, but I guess you love Haley better than me or you wouldn't let him keep me away. But when your champ hon we can do as we please and tell Haley to go to the devil.

Well hon I will send you a telegram Saturday and I almost forgot to tell you I will need some more money, a couple hundred say and you will have to wire it to me as soon as you get this. You will won't you hon.

I will send you a telegram Saturday and remember hon I am pulling for you.

Well good-by sweetheart and good luck.

                                                            Grace.

"They're all alike," said Midge. "Money, money, money."

Tommy Haley, shining from his ablutions, came in from the adjoining room.

"Thought you'd be layin' down," he said.

"I'm goin' to," said Midge, unbuttoning his orange shoes.

"I'll call you at six and you can eat up here without no bugs to pester you. I got to go down and give them birds their tickets."

"Did you hear from Goldberg?" asked Midge.

"Didn't I tell you? Sure; fifteen weeks at five hundred, if we win. And we can get a guarantee o' twelve thousand, with privileges either in New York or Milwaukee."

"Who with?"

"Anybody that'll stand up in front of you. You don't care who it is, do you?"

"Not me. I'll make 'em all look like a monkey."

"Well you better lay down aw'ile."

"Oh, say, wire two hundred to Grace for me, will you? Right away; the New York address."

"Two hundred! You just sent her three hundred last Sunday."

"Well, what the hell do you care?"

"All right, all right. Don't get sore about it. Anything else?"

"That's all," said Midge, and dropped onto the bed.

"And I want the deed done before I come back," said Grace as she rose from the table. "You won't fall down on me, will you, hon?"

"Leave it to me," said Midge. "And don't spend no more than you have to."

Grace smiled a farewell and left the café. Midge continued to sip his coffee and read his paper.

They were in Chicago and they were in the middle of Midge's first week in vaudeville. He had come straight north to reap the rewards of his glorious victory over the broken down Dutchman. A fortnight had been spent in learning his act, which consisted of a gymnastic exhibition and a ten minutes' monologue on the various excellences of Midge Kelly. And now he was twice daily turning 'em away from the Madison Theater.

His breakfast over and his paper read, Midge sauntered into the lobby and asked for his key. He then beckoned to a bell-boy, who had been hoping for that very honor.

" Find Haley, Tommy Haley," said Midge. " Tell him to come up to my room."

" Yes, sir, Mr. Kelly," said the boy, and proceeded to break all his former records for diligence.

Midge was looking out of his seventh-story window when Tommy answered the summons.

" What'll it be? " inquired his manager.

There was a pause before Midge replied.

" Haley," he said, " twenty-five per cent's a whole lot o' money."

" I guess I got it comin', ain't I? " said Tommy.

" I don't see how you figger it. I don't see where you're worth it to me."

" Well," said Tommy, " I didn't expect nothin' like this. I thought you was satisfied with the bargain. I don't want to beat nobody out o' nothin', but I don't see where you could have got anybody else that would of did all I done for you."

" Sure, that's all right," said the champion. " You done a lot for me in Philly. And you got good money for it, didn't you? "

" I ain't makin' no holler. Still and all, the big money's still ahead of us yet. And if it hadn't of been for me, you wouldn't of never got within grabbin' distance."

" Oh, I guess I could of went along all right," said Midge. " Who was it that hung that left on the Dutchman's jaw, me or you? "

" Yes, but you wouldn't been in the ring with the Dutchman if it wasn't for how I handled you."

" Well, this won't get us nowheres. The idear is that you ain't worth no twenty-five per cent now and it don't make no diff'rence what come off a year or two ago."

" Don't it? " said Tommy. " I'd say it made a whole lot of difference."

" Well, I say it don't and I guess that settles it."

" Look here, Midge," Tommy said, " I thought I was fair with you, but if you don't think so, I'm willin' to hear what you think is fair. I don't want nobody callin' me a Sherlock. Let's go down to business and sign up a contrac'. What's your figger? "

"I ain't namin' no figger," Midge replied. "I'm sayin' that twenty-five's too much. Now what are you willin' to take?"

"How about twenty?"

"Twenty's too much," said Kelly.

"What ain't too much?" asked Tommy.

"Well, Haley, I might as well give it to you straight. They ain't nothin' that ain't too much."

"You mean you don't want me at no figger?"

"That's the idear."

There was a minute's silence. Then Tommy Haley walked toward the door.

"Midge," he said, in a choking voice, "you're makin' a big mistake, boy. You can't throw down your best friends and get away with it. That damn woman will ruin you."

Midge sprang from his seat.

"You shut your mouth!" he stormed. "Get out o' here before they have to carry you out. You been spongin' off o' me long enough. Say one more word about the girl or about anything else and you'll get what the Dutchman got. Now get out!"

And Tommy Haley, having a very vivid memory of the Dutchman's face as he fell, got out.

Grace came in later, dropped her numerous bundles on the lounge and perched herself on the arm of Midge's chair.

"Well?" she said.

"Well," said Midge, "I got rid of him."

"Good boy!" said Grace. "And now I think you might give me that twenty-five per cent."

"Besides the seventy-five you're already gettin'?" said Midge.

"Don't be no grouch, hon. You don't look pretty when you're grouchy."

"It ain't my business to look pretty," Midge replied.

"Wait till you see how I look with the stuff I bought this mornin'!"

Midge glanced at the bundles on the lounge.

"There's Haley's twenty-five per cent," he said, "and then some."

The champion did not remain long without a manager. Haley's successor was none other than Jerome Harris, who saw in Midge a better meal ticket than his popular-priced musical show had been.

The contract, giving Mr. Harris twenty-five per cent of Midge's earnings, was signed in Detroit the week after Tommy Haley had heard his dismissal read. It had taken Midge just six days to learn that a popular actor cannot get on without the ministrations of a man who thinks, talks and means business. At first Grace objected to the new member of the firm, but when Mr. Harris had demanded and secured from the vaudeville people a one-hundred dollar increase in Midge's weekly stipend, she was convinced that the champion had acted for the best.

" You and my missus will have some great old times," Harris told Grace. " I'd of wired her to join us here, only I seen the Kid's bookin' takes us to Milwaukee next week, and that's where she is."

But when they were introduced in the Milwaukee hotel, Grace admitted to herself that her feeling for Mrs. Harris could hardly be called love at first sight. Midge, on the contrary, gave his new manager's wife the many times over and seemed loath to end the feast of his eyes.

" Some doll," he said to Grace when they were alone.

" Doll is right," the lady replied, " and sawdust where her brains ought to be."

" I'm li'ble to steal that baby," said Midge, and he smiled as he noted the effect of his words on his audience's face.

On Tuesday of the Milwaukee week the champion successfully defended his title in a bout that the newspapers never reported. Midge was alone in his room that morning when a visitor entered without knocking. The visitor was Lou Hersch.

Midge turned white at sight of him.

" What do you want? " he demanded.

" I guess you know," said Lou Hersch. " Your wife's starvin' to death and your baby's starvin' to death and I'm starvin' to death. And you're dirty with money."

" Listen," said Midge, " if it wasn't for you, I wouldn't never saw your sister. And, if you ain't man enough to hold a job, what's that to me? The best thing you can do is keep away from me."

" You give me a piece o' money and I'll go."

Midge's reply to the ultimatum was a straight right to his brother-in-law's narrow chest.

" Take that home to your sister."

And after Lou Hersch had picked himself up and slunk away, Midge thought: " It's lucky I didn't give him my left or I'd of croaked him. And if I'd hit him in the stomach, I'd of broke his spine."

There was a party after each evening performance during the

Milwaukee engagement. The wine flowed freely and Midge had more of it than Tommy Haley ever would have permitted him. Mr. Harris offered no objection, which was possibly just as well for his own physical comfort.

In the dancing between drinks, Midge had his new manager's wife for a partner as often as Grace. The latter's face as she floundered round in the arms of the portly Harris, belied her frequent protestations that she was having the time of her life.

Several times that week, Midge thought Grace was on the point of starting the quarrel he hoped to have. But it was not until Friday night that she accommodated. He and Mrs. Harris had disappeared after the matinee and when Grace saw him again at the close of the night show, she came to the point at once.

" What are you tryin' to pull off ? " she demanded.

" It's none o' your business, is it ? " said Midge.

" You bet it's my business ; mine and Harris's. You cut it short or you'll find out."

"Listen," said Midge, " have you got a mortgage on me or somethin' ? You talk like we was married."

" We're goin' to be, too. And to-morrow's as good a time as any."

" Just about," Midge said. " You got as much chanct o' marryin' me to-morrow as the next day or next year and that ain't no chanct at all."

" We'll find out," said Grace.

" You're the one that's got somethin' to find out."

" What do you mean ? "

" I mean I'm married already."

" You lie ! "

" You think so, do you ? Well, s'pose you go to this here address and get acquainted with my missus."

Midge scrawled a number on a piece of paper and handed it to her. She stared at it unseeingly.

" Well," said Midge, " I ain't kiddin' you. You go there and ask for Mrs. Michael Kelly, and if you don't find her, I'll marry you to-morrow before breakfast."

Still Grace stared at the scrap of paper. To Midge it seemed an age before she spoke again.

" You lied to me all this w'ile."

" You never ast me was I married. What's more, what the hell diff'rence did it make to you ? You got a split, didn't you ? Better'n fifty-fifty."

He started away.

" Where you goin'? "

" I'm goin' to meet Harris and his wife."

" I'm goin' with you. You're not goin' to shake me now."

" Yes, I am, too," said Midge quietly. " When I leave town to-morrow night, you're going to stay here. And if I see where you're goin' to make a fuss, I'll put you in a hospital where they'll keep you quiet. You can get your stuff to-morrow mornin' and I'll slip you a hundred bucks. And then I don't want to see no more o' you. And don't try and tag along now or I'll have to add another K. O. to the old record."

When Grace returned to the hotel that night, she discovered that Midge and the Harrises had moved to another. And when Midge left town the following night, he was again without a manager, and Mr. Harris was without a wife.

Three days prior to Midge Kelly's ten-round bout with Young Milton in New York City, the sporting editor of *The News* assigned Joe Morgan to write two or three thousand words about the champion to run with a picture lay-out for Sunday.

Joe Morgan dropped in at Midge's training quarters Friday afternoon. Midge, he learned, was doing road work, but Midge's manager, Wallie Adams, stood ready and willing to supply reams of dope about the greatest fighter of the age.

" Let's hear what you've got," said Joe, " and then I'll try to fix up something."

So Wallie stepped on the accelerator of his imagination and shot away.

" Just a kid; that's all he is; a regular boy. Get what I mean? Don't know the meanin' o' bad habits. Never tasted liquor in his life and would prob'bly get sick if he smelled it. Clean livin' put him up where he's at. Get what I mean? And modest and unassumin' as a school girl. He's so quiet you wouldn't never know he was round. And he'd go to jail before he'd talk about himself.

"No job at all to get him in shape, 'cause he's always that way. The only trouble we have with him is gettin' him to light into these poor bums they match him up with. He's scared he'll hurt somebody. Get what I mean? He's tickled to death over this match with Milton, 'cause everybody says Milton can stand the gaff. Midge'll maybe be able to cut loose a little this time. But the last two bouts he had, the guys hadn't no business in the ring with him, and he was holdin' back all the w'ile for the fear he'd kill somebody. Get what I mean? "

" Is he married ? " inquired Joe.

" Say, you'd think he was married to hear him rave about them kiddies he's got. His fam'ly's up in Canada to their summer home and Midge is wild to get up there with 'em. He thinks more o' that wife and them kiddies than all the money in the world. Get what I mean? "

" How many children has he? "

" I don't know, four or five, I guess. All boys and every one of 'em a dead ringer for their dad."

" Is his father living? "

" No, the old man died when he was a kid. But he's got a grand old mother and a kid brother out in Chi. They're the first ones he thinks about after a match, them and his wife and kiddies. And he don't forget to send the old woman a thousand bucks after every bout. He's goin' to buy her a new home as soon as they pay him off for this match."

" How about his brother? Is he going to tackle the game? "

" Sure, and Midge says he'll be a champion before he's twenty years old. They're a fightin' fam'ly and all of 'em honest and straight as a die. Get what I mean? A fella that I can't tell you his name come to Midge in Milwaukee onct and wanted him to throw a fight and Midge give him such a trimmin' in the street that he couldn't go on that night. That's the kind he is. Get what I mean? "

Joe Morgan hung around the camp until Midge and his trainers returned.

" One o' the boys from *The News*," said Wallie by way of introduction. " I been givin' him your fam'ly hist'ry."

" Did he give you good dope? " he inquired.

" He's some historian," said Joe.

" Don't call me no names," said Wallie smiling. " Call us up if they's anything more you want. And keep your eyes on us Monday night. Get what I mean? "

The story in Sunday's *News* was read by thousands of lovers of the manly art. It was well written and full of human interest. Its slight inaccuracies went unchallenged, though three readers, besides Wallie Adams and Midge Kelly, saw and recognized them. The three were Grace, Tommy Haley and Jerome Harris and the comments they made were not for publication.

Neither the Mrs. Kelly in Chicago nor the Mrs. Kelly in Milwaukee knew that there was such a paper as the New York *News*. And even if they had known of it and that it contained two columns of reading matter about Midge, neither mother nor wife could have bought it. For *The News* on Sunday is a nickel a copy.

Joe Morgan could have written more accurately, no doubt, if instead of Wallie Adams, he had interviewed Ellen Kelly and Connie Kelly and Emma Kelly and Lou Hersch and Grace and Jerome Harris and Tommy Haley and Hap Collins and two or three Milwaukee bartenders.

But a story built on their evidence would never have passed the sporting editor.

" Suppose you can prove it," that gentleman would have said, " It wouldn't get us anything but abuse to print it. The people don't want to see him knocked. He's champion."

DEATH IN THE WOODS
A Story

BY SHERWOOD ANDERSON

S HE was an old woman and lived on a farm near the town in which I lived. All country and small-town people have seen such old women, but no one knows much about them. Such an old woman comes into town driving an old worn-out horse or she comes afoot carrying a basket. She may own a few hens and have eggs to sell. She brings them in a basket and takes them to a grocer. There she trades them in. She gets some salt pork and some beans. Then she gets a pound or two of sugar and some flour.

Afterward she goes to the butcher's and asks for some dog meat. She may spend ten or fifteen cents, but when she does she asks for something. In my day the butchers gave liver to anyone who wanted to carry it away. In our family we were always having it. Once one of my brothers got a whole cow's liver at the slaughter-house near the fair-grounds. We had it until we were sick of it. It never cost a cent. I have hated the thought of it ever since.

The old farm woman got some liver and a soup bone. She never visited with anyone, and as soon as she got what she wanted she lit out for home. It made quite a load for such an old body. No one gave her a lift. People drive right down a road and never notice an old woman like that.

There was such an old woman used to come into town past our house one summer and fall when I was sick with what was called inflammatory rheumatism. She went home later carrying a heavy pack on her back. Two or three large gaunt-looking dogs followed at her heels.

The old woman was nothing special. She was one of the nameless ones that hardly anyone knows, but she got into my

407

thoughts. I have just suddenly now, after all these years, remembered her and what happened. It is a story. Her name was, I think, Grimes, and she lived with her husband and son in a small unpainted house on the bank of a small creek four miles from town.

The husband and son were a tough lot. Although the son was but twenty-one, he had already served a term in jail. It was whispered about that the woman's husband stole horses and ran them off to some other county. Now and then, when a horse turned up missing, the man had also disappeared. No one ever caught him. Once, when I was loafing at Tom Whitehead's livery barn, the man came there and sat on the bench in front. Two or three other men were there, but no one spoke to him. He sat for a few minutes and then got up and went away. When he was leaving he turned around and stared at the men. There was a look of defiance in his eyes. "Well, I have tried to be friendly. You don't want to talk to me. It has been so wherever I have gone in this town. If, some day, one of your fine horses turns up missing, well, then what?" He did not say anything actually. "I'd like to bust one of you on the jaw," was about what his eyes said. I remember how the look in his eyes made me shiver.

The old man belonged to a family that had had money once. His name was Grimes, Jake Grimes. It all comes back clearly now. His father, John Grimes, had owned a sawmill when the country was new and had made money. Then he got to drinking and running after women. When he died, there wasn't much left.

Jake blew in the rest. Pretty soon there wasn't any more lumber to cut and his land was nearly all gone.

He got his wife off a German farmer, for whom he went to work one June day in the wheat harvest. She was a young thing then and scared to death. You see, the farmer was up to something with the girl—she was, I think, a bound girl, and his wife had her suspicions. She took it out on the girl when the man wasn't around. Then, when the wife had to go off to town for supplies, the farmer got after her. She told young Jake that nothing really ever happened, but he didn't know whether to believe it or not.

He got her pretty easy himself, the first time he was out with her. He wouldn't have married her if the German

farmer hadn't tried to tell him where to get off. He got her
to go riding with him in his buggy one night when he was
threshing on the place, and then he came for her the next
Sunday night.

She managed to get out of the house without her employer's
seeing, but when she was getting into the buggy he showed
up. It was almost dark, and he just popped up suddenly
at the horse's head. He grabbed the horse by the bridle and
Jake got out his buggy whip.

They had it out all right! The German was a tough one.
Maybe he didn't care whether his wife knew or not. Jake
hit him over the face and shoulders with the buggy whip,
but the horse got to acting up and he had to get out.

Then the two men went for it. The girl didn't see it. The
horse started to run away and went nearly a mile down the
road before the girl got him stopped. Then she managed to
tie him to a tree beside the road. (I wonder how I know all
this. It must have stuck in my mind from small-town tales
when I was a boy.) Jake found her there after he got through
with the German. She was huddled up in the buggy seat,
crying, scared to death. She told Jake a lot of stuff, how the
German had tried to get her, how he chased her once into the
barn, how another time, when they happened to be alone in
the barn together, he tore her dress open clear down the
front. The German, she said, might have got her that time
if he hadn't heard his old woman drive in at the gate. She
had been off to town for supplies. Well, she would be putting
the horse in the barn. The German managed to sneak off
to the fields without his wife seeing. He told the girl he
would kill her if she told. What could she do? She told a
lie about ripping her dress in the barn when she was feeding
the stock. I remember now that she was a bound girl and
did not know where her father and mother were. Maybe she
did not have any father. You know what I mean.

II

She married Jake and had a son and daughter but the
daughter died.

Then she settled down to feed stock. That was her job.
At the German's place she had cooked the food for the Ger-

man and his wife. The wife was a strong woman with big hips and worked most of the time in the fields with her husband. She fed them and fed the cows in the barn, fed the pigs, the horses, and the chickens. Every moment of every day as a young girl was spent feeding something.

Then she married Jake Grimes and he had to be fed. She was a slight thing, and when she had been married for three or four years, and after the two children were born, her slender shoulders became stooped.

Jake always had a lot of big dogs around the house, that stood near the unused sawmill near the creek. He was always trading horses when he wasn't stealing something, and had a lot of poor bony ones about. Also, he kept three or four pigs and a cow. They were all pastured in the few acres left of the Grimes place and Jake did little.

He went into debt for a threshing outfit and ran it for several years, but it did not pay. People did not trust him. They were afraid he would steal the grain at night. He had to go a long way off to get work, and it cost too much to get there. In the winter he hunted and cut a little firewood, to be sold in some near-by town. When the boy grew up he was just like his father. They got drunk together. If there wasn't anything to eat in the house when they came home the old man gave his old woman a cut over the head. She had a few chickens of her own and had to kill one of them in a hurry. When they were all killed she wouldn't have any eggs to sell when she went to town, and then what would she do?

She had to scheme all her life about getting things fed, getting the pigs fed so they would grow fat and could be butchered in the fall. When they were butchered her husband took most of the meat off to town and sold it. If he did not do it first the boy did. They fought sometimes and when they fought the old woman stood aside trembling.

She had got the habit of silence anyway—that was fixed. Sometimes, when she began to look old—she wasn't forty yet —and when the husband and son were both off, trading horses or drinking or hunting or stealing, she went around the house and the barnyard muttering to herself.

How was she going to get everything fed?—that was her problem. The dogs had to be fed. There wasn't enough

hay in the barn for the cow and the horses.   If she didn't feed
the chickens how could they lay eggs?   Without eggs to sell
how could she get things in town, things she had to have to
keep the life of the farm going?   Thank heaven, she did not
have to feed her husband—in a certain way.   That hadn't
lasted long after their marriage and after the babies came.
Where he went on his long trips she did not know.   Sometimes he was gone from home for weeks, and after the boy
grew up they went off together.

They left everything at home for her to manage and she
had no money.   She knew no one.   No one ever talked to
her in town.   When it was winter she had to gather sticks
of wood for her fire, had to try to keep the stock fed with
very little grain.

The stock in the barn cried to her hungrily, the dogs followed her about.   In the winter the hens laid few enough eggs.
They huddled in the corners of the barn and she kept watching
them.   If a hen lays an egg in the barn in the winter and you
do not find it, it freezes and breaks.

One day in winter the old woman went off to town with a
few eggs and the dogs followed her.   She did not get started
until nearly three o'clock and the snow was heavy.   She
hadn't been feeling very well for several days and so she went
muttering along, scantily clad, her shoulders stooped.   She
had an old grain bag in which she carried her eggs, tucked
away down in the bottom.   There weren't many of them, but
in winter the price of eggs is up.   She would get a little meat
for the eggs, some salt pork, a little sugar, and some coffee,
perhaps.   It might be the butcher would give her a piece of
liver.

When she had got to town and was trading in her eggs the
dogs lay by the door outside.   She did pretty well, got the
things she needed, more than she had hoped.   Then she went
to the butcher and he gave her some liver and some dog meat.

It was the first time anyone had spoken to her in a friendly
way for a long time.   The butcher was alone in his shop when
she went in and was annoyed by the thought of such a sick-
looking old woman out on such a day.   It was bitter cold and
the snow, that had let up during the afternoon, was falling
again.   The butcher said something about her husband and
her son, swore at them, and the old woman stared at him, a

look of mild surprise in her eyes as he talked.   He said that
if either the husband or the son were going to get any of the
liver or the heavy bones with scraps of meat hanging to them
that he had put into the grain bag, he'd see him starve first.

Starve, eh?   Well, things had to be fed.   Men had to be
fed, and the horses that weren't any good but maybe could be
traded off, and the poor thin cow that hadn't given any milk
for three months.

Horses, cows, pigs, dogs, men.

III.

The old woman had to get back before darkness came if
she could.   The dogs followed at her heels, sniffing at the
heavy grain bag she had fastened on her back.   When she
got to the edge of town she stopped by a fence and tied the
bag on her back with a piece of rope she had carried in her
dress pocket for just that purpose.   That was an easier way
to carry it.   Her arms ached.   It was hard when she had to
crawl over fences, and once she fell over and landed in the
snow.   The dogs went frisking about.   She had to struggle
to get to her feet again, but she made it.   The point of climbing over the fences was that there was a short cut over a hill
and through a wood.   She might have gone around by the
road, but it was a mile farther that way.   She was afraid
she couldn't make it.   And then, besides, the stock had to
be fed.   There was a little hay left, a little corn.   Perhaps
her husband and son would bring some home when they came.
They had driven off in the only buggy the Grimes family had,
a rickety thing, a rickety horse hitched to the buggy, two
other rickety horses led by halters.   They were going to trade
horses, get a little money if they could.   They might come
home drunk.   It would be well to have something in the
house when they came back.

The son had an affair on with a woman at the county seat,
fifteen miles away.   She was a bad woman, a tough one.
Once, in the summer, the son had brought her to the house.
Both she and the son had been drinking.   Jake Grimes was
away and the son and his woman ordered the old woman
about like a servant.   She didn't mind much; she was used
to it.   Whatever happened, she never said anything.   That

was her way of getting along. She had managed that way when she was a young girl at the German's and ever since she had married Jake. That time her son brought his woman to the house they stayed all night, sleeping together just as though they were married. It hadn't shocked the old woman, not much. She had got past being shocked early in life.

With the pack on her back she went painfully along across an open field, wading in the deep snow, and got into the woods.

There was a path, but it was hard to follow. Just beyond the top of the hill, where the wood was thickest, there was a small clearing. Had someone once thought of building a house there? The clearing was as large as a building lot in town, large enough for a house and a garden. The path ran along the side of the clearing and when she got there the old woman sat down to rest at the foot of a tree.

It was a foolish thing to do. When she got herself placed, the pack against the tree's trunk, it was nice, but what about getting up again? She worried about that for a moment and then quietly closed her eyes.

She must have slept for a time. When you are about so cold you can't get any colder. The afternoon grew a little warmer and the snow came thicker than ever. Then after a time the weather cleared. The moon even came out.

There were four Grimes dogs that had followed Mrs. Grimes into town, all tall gaunt fellows. Such men as Jake Grimes and his son always keep just such dogs. They kick and abuse them, but they stay. The Grimes dogs, in order to keep from starving, had to do a lot of foraging for themselves, and they had been at it while the old woman slept with her back to the tree at the side of the clearing. They had been chasing rabbits in the woods and in adjoining fields, and in their ranging had picked up three other farm dogs.

After a time all the dogs came back to the clearing. They were excited about something. Such nights, cold and clear and with a moon, do things to dogs. It may be that some old instinct, come down from the time when they were wolves and ranged the woods in packs on winter nights, comes back into them.

The dogs in the clearing, before the old woman, had caught

two or three rabbits and their immediate hunger had been satisfied. They began to play, running in circles in the clearing. Round and round they ran, each dog's nose at the tail of the next dog. In the clearing, under the snow-laden trees and under the wintry moon they made a strange picture, running thus silently, in a circle their running had beaten in the soft snow. The dogs made no sound. They ran around and around in the circle.

It may have been that the old woman saw them doing that before she died. She may have awakened once or twice and looked at the strange sight with dim old eyes.

She wouldn't be very cold now, just drowsy. Life hangs on a long time. Perhaps the old woman was out of her head. She may have dreamed of her girlhood, at the German's, and before that, when she was a child and before her mother lit out and left her.

Her dreams couldn't have been very pleasant. Not many pleasant things had happened to her. Now and then one of the Grimes dogs left the running circle and came to stand before her. The dog thrust his face close to her face. His red tongue was hanging out.

The running of the dogs may have been a kind of death ceremony. It may have been that the primitive instinct of the wolf, having been aroused in the dogs by the night and the running, made them somehow afraid.

"Now we are no longer wolves. We are dogs, the servants of men. Keep alive, man! When man dies we become wolves again."

When one of the dogs came to where the old woman sat with her back against the tree and thrust his nose close to her face he seemed satisfied and went back to run with the pack. All the Grimes dogs did it at some time during the evening, before she died. I knew all about it afterward, when I grew to be a man, because once in a wood on another winter night I saw a pack of dogs act just like that. The dogs were waiting for me to die as they had waited for the old woman that night when I was a child, but when it happened to me I was a young man and had no intention whatever of dying.

The old woman died softly and quietly. When she was dead and when one of the Grimes dogs had come to her and had found her dead all the dogs stopped running.

They gathered about her.

Well, she was dead now. She had fed the Grimes dogs when she was alive, what about now?

There was the pack on her back, the grain bag containing the piece of salt pork, the liver the butcher had given her, the dog meat, the soup bones. The butcher in town, having been suddenly overcome with a feeling of pity, had loaded her grain bag heavily. It had been a big haul for the old woman.

A big haul for the dogs now.

IV

One of the Grimes dogs sprang suddenly out from among the others and began worrying the pack on the old woman's back. Had the dogs really been wolves that one would have been the leader of the pack. What he did, all the others did.

All of them sank their teeth into the grain bag the old woman had fastened with ropes to her back.

They dragged the old woman's body out into the open clearing. The worn-out dress was quickly torn from her shoulders. When she was found, a day or two later, the dress had been torn from her body clear to the hips but the dogs had not touched her body. They had got the meat out of the grain bag, that was all. Her body was frozen stiff when it was found and the shoulders were so narrow and the body so slight that in death it looked like the body of some charming young girl.

Such things happened in towns of the Middle West, on farms near town, when I was a boy. A hunter out after rabbits found the old woman's body and did not touch it. Something, the beaten round path in the little snow-covered clearing, the silence of the place, the place where the dogs had worried the body trying to pull the grain bag away or tear it open—something startled the man and he hurried off to town.

I was in Main Street with one of my brothers, who was taking the afternoon papers to the stores. It was almost night.

The hunter came into a grocery and told his story. Then he went to a hardware shop and into a drug store. Men began to gather on the sidewalks. Then they started out along the road to the place in the wood.

My brother should have gone on about his business of distributing papers, but he didn't.   Everyone was going to the woods.   The undertaker went and the town marshal.   Several men got on a dray and rode out to where the path left the road and went into the woods, but the horses weren't very sharply shod and slid about on the slippery roads. They made no better time than those of us who walked.

The town marshal was a large man whose leg had been injured in the Civil War.   He carried a heavy cane and limped rapidly along the road.   My brother and I followed at his heels, and as we went other men and boys joined the crowd.

It had grown dark by the time we got to where the old woman had left the road, but the moon had come out.   The marshal was thinking there might have been a murder.   He kept asking the hunter questions.   The hunter went along with his gun across his shoulders, a dog following at his heels. It isn't often a rabbit hunter has a chance to be so conspicuous. He was taking full advantage of it, leading the procession with the town marshal.   "I didn't see any wounds.   She was a beautiful young girl.   Her face was buried in the snow.   No, I didn't know her."   As a matter of fact, the hunter had not looked closely at the body.   He had been frightened.   She might have been murdered and someone might spring out from behind a tree and murder him too.   In a woods, in the late afternoon, when the trees are all bare and there is white snow on the ground, when all is silent, something creepy steals over the mind and body.   If something strange or uncanny has happened in the neighbourhood, all you think about is getting away from there as fast as you can.

The crowd of men and boys had got to where the old woman crossed the field and went, following the marshal and the hunter up the slight incline and into the woods.

My brother and I were silent.   He had his bundle of papers in a bag slung across his shoulder.   When he got back to town he would have to go on distributing his papers before he went home to supper.   If I went along, as he had no doubt already determined I should, we would both be late.   Either Mother or our younger sister would have to warm our supper.

Well, we would have something to tell.   A boy did not get such a chance very often.   It was lucky we just happened to go into the grocery when the hunter came in. The hunter was a country fellow. Neither of us had ever seen him before.

Now the crowd of men and boys had got to the clearing. Darkness comes quickly on such winter nights, but the full moon made everything clear. My brother and I stood near the trees beneath which the old woman had died.

She did not look old, lying there frozen in that light. One of the men turned her over in the snow and I saw everything. My body trembled with some strange mystical feeling, and so did my brother's. It might have been the cold.

Neither of us had ever seen a woman's body before. It may have been the snow, clinging to the frozen flesh, that made it look so white and lovely, so like marble. No woman had come with the party from town, but one of the men, he was the town blacksmith, took off his overcoat and spread it over her. Then he gathered her into his arms and started off to town, all the others following silently. At that time no one knew who she was.

V

I had seen everything, had seen the oval in the snow, like a miniature race track, where the dogs had run, had seen how the men were mystified, had seen the white, bare, young-looking shoulders, had heard the whispered comments of the men.

The men were simply mystified. They took the body to the undertaker's, and when the blacksmith, the hunter, the marshal, and several others had got inside, they closed the door. If Father had been there, perhaps he could have got in, but we boys couldn't.

I went with my brother to distribute the rest of his papers, and when we got home it was my brother who told the story.

I kept silent and went to bed early. It may have been I was not satisfied with the way he told it.

Later, in the town, I must have heard other fragments of the old woman's story. She was recognized the next day and there was an investigation.

The husband and son were found somewhere and brought

to town, and there was an attempt to connect them with the woman's death, but it did not work. They had perfect enough alibis.

However, the town was against them. They had to get out. Where they went, I never heard.

I remember only the picture there in the forest, the men standing about, the naked, girlish-looking figure, face down in the snow, the tracks made by the running dogs, and the clear, cold winter sky above. White fragments of clouds were drifting across the sky. They went racing across the little open space among the trees.

The scene in the forest had become for me, without my knowing it, the foundation for the real story I am now trying to tell. The fragments. you see, had to be picked up slowly, long afterward.

Things happened. When I was a young man I worked on the farm of a German. The hired girl was afraid of her employer. The farmer's wife hated her.

I saw things at that place. Once, later, I had a half-uncanny, mystical sort of adventure with dogs in a forest on a clear, moonlit winter night. When I was a schoolboy, and on a summer day, I went with a boy friend out along a creek some miles from town and came to the house where the old woman had lived. No one had lived in the house since her death. The doors were broken from the hinges, the window lights were all broken. As the boy and I stood in the road outside, two dogs, just roving farm dogs, no doubt, came running around the corner of the house. The dogs were tall, gaunt fellows and came down to the fence and glared through at us, standing in the road.

The whole thing, the story of the old woman's death, was to me, as I grew older, like music heard from far off. The notes had to be picked up slowly one at a time. Something had to be understood.

The woman who died was one destined to feed animal life. Anyway, that is all she ever did. She was feeding animal life before she was born, as a child, as a young woman working on the farm of the German, after she married, when she grew old, and when she died. She fed animal life in cows, in chickens, in pigs, in horses, in dogs, in men. Her daughter had died in childhood, and with her one son she had no articulate relations. On the night when she died she was hurrying homeward, bearing on her body food for animal life.

She died in the clearing in the woods, and even after her death continued feeding animal life.

You see it is likely that, when my brother told the story, that night when we got home and my mother and sister sat listening, I did not think he got the point. He was too young and so was I. A thing so complete has its own beauty.

I shall not try to emphasize the point. I am only explaining why I was dissatisfied then, and have been ever since. I speak of that only that you may understand why I have been impelled to try to tell the simple story over again.

Mary of Scotland

A Play

BY MAXWELL ANDERSON

NOTE

CHARACTERS

(In the Order of their Appearance):

First Guard, JAMIE
Second Guard
Third Guard
JOHN KNOX
JAMES HEPBURN, Earl of Bothwell
CHATELARD
MARY STUART
DUC DE CHATELHERAULT
MARY BEATON
MARY SETON
MARY LIVINGSTONE
MARY FLEMING
ELIZABETH TUDOR
LORD BURGHLEY
HENRY, LORD DARNLEY
LORD GORDON
DAVID RIZZIO
JAMES STUART, Earl of Moray
MAITLAND of Lethington
LORD HUNTLEY
LORD MORTON
LORD ERSKINE
LORD THROGMORTON
A Porter
LORD RUTHVEN
LORD DOUGLAS
Young RUTHVEN
First Sentinel
Second Sentinel
A Sergeant
A Warden
Soldiers and others

Mary of Scotland

ACT ONE

ACT ONE

Scene One

Scene: *A half-sheltered corner of the pier at Leith. It is a sleety, windy night, and the tall piles of the background and the planks underfoot shine black and icy with their coating of freezing rain. Long cables stretch away into the dark. The only light comes from the lantern of two iron-capped* Guards *who are playing cards morosely on the head of a fish-tub in the lee of a great coil of rope.*

FIRST GUARD

Na, na, put them away. I'm fair clabbered with the cold.

SECOND GUARD

Aye, you'd say that, wi' ma siller-piece laced in youɪ brogues!

FIRST GUARD

Gie me the hand, then. But man, it's an unco bitter nicht for indoor pleasures.

SECOND GUARD

[*Throwing out cards*]
It's a blastit wonner—

FIRST GUARD

Put out, put out!

SECOND GUARD

[*Laying down a coin*]
Aye.

FIRST GUARD

And we'll just stop now, forbye to go on 'ud strain
your two-year credit.
[*He shows his hand*]

SECOND GUARD

Dod, mon, ye hae luck wi' the titties. Ye'll no refuse
me ma revenge, Jamie?
[*A tall bearded* FIGURE, *muffled in a cloak, has
come in from the left*]

FIRST GUARD

When ye can afford it. No earlier.

SECOND GUARD

Ye see yoursel', Jamie. I'm gouged out clean—

FIRST GUARD

And is that a reason I should risk my gains—?

THE OLD MAN

Aye, dicing, gaming, cards, drinking, dancing, whoring, and all the papistical uses of the flesh—they run
before her like a foul air—

SECOND GUARD

It's the Master—wheest—put them awa'.

FIRST GUARD
An' what of it? I'm na member of his congregation.
[*A third* GUARD *runs in from the right*]

THIRD GUARD
I was right, Jamie! 'Tis the queen's ship!

FIRST GUARD
The Queen's ship, you goik! How could it be the
queen's ship? She's to come in a galley, and she's none
due this month yet.

THIRD GUARD
My word on it, Tod, I rid out wi' the fishermen, and
she's a galley wi' oars, and by God she carries the ori-
flamme!

SECOND GUARD
Would the queen's ship dock without notice to the
lords, and no retinue at the pier?

THIRD GUARD
There it lies—yon wi' the lights!

FIRST GUARD
She's lights aplenty, afore God. Aweel, we've no
orders aboot it.

THIRD GUARD
But we can do no less than give her what escort we
can—

FIRST GUARD
We're set to guard the pier, and for nowt else.—And
why are you so hot for a Romish sovereign to set foot

on Scottish soil, do you mind if I ask?—For myself,
I'm no member of the congregation, I'm a sojer doing
what I'm set to, but it runs in my head we've had
enough of the Guises and their Holy Father. Let them
stick to their warm climates where they're welcome—
and may they come to a hotter place before they set
up another standard here!

THE OLD MAN

Ye may be na member of the congregation, friend,
but you will be if you keep in that opinion. For her
or against her it's to be in this land, and no half-way
to stand on. The kirk of Christ or the hussy of Rome,
drowned in wine, bestial with fornication, corrupt
with all diseases of mind and blood—

SECOND GUARD

Is it the queen's galley, Master?

THE OLD MAN

Aye, is it.

SECOND GUARD

For there's been no herald of it, nor anyone told—

THE OLD MAN

I have my ways of knowing. And, hearing of it, I
came myself to see this white face they speak of, and
these taking graces, and to tell her to that white face
of hers and despite her enchantments that we want
and will have none of her here. For whatever beauty
she may possess, or whatever winning airs, they are
given her of the devil to cozen us, they are born solely
of the concupiscence of hell and set upon her like a

sign. They say when she speaks she drips honey and she smells sweet with boughten perfumes, but I say the man who tastes of her or the people who trust in her will chew on dry ashes in the last day and find no remedy for that thirst! I say she comes with a milk-white body and a tongue of music, but beware her, for she will be to you a walking curse and a walking death!

THIRD GUARD

You will say this to the queen?

THE OLD MAN

I will say this to her whey face!
　　[BOTHWELL *enters from the right*]

BOTHWELL

Leg it over to the inn, one of you lads, and fetch a chair—

FIRST GUARD

We're on guard here, my lord.

BOTHWELL

Damn your guard duty! The queen of Scotland's stepping out of a boat in velvet shoes—

THIRD GUARD

I doubt there's a chair nearer than Edinburgh town—

BOTHWELL

There's one at the Leith inn, as ye well know—

FIRST GUARD

We'd need the silver for that, in any case—

BOTHWELL

My mannie, if I was to lay a fist to the side of that iron pot of yours I doubt the dinge would come out in a hurry—. What the devil do ye mean bauchling over a dirty chair? Seize it, seize it in the queen's name!

THIRD GUARD

I'll fetch it, sir.
[*He starts out*]

BOTHWELL

And do you go with him. I suspect ye of being a psalm-singer with that face.
[*The first* GUARD *goes with the third*]
A verra braw evening to you, Master Knox.

THE OLD MAN

And to you, my lord.

BOTHWELL

It seems some here heard of her coming, though not perhaps those she'd have chosen. You're not here, by chance, to greet the daughter of Mary of Guise?

THE OLD MAN

If I have aught to say to her, it will be for her own ears.

BOTHWELL

No doubt, no doubt. And I have a little observe to make to you about that, too, sir. Whatever it is you have to say to her you won't say it.

THE OLD MAN

And why not? Are the Papists muzzling the ministers
of God?

BOTHWELL

I'm no Papist, as ye're aware, Master Knox, and if I
were I'm no such fool as to try to muzzle a minister,
nevertheless, whatever it was you were going to say,
you won't say it, that's my observe to you—

KNOX

I shall say what I have come to say.
    [BOTHWELL *follows the Soldiers. A man's voice,
speaking French in a light tenor comes in from the
right*]

CHATELARD

    [*Outside*]
It is a badge of honor, I assure Your Majesty.

MARY

    [*Outside*]
Still, when next you toss your cloak in the mud, take
note whether there are any watching to report it—

CHATELARD

    [*Outside*]
But if my queen and lady note it—ah, what other
advertisement would a man desire?
    [MARY *the Queen enters with* CHATELARD, CHATEL-
HERAULT, *and the* FOUR MARYS-IN-WAITING]

MARY

Tut, if it were not known, or suspected, that I was queen, I should have stepped in bog like a drover's daughter—

CHATELARD

Madame, that you are queen would be known if the world were stripped of subjects. The very trees and frozen mountains would bow down to you!

MARY

[*Laughing*]
I can well imagine.
Body o' me, I could wish the clouds would stoop less to their queen in my native land.

CHATELHERAULT

One forgets how damn dismal this Scotland can be.

MARY

Dismal? Traitor, have you never plucked a gowan in spring—a fairy fresh gowan—?

CHATELHERAULT

Late—it comes late here—

MARY

Or gorged with bright thorn-apples in mid-August?

CHATELHERAULT

Is there an August in this heathenish climate? God, I can't remember it!

MARY

They are sweeter here than in France, as I recall, and all fruits are sweeter here, of those that grow—and the summer's sweeter—

CHATELHERAULT

They're short enough, God knows.

THE OLD MAN

And when they come they will bring excellent devices of masks and ornament to deceive the eye, and soft words and stenches to cumber the senses of mankind. Adulterers, jig-masters and the like will come in authority, and their counsel will be whoring and carousing, the flowers and fruits of evil, of that great sin, that sin that eats at the heart of the world, the church of abominations, the church of Rome.
    [*He pauses.* MARY *stops to look back at him*]

MARY

Chatelherault, I have been long away, and the speech of Scotland falls strangely on my ears, but is this talk usual among my people?

THE OLD MAN

Yet is there a place reserved for them, where the fire is unending and abates not, even as their desires abate not, where their tender flesh shall be torn from them with white-hot pincers, nor shall rank or station avail them, whether they be queens or kings or the lemans of queens and kings—!

MARY

[*Tremulous*]

Surely this is some jest, sir. Surely this is not said in welcome to me.

THE OLD MAN

And what other welcome shall we give the whore of Babylon—the leprous and cankerous evangel of the Beast!

[BOTHWELL *returns from the right*]

BOTHWELL

Your Majesty, they are preparing a room at the inn, and the chair will be here at once. If you would deign to take my cloak for your shoulders—

[*He lays his cloak around her*]

MARY

Thank you. I wish to speak to this gentleman—

BOTHWELL

This is Master John Knox, of whom your Grace may have heard.

MARY

Nay, then I have heard of him, and I wish to speak to him. Master Knox, it is true that I am Mary Stuart, and your queen, and I have come back from France after many years away, to take up my rule in this country. It is true, too, that I am sad to leave the south and the sun, and I come here knowing that I shall meet with difficulties that would daunt many older and wiser than I am—for I am young and inexperienced and perhaps none too adept in statecraft.

Yet this is my native place, Master Knox, and I loved it as a child and still love it—and whatever I may lack in experience, whatever I may have too much of youth, I shall try to make up for, if my people will help me, in tolerance and mercy, and a quick eye for wrongs and a quick hand to right them—

THE OLD MAN

Aye, they told me you spoke honey—

MARY

And cannot you also—you and your people and those you know—cannot you too be tolerant toward me a little space while I find my way? For it will be hard enough at the friendliest.

THE OLD MAN

Woman, I remember whose daughter and whose voice you are—

MARY

If I were your daughter, Master Knox, and this task before me, would you think it fitting to lay such hard terms on me, beast and whore and I know not what? For I am not a whore, I can say truly, but the daughter of a prince, softly nurtured and loving honor and truth. Neither is my body corrupt, nor my mind. Nay, I am near to tears that you should think so, and I was not far from tears before, finding myself unexpected on this coast, and no preparation to receive me. What you have said comes as very cold comfort now when I need greeting and reassurance.

BOTHWELL

Your Majesty, if the old goat has said anything that needs retracting—

MARY

He shall retract nothing in fear! I would have all men my friends in Scotland!

BOTHWELL

I'm afraid that's past praying for.

MARY

Look on me, sir—and judge my face and my words. In all fairness, am I the evangel of the Beast? Can we not be friends?

THE OLD MAN

I fear not, madam.

MARY

I strongly desire it. I have no wish for any enemy of mine except that he become my friend. You most of all, for I have met you first, and it is an augury.

THE OLD MAN

Your Majesty, I have said what I came to say.

MARY

But you no longer mean it! See—I give you my hand, Master Knox—it is a queen's hand, and fair—and I look at you out of honest eyes—and I mean well and fairly—you cannot refuse me! Do you still hesitate? It is clean.

[*She smiles. He bows stiffly over her hand*]

And will you come to see me at Holyroodhouse, and give me counsel? For God knows I shall need counsel —and I shall listen, that I promise.

THE OLD MAN

Your Majesty, I should be untrue to myself and my calling if I refused counsel where it is asked.

MARY

You will come?

THE OLD MAN

I will come.

MARY

I will send for you, and soon.
[*Her words are a kindly dismissal*]

THE OLD MAN

Good night, Your Majesty—

MARY

Goodnight, Master Knox.
[KNOX *goes to the left*]
Now I wonder, will he hate me more or less?

BOTHWELL

More, probably. However, it's just as well to have him where you can watch him.

MARY

You're an outspoken man yourself, Captain.

BOTHWELL

I am.

MARY

You will forgive me, but so far I have not heard your name.

CHATELHERAULT

The Captain is James Hepburn, madame—the Earl of Bothwell.

MARY

Ah—you fought ably for my mother.

BOTHWELL

I have been of some slight service here and there.

MARY

You have indeed! Tell me, my lord of Bothwell, have I done well so far? Shall I not make this Scotland mine?

BOTHWELL

Madame, it is a cold, dour, sour, bastardly villainous country, and the folk on it are a cold, dour, sour, bastardly lot of close-shaving psalm-retching villains, and I can only hope no harm will come here to that bonny face of yours, and no misery to the spirit you bring.

MARY

Now here's a new kind of courtesy!

BOTHWELL

You'll hear far and wide I'm no courtier, madame— but I have eyes, and I can see that the new sovereign is a sonsie lass and a keen one, and I was for her from

the first I saw her face—but from my heart I could
wish her a better country to rule over—

MARY

Now, will no one speak well of this poor Scotland of
mine—?

BOTHWELL

Your Majesty, shall I praise it for you—as high as it
deserves—?

MARY

Say whatever good you can!

BOTHWELL

Then this is Scotland, my lady: To the north a few
beggarly thousands of Highland Catholics who have
not yet learned the trick of wearing britches, and to
the south a few beggarly thousands of Lowland
Protestants whose britches have no pockets to them
—Their pleasures are drinking and fighting, both of
which they do badly, and what they fight about is
that half of them are willing to sell their souls for a
florin, whereas the other half has no expectation of
getting so much. What business they have is buying
cheap and selling dear, but since none of them will sell
cheap, and none will pay dear, the upshot is there's
no business done—

MARY

Enough, enough!—solemnly and truly, sir—it may
be they are not a happy race, but they have beliefs—
and what they believe they believe from the heart!
Even this Master Knox—

BOTHWELL

He? He believes whatever's to his own advantage,
and prophesies whatever will line his nest if it comes
to pass. He makes his living yelling nonsense into the
lugs of these poor, benighted, superstitious savages—
he's split the country wide open over your coming
and leads the pack against you, brawling from his
dung-hill! We'll have bloodshed over it yet—

MARY

Blood-shed?

BOTHWELL

And plenty.

MARY

No. If I thought that I should turn now and bid the
mariners hoist sail and put back for France. I shall
win, but I shall win in a woman's way, not by the
sword.

BOTHWELL

Let us hope so.

MARY

Hope so! But I shall!

BOTHWELL

I am no courtier, madame. I say, let us hope so.

MARY BEATON

The chair has come, madame.

MARY

Yes, and in time.   We're chilled to the heart here.
Come.
[*She goes out with* BOTHWELL, *the others following.
The first and third* GUARDS *return*]

FIRST GUARD

Did the old man spit his venom?

SECOND GUARD

You'll not believe it. He kissed her hand.

THIRD GUARD

She's a witch, then.

SECOND GUARD

Aye, is she. The kind a man wouldna mind being be-
witched by.

THIRD GUARD

No.

SECOND GUARD

I tell you she fair wenched him. The old man doddert
a bit and then bent over like a popinjay.

FIRST GUARD

She's tha' kind then?

SECOND GUARD

She's tha' kind.

Curtain

ACT ONE

SCENE TWO

SCENE: *A corner of Queen Elizabeth's study at Whitehall. It is
  morning, but the sun has not yet risen. She is up early to
  go over plans with* LORD BURGHLEY, *who sits opposite
  her at a small table on which an hour-glass stands like a
  paper-weight on their notes. She is a young woman, still
  beautiful, with a crafty face. Tall candles burn behind
  them in a sconce. Outside the circle of light the scene is
  indefinite.*

BURGHLEY

It still lacks something of dawn, Your Majesty.

ELIZABETH

We have one more hour before the palace will be
stirring. You said, I believe, that you have made
memoranda in regard to Mary Stuart?

BURGHLEY

I have set down the facts as we must face them, and
alternative policies.

ELIZABETH

Read them, if you will. And turn the glass. It's run
out.

BURGHLEY

[*Turning the glass and taking up a paper*]
They are not in order, but the main points are cov-
ered. First, Mary Stuart has crossed from France to
Scotland against your advice and without your safe-

conduct. This is in itself a slight to Your Majesty, and almost a challenge, though not one of which you can take public cognizance.

ELIZABETH

Yes.

BURGHLEY

Second, she has been crowned queen of Scotland, this also against your wish and in defiance of your policy. This may be construed as an open breach of friendship, or may be overlooked, as Your Majesty may desire—and as it may seem best.

ELIZABETH

Yes.

BURGHLEY

Third, she is a Catholic and related by blood to the most powerful Catholic house in France, which constitutes her a public danger to Protestant England. Fourth, she is next heir after Your Majesty to the throne of England, and is held by Catholic Europe to be the rightful queen of England at the present time, Your Majesty being regarded by all Catholics as a pretender, unjustly seated on your throne.

ELIZABETH

True. Proceed. You have more on that point. They believe me a bastard and say so. Very well, let us face that, too.

BURGHLEY

Fifth, then—you are held by the Catholic Europe to be the illegitimate daughter of Henry the Eighth, the divorce of Henry from Catherine of Arragon being unrecognized by the Church of Rome and his marriage to your mother, Anne Boleyn, deemed invalid. Sixth, these things being true, Your Majesty must not allow Marie Stuart to succeed as Queen of Scotland. For in so far as she is secure in Scotland you are insecure in England. Your Majesty will forgive my bad habit of setting down in writing what is so obvious, but it is only by looking hard at these premises that I am able to discover what must be done.

ELIZABETH

Out with it then. What must be done?

BURGHLEY

She must be defeated.

ELIZABETH

How?

BURGHLEY

Is there more than one way? We must pick our quarrel and send an army into Scotland.

ELIZABETH

Declare war?

BURGHLEY

Perhaps not openly—but we have excuse for it.

ELIZABETH

And reason?

BURGHLEY

She must be defeated.

ELIZABETH

Truly, but not so quick, not so quick with wars and troops and expenses. Have you no better counsel?

BURGHLEY

In all my reading I have found no case of a sovereign deposed without violence.

ELIZABETH

And in all those voluminous notes of yours you have set down no other method save warfare? The last resort, the most difficult, costly and hazardous of all?

BURGHLEY

It is the only sure method, and you cannot afford to fail.

ELIZABETH

My dear Burghley, in any project which affects England and our own person so nearly we have no intention of failing. But you have overlooked in your summary two considerations which simplify the problem. One is the internal dissension in Scotland, half Protestant, half Catholic, and divided in a mortal enmity—

BURGHLEY

Overlooked it! Madame, it is the main argument for an immediate declaration of war—Edinburgh would rally to your arms overnight! This is our opportunity to unite England and Scotland!

ELIZABETH

A war would unite Scotland against us—unite Scotland under Mary. No—it is necessary first to undermine her with her own subjects.

BURGHLEY

And how would that be accomplished?

ELIZABETH

This brings me to the second consideration which you overlook—the conduct and reputation of Mary herself.

BURGHLEY

Would that affect our policy?

ELIZABETH

It will make it. Merely to remind us, will you read over again the report of Mary's character in Randolph's latest budget of news?

BURGHLEY

This? "As for the person of Marie, our new Queen, I must say in truth that she is of high carriage, beautiful in a grave way—"?

ELIZABETH

So—go on.

BURGHLEY

"Beautiful, in a grave way, somewhat gamesome and given to lightness of manner among her lords as well as with other company, very quick-witted to answer back, and addicted to mirth and dancing, wherewith she hath made many converts to her cause among those most disaffected, though there be also those found to say her manners might more beseem the stews or places of low resort than so ancient a palace and line—"

ELIZABETH

You see, she is a Stuart.

BURGHLEY

"Moreover, she hath allowed herself to be seen much in the company of certain men, among them the Earl of Bothwell, and hath borne herself among these men, they being known of somewhat loose report, in such fashion as to give scandal to the stricter sort here, she not scanting to lend her eyes or hands or tongue to a kind of nimble and facile exchange of smiles and greetings which might better become the hostess of an ale-house, seeking to win custom. Natheless she is liked, and greatly liked by those on whom she hath smiled closely, they being won not as a wise sovereign wins subjects, but as a woman wins men."

ELIZABETH

Yes, a Stuart.

BURGHLEY

"Yet to be true again I must say also that she is of noble mind, greatly religious in her way, and the whispers against her name not justified by what she is in herself, but only by her manners, which she hath brought from France."

ELIZABETH

She has won our Randolph among others. He shall go north no more.

BURGHLEY

"And in addition she hath borne her power thus far with so discreet and tolerant a justness, impartial to north and south, to Catholic and Protestant alike, that if she persevere in this fashion she is like to reconcile the factions and establish herself firmly on the throne of Scotland. For vast numbers who thought to curse her now remain her fast friends."

ELIZABETH

Have you yet seen what we must do?

BURGHLEY

I find in this only a graver and more malicious danger.

ELIZABETH

And you would still make war?

BURGHLEY

Your Majesty, it will be war whether we like it or not —and there is imminent danger, danger to your throne and life. The more suddenly you act the less effort will be needed—

ELIZABETH

My lord, my lord, it is hard to thrust a queen from her throne, but suppose a queen were led to destroy herself, led carefully from one step to another in a long descent until at last she stood condemned among

her own subjects, barren of royalty, stripped of force,
and the people of Scotland were to deal with her for
us?

BURGHLEY

She would crush a rebellion.

ELIZABETH

She would now, but wait. She is a Catholic, and for
that half her people distrust her. She has a name for
coquetry and easy smiling, and we shall build that
up into a name for wantonness and loose behaviour.
She is seen to have French manners; we shall make it
appear that these manners indicate a false heart and
follow faith.

BURGHLEY

Can this be done?

ELIZABETH

She is a woman, remember, and open to attack as a
woman. We shall set tongues wagging about her.
And since it may be true that she is of a keen and
noble mind, let us take care of that too. Let us marry
her to a weakling and a fool. A woman's mind and
spirit are no better than those of the man she lies
under in the night.

BURGHLEY

She will hardly marry to our convenience, madame.

ELIZABETH

Not if she were aware of it. But she is next heir to my
throne; she will hope for children to sit on it, and she

will therefore wish to marry a man acceptable as the father of kings. We can make use of that.

BURGHLEY

Only perhaps.

ELIZABETH

No, certainly. She is a woman and already jealous for the children she may bear. To my mind the man she marries must be of good appearance, in order that she may want him, but a fool, in order that he may ruin her, and a Catholic, in order to set half her people against her.

BURGHLEY

We know that she is seen much with Bothwell.

ELIZABETH

And he is a Protestant.

BURGHLEY

He is a Protestant. Now suddenly it occurs to me. If she were to marry a Protestant and turn Protestant herself, would she not make an acceptable ally?—

ELIZABETH

[Rising]

I do not wish her for an ally! Have you not yet understood? I wish her a Catholic and an enemy, that I may see her blood run at my feet! Since Bothwell is a Protestant, the more reason for dangling some handsome youngster instantly in the north, as if by accident, nay, as if against my will, some youngster with courtly manners, lacking in brain, a Catholic, and

of a bloodstrain that would strengthen pretensions to
the throne of England.

BURGHLEY

You have thought of someone?

ELIZABETH

I have thought of several. I shall even let it be
rumored that I oppose such a marriage. I shall let it
go abroad that I favor someone else.

BURGHLEY

Who is the man?

ELIZABETH

I have thought of Darnley.

BURGHLEY

But after herself Darnley is in fact heir to the English
throne. An alliance with him would actually strengthen her claim to succeed to your place.

ELIZABETH

The better, the better. He is handsome, and of good
bearing?

BURGHLEY

Yes.

ELIZABETH

And a fool?

BURGHLEY

A boasting, drunken boy.

ELIZABETH

And a Catholic.

BURGHLEY

As you know.

ELIZABETH

If I give out that I am determined against it, she will
marry him, and he will drag her down, awaken her
senses to become his slave, turn her people against
her, make her a fool in council, curb this pretty
strumpetry that gains her friends, haul her by the
hair for jealousy, get her big with child, too, and spoil
her beauty. I tell you a queen who marries is no
queen, a woman who marries is a puppet—and she
will marry—she must marry to staunch that Stuart
blood.

BURGHLEY

This will take time.

ELIZABETH

It may take many years. I can wait.

BURGHLEY

And we shall need many devices.

ELIZABETH

You shall not find me lacking in devices, in the word
to drop here, the rumor started there. We must have
constant knowledge of her, and agents about her continually, so that her acts and sayings may be miscon-
strued and a net of half-lies woven about her, yes, till

her people believe her a voluptuary, a scavenger of dirty loves, a bedder with grooms. Aye, till she herself think ill of herself and question her loves, lying awake in torment in the dark.—There is a man called Knox who can be used in this.

BURGHLEY

But that—to accomplish that—

ELIZABETH

We live in a world of shadows, my lord; we are not what we are, but what is said of us and what we read in others' eyes. More especially is this true of queens and kings. It will grow up about her in whispers that she is tainted in blood, given over to lechery and infamous pleasures. She will be known as double-tongued, a demon with an angel's face, insatiable in desire, an emissary of Rome, a prophetess of evil addicted to lascivious rites and poisonous revenges. And before all this her own mind will pause in doubt and terror of what she may be that these things should be said of her—she will lie awake in torment in the dark—and she will lie broken, nerveless there in the dark. Her own people will rise and take her sceptre from her.

BURGHLEY

[*Rising*]
But Your Majesty—you—

ELIZABETH

However, I am not to appear in this. Always, and above all, I am to seem her friend.—You would say

that I am in myself more nearly what will be said of
her.

ELIZABETH
BURGHLEY

No, no—

ELIZABETH

Why, perhaps. But that is not what is said of me.
Whatever I may be, it shall be said only that I am
the queen of England, and that I rule well.

Curtain

ACT ONE

Scene Three

SCENE: *A great hall in Mary Stuart's apartments at Holyroodhouse. The room is rectangular with wide fireplaces
glowing to the left and right. An entrance door opens to
the right, and two doors at the left lead, one to Mary's
study, and the other to her bedroom. The stone of the walls
is largely covered with stamped leather hangings. A chair,
slightly elevated, stands in the middle of the rear wall, the
royal arms of Scotland draped above it. The floor is stone
with a few Eastern rugs. There are two high, heavily
draped windows at the rear, on either side of the queen's
chair.*

MARY BEATON, MARY SETON, *and* MARY LIVINGSTONE
are concerning themselves with the hanging of the ensign

behind the chair, and LIVINGSTONE *has stepped upon a stool to reach a fold of it.* LORD DARNLEY *and* LORD GORDON *are warming themselves at one of the fires, having just come in.*

BEATON
[*To the men*]
It's to hang there because she wants it there. Isn't that enough?

GORDON
I've heard my father say the kings of Scotland were always plain folk, but queens are a fancy breed, and their ways are fancy.

DARNLEY
A thought higher with that fold, my dear—just a thought higher.

LIVINGSTONE
[*Turning*]
And why?

DARNLEY
Dod, lady, it's a neat turn of ankle you show when you reach up. Reach a bit higher.

LIVINGSTONE
[*Back to her work*]
Look your eyes full if it does you any good, my Lord Darnley.

DARNLEY
Man, man, but that's a pretty foot!

GORDON

Aye.

DARNLEY

Ye have heard it said, no doubt, what they say about a woman's foot?

GORDON

Aye.

SETON

What do they say?

DARNLEY

About a woman's foot? Only that it's, in a sort, a measure of her capacities.

BEATON

Oh, is it, indeed? I've heard the same in respect to a man's nose, and I can only say if it's true your nose is no great advertisement for you.

DARNLEY

The nose is a fallible signal, my lady, as I'll prove to you—you naming your own place and time.

BEATON

I to name the place?

DARNLEY

It is your privilege.

BEATON

Your own bed-chamber, then.

LIVINGSTONE

Beaton!

DARNLEY

Accepted! Accepted! My own bed-chamber! And the time?

BEATON

The night of your wedding, by God!

DARNLEY

My dear lady—

GORDON

She has you there, Darnley.

BEATON

Moreover, if there is one kind of man a woman dislikes more than another it's one so little experienced that he goes peeping at ankles for lack of better satisfaction.

DARNLEY

Stop there! I will furnish you with data—

BEATON

Unless indeed it be the kind of man whose experiences with women have been like nothing so much as those of a dog with lamp-posts—

LIVINGSTONE

Beaton!
[MARY FLEMING *enters from the queen's study*]

BEATON

[*Clapping a hand to her mouth in mock chagrin*]
Oh, what have I said, what have I said?

SETON

A great plenty!

DARNLEY

Mistress Fleming, is it true our sovereign is inaccessible this day?

FLEMING

Quite true, I fear.

DARNLEY

God help the man who tries to woo a queen.

FLEMING

And so he might if your Lordship prayed to him with any serious intent.

DARNLEY

Perhaps. And yet I doubt it might do more good if a man were to have studied in France.

FLEMING

Studied?

DARNLEY

The arts. The arts of Ovid. The arts of pleasing a maid.

BEATON

They are the same in France as elsewhere, no doubt.

DARNLEY

No doubt, says she, and a very pretty innocence.

GORDON

Aye, as though she'd never been there.

FLEMING

We're not denying that we've been in France.

DARNLEY

Then don't tell us that the art of Love is the same there as in England and Scotland, for the report runs different.

GORDON

It's a kennt thing that French love is none the same.

LIVINGSTONE

Will you tell us how?

GORDON

Eh, we're to tell you who've lived among them?

FLEMING

Aside from better manners the people of France are like the people of Scotland, both in love and war.

DARNLEY

It's not an easy matter to go into with my lady's bevy of beauty, nevertheless they say there are no virgins there above four years old.

LIVINGSTONE

Then they lie who say it, and you're fools to believe it.

DARNLEY

Nay, it may be a bit exaggerated, but I'd lay no more than a groat on any piece of French virginity. They have summat to tell in confession; they have had their three of a night; they have had their what-for, and come up all the fresher and more lisping for it.

BEATON

I must say I ve never met nastier minds than hereabout, and that's something for John Knox to ponder on, too.

GORDON

Will ye come, man? Ye'll have no sight of the queen today, and these trollops have no time for plain Scotchmen.

DARNLEY

Aye.

FLEMING

Lord Darnley is to remain within call. It is her Majesty's pleasure.

DARNLEY

Ah, well that's something.

GORDON

It's dangling, to give it a plain name.
    [BOTHWELL *enters from the right*]

LIVINGSTONE

Oh, my lord Bothwell.

BOTHWELL

By God, my name's remembered, and that's a
   triumph,
Tell the sweet queen Lord Bothwell would see her
   alone.

LIVINGSTONE

Sir, she is closeted with her secretary—
We are not free to speak with her.

BOTHWELL

Closeted? So?
I like not that word closeted. Who is there here
Who can speak with her and tell her?

FLEMING

My Lord, she has spaced
This day off into hours, so many to each,
And I fear your name is not scheduled.

BOTHWELL

Distrust your schedule,
Then, my prim, for I'll see her.

FLEMING

The ambassador
From England arrives today, for his audience,
And before that Her Majesty plans to hold
A conclave with the lords.

DARNLEY

We've been sloughed off
Much the same way, my lord.

BOTHWELL

Run along then, and practise
Wearing that tin sword you've got hung on you,
Before it trips you.

DARNLEY

Trips me?

BOTHWELL

Aye, run and play!
This one's been used. The nicks along the edge
Were made on tougher than you. Tell my lady queen
I wish to see her now.

FLEMING

I cannot myself.
I might speak to Master Rizzio.

BOTHWELL

Then do that. Is Scotland grown so formal
That a man's received like a money-lender?
    [FLEMING *goes out*]

LIVINGSTONE

No,
But these matters must be arranged.

BOTHWELL

    [*To* DARNLEY]
Are you still here?

DARNLEY

Still here.

BOTHWELL

I knew a pimp in Paris had much your look,
But the women he brought me were foul.

DARNLEY

But good enough,
I daresay.

BOTHWELL

You might have thought so.
 [RIZZIO *enters*, FLEMING *following*]

RIZZIO

Oh, my lord Bothwell,
There's such great pressure on our time today—
Matters that must be seen to; if you could come
Tomorrow—

BOTHWELL

Well, I cannot come tomorrow.
Tomorrow will not do. I am here today.
And will not be here tomorrow. Is that understood?
 [RIZZIO *pauses*]

DARNLEY

Let him run his suit into the ground.

GORDON

Aye, and himself.
 [DARNLEY *and* GORDON *go out*]

RIZZIO

My orders are strict, my lord. Her Majesty
Has great problems of state—

BOTHWELL

And they concern me
More than some others. Now, before Christ, I've
    argued
Enough with women and women-faced men! A room's
    a room
And a door's a door! Shall I enter without warning
Or will you announce me to her? Great pressure on
Our time! Our time, he says! My fine Italian—
    [MARY STUART *enters. There is sudden quiet*]

MARY

I will speak with my lord alone.
    [*One by one, and silently,* RIZZIO *and the girls go
    out*]
Do I find you angry?

BOTHWELL

At these pests and midges.

MARY

You saw me yesterday.

BOTHWELL

I have been standing since this early morning—
I and some hundred crows, out in the coppice
On the cliff's edge, waiting for the smoke to rise
From your breakfast chimney. And by the Lord these
    crows
Are a funny company. I've had four full hours
To study them.

MARY

You come to tell me this?

BOTHWELL

I come to tell you
I've never shown such patience for a woman,
Not in my life before.

MARY

Did you call it patience
On a time when I could not see you, to wreck an inn,
Leave mine host in the road with a broken head
And lie with his daughter?

BOTHWELL

That was not true. Or at least
I had her good will for it.

MARY

And another time
To besiege the governor's house with your border
    knaves
And rouse all Edinburgh? Are you a man
Or a storm at sea, not to be brought indoors?

BOTHWELL

When I would see my girl, why I must see her
Or I am a storm, and indoors, too.

MARY

Your girl? Give me leave,
Since I am a queen, with a kingdom to reign over,
To queen it once in a while.

BOTHWELL

I tell you truly
I've the manners of a rook, for we're all crows here,
And that's what's understood in this town, but I
    could
Be tame and split my tongue with courtly speeches
If I could be sure of you—if I could know from one
    day
To another what to make of your ways. You shut
    yourself up
With secretaries and ministers, harking for weeks
On end to their truffle—while I perch me on the rocks
And look my eyes out.

MARY

When I was but thirteen
A pretty lad fell in love with me; he'd come,
Oh, afternoons, late midnight, early dawn
Sopping with dew-fall; he'd stand there, waiting for a
    glance—
I've never had such tribute.

BOTHWELL

This is no boy.
This is a man comes beating your door in now.
It may be you're too young to know the difference,
But it's time you learned.

MARY

You've had your way, my lord;
We've spoken together, though I had no time to give,
And now, with your pardon—

BOTHWELL

You'll go about the business
Of marrying someone else. That's what this mangy
Meeting of councillors means, and that's what por-
    tends
From Elizabeth's ambassador! I warn you,
Make no decisions without me!

MARY

I cannot marry you.
I beg you, ask it not; speak not of it. Our day
Has come between us. Let me go now.

BOTHWELL

My lady,
I will speak softly. Have no fear of me
Or what I intend. But there have been days I remem-
    ber
When you had less care what hostages you gave
The world. I think you showed more royally then
Than now, for you loved then and spoke your love,
    and I
Moved more than mortal for that while. Oh, girl,
If we would be as the high gods, we must live
From within outward! Let the heavens rain fire
Or the earth mud. This is a muddy race
That breeds around us. Will you walk in fear of mud-
    slingers,
Or walk proudly, and take my hand?

MARY

I am a queen.

BOTHWELL

They've made a slave of you,
This bastard half-brother of yours, this fox of a Mait-
    land,
This doddering Chatelherault! They frighten you
With consequences. They're afraid of men's tongues
And they've made you afraid. But what they truly
    fear
Is that you'll win the country, be queen here truly
And they'll be out of it. What they'd like best of all
Is to wreck you, break you completely, rule the coun-
    try themselves,
And why they fear me is because I'm your man alone,
And man enough to stop them.

MARY

Yes. You are man enough.
It's dangerous to be honest with you, my Bothwell,
But honest I'll be. Since I've been woman grown
There's been no man save you but I could take
His hand steadily in mine, and look in his eyes
Steadily, too, and feel in myself more power
Than I felt in him. All but yourself. There is aching
Fire between us, fire that could take deep hold
And burn down all the marches of the west
And make us great or slay us. Yet it's not to be
    trusted.
Our minds are not the same. If I gave my hand
To you, I should be pledged to rule by wrath
And violence, to take without denial,
And mount on others' ruin. That's your way
And it's not mine.

BOTHWELL

You'll find no better way.
There's no other way for this nation of churls and
   cravens.

MARY

I have been queen of France—a child-queen and
   foolish—
But one thing I did learn, that to rule gently
Is to rule wisely. The knives you turn on your people
You must sometime take in your breast.

BOTHWELL

You know not Scotland.
Here you strike first or die. Your brother Moray
Seeks your death, Elizabeth of England
Seeks your death, and they work together.

MARY

Nay—
You mistrust too much—and even if this were true
A sovereign lives always with death before and after,
And many have tried to murder their way to safety—
But there's no safety there. For each enemy
You kill you make ten thousand, for each one
You spare, you make one friend.

BOTHWELL

Friends? Friends? Oh, lass,
Thou'lt nurse these adders and they'll fang thee—
   Thou'rt
Too tender and too just. My heart cries for thee—
Take my help, take my hands!

MARY

I would I could take both.
God knows how I wish it. But as I am queen
My heart shall not betray me, what I believe
And my faith. This is my faith, dear my lord, that
    all men
Love better good than evil, cling rather to truth
Than falseness, answer fair dealing with fair return;
And this too; those thrones will fall that are built on
    blood
And craft, that as you'd rule long, you must rule
    well.—
This has been true, and is true.

BOTHWELL

God help thee, child.

MARY

Be staunch to me. You have been staunchest of all.
Let me not lose your arm. No, nor your love—
You know how much you have of mine. I'm here
Alone, made queen in a set, hard, bitter time.
Aid me, and not hinder.

BOTHWELL

So it shall be.

MARY

And give me the help I'd have.

BOTHWELL

That I can't promise.
I'll help thee and defend thee. Lady dear,
Do you use guile on me?

MARY

No, sweet, I love thee,
And I could love thee well.
> [*She goes to him. He kisses her hand and then her lips.*]

Go now, and leave me.
We've been seen too much together.

BOTHWELL

You must lay this hand
In no one's else. It's mine.

MARY

I have but lease on it,
Myself. It's not my own. But it would be yours
If it were mine to give.
> [MARY LIVINGSTONE *comes to the right hand door*]

LIVINGSTONE

Your Majesty,
The Lords of the council are here.

MARY

Let them be admitted.
> [LIVINGSTONE *goes out*]

BOTHWELL

Has Your Majesty forgotten
That I am of the council, under your seal?

MARY

I could wish you were elsewhere. These are the men
   I least

Have wanted to find us alone. But stay, now you're
here.

> [*She goes pensively to her chair of state and seats
> herself.* LORD JAMES STUART, *Earl of Moray,*
> MAITLAND OF LETHINGTON, *the* DUC DE CHATEL-
> HERAULT, HUNTLEY, MORTON, *and* ERSKINE *are
> ushered in by* MARY LIVINGSTONE, *who withdraws.
> There is a brief silence*]

MAITLAND

We have not interrupted Your Majesty?

MARY

No. The Earl of Bothwell is of the council.
I have asked him to take part.

MAITLAND

There was some agreement
That since the Earl's name might come up, it would
    be as well
If he were not here.

BOTHWELL

And then again, since my name
May be mentioned, and there's none so able as I
To defend it, it may be as well that I'm here.

MAITLAND

My lord,
There was small thought to attack you.

BOTHWELL

Less now, perhaps,

MARY

Lord Bothwell will remain.

MORAY

Sister, it may be that Bothwell will be offended
By something said.

MARY

You are courtier enough
To couch it not to offend, my brother.

MAITLAND

Nay, then,
What we have come to say must be softly said,
But meant no less strictly. The question of our
  queen's marriage,
Of which everyone has spoken, let me add,
But which we have avoided here, must now come up
Whether or no we like it.

MARY

Be not so tender
With me, dear Maitland. I have been married. I am
A widow, and free to marry again.

HUNTLEY

That's the lass!
They say widows are always ready.

MARY

Do they say that?
Do they not say ready but—wary?

HUNTLEY

Aye, that too.

MARY

But the truth is I should prefer my own time for
    wedding.
I know of no prince or king whose hand is offered,
And whose hand I'd take.

MAITLAND

It's not to be treated lightly
I'm much afraid. The thrones of all the world
Are shaken with broils even as we stand here. The
    throne
On which you sit, our sovereign, is shaken, too,
Though Your Majesty has done more than I'd have
    dreamed
Could be done to still the factions. It's our belief
That a marriage, if the right one, would seat you
    more firmly,
Put an end to many questions.

MARY

There's more of this?

MAITLAND

That's all we wish—to see you safe on your throne
So that we may be safe in our houses. Until men know
What alliance we're to make, what hangs over us
In the way of foreign treaties, the clans will sleep
With dirks in their brogans, and a weather eye still
    open
For fire in the thatch. And yet to choose the man—
That's a point we can't agree on.

MARY

I'm with you there.
For you see, I'm hard to please.

MAITLAND

And more than that,
Of princes that offer, or have been suggested, each
  one
Commits us to some alliance of church or state
We'd find embarrassing. Philip of Spain, the Duke
Of Anjou—these are Catholic—

BOTHWELL

Has it crossed your mind
That there are lords in Scotland?

MAITLAND

And there, too—
If the choice were to fall on a Scottish earl, the houses
Passed over would take it ill—and it might well lead
To a breach in our peace—

BOTHWELL

Yes?

MAITLAND

Nay, even to civil war.

MARY

I cannot give myself out
As a virgin queen, yet our cousin Elizabeth's plan
Has virtues. Must I marry at all?

MORTON

Your Majesty,
We have not yet said what we came to say,
And it needs saying bluntly. The people of Scotland
Are given to morals almost as much as to drink.
I'll not say they're moral themselves, but they'll
    insist
On morals in high places. And they've got in their
    heads
That you're a light woman.
    [MARY *rises*]
I don't know how it got there,
And I daresay it's not true—

MARY

Thank you. For your daresay.

MAITLAND

I could have wished to speak more delicately
Of this, but it's before us, and can't be denied.
Your Majesty, when you came to us from France
And I saw you first, I said to myself in my heart,
All will be well with Scotland. What I thought then
I can say now, for you are wiser even
Than I had supposed, and you have dealt more justly
Than any could have hoped, yet still it's true
Some spreading evil has gone out against you,
A crawling fog of whispers.

MARY

Who believes them?

MAITLAND

I'll not say they're believed. I'm not sure they are.
But there was the episode of the boy who was hidden
In your bed-chamber—

ERSKINE

Chatelard.

MAITLAND

Aye, he, and
That may have begun it. I believed at first it stemmed
From John Knox's preaching, for he holds all Catholics
To be the devil's own, but there's more than that—
A much more seeded, intentional crop of lyings
Planted here, till I've wondered if Chatelard
May not have been an agent, or one of many.

MARY

Planted by whom?

HUNTLEY

Why, by Elizabeth.
Who else?

MAITLAND

But that's not certain, either.
Chatelard came from France, and in all this scurril
I've traced no word to London.

MARY

It's what they say.
Not what they believe.

HUNTLEY

You've lent them some color for it,
Your Majesty. You've been no statue.

MARY

No,
Nor wish to be. My lord of Lethington,
What you have said of me, how I was when you saw
    me,
How I seem to you now, I swear to you, you were
    not wrong.
I have not betrayed myself as woman or queen.

MAITLAND

I would swear that, too.

MARY

And since I know that is true,
I have thought very little of whispers. For there is
    judgment
Somehow in the air; what I am will be known, what's
    false
Will wash out in the rains.
    [*She seats herself again*]

MAITLAND

My sovereign, you are yet young.
I once believed that. But I have lived long enough
To see error grow up and prosper, and send its roots
A century deep. There's force enough in these winds
Of malice to blow us all down—

MARY

I'll try to be serious,
For I see you are. It's your thought, then, that a
    marriage
Would end the rumors?

MAITLAND

Aye.

MARY

But as to whom I'll marry—
Happily, that's not decided for me yet.

MORTON

By God,
If it was we'd see you to bed with him tonight.

MARY

Has the woman no voice in such matters?

MORTON

Not in such cases.

MARY

And what is my case, may I ask?

MORTON

Why, we've said nothing
About my Lord Bothwell. It's his name's coupled
    with yours;
His and young Rizzio's.

BOTHWELL

I've thought often, Morton,
One of us would die before the other. Now
I'm sure of it. And soon.

MORTON

I have you.

MARY

My lords,
Will you quarrel in council over your queen's virtue?
Let me defend my own honor, and let you
Defend your own. Do I understand that I
Am accused with Bothwell or Rizzio? Or both?

MAITLAND

You are accused of nothing.

MORTON

You are not accused,
Your Majesty. Morevoer, you are queen
Of Scotland, and therefore no man here would dare
Accuse you—

MARY

Oh, speak out, man! Are you afraid?
When have I punished plain dealing?

MORTON

Why, then, you are queen,
And may set your own customs, but if my wife were
    seen
Abroad as you are, and half so free of contact
With young and old as you are, I'd not answer
For what was said about her!

MARY

I'm no man's wife.

MORTON

No. And the sense of this council
Is that it might be better if you were,
Better for your good name and better for Scotland.

MARY

I will answer these things: as for Rizzio,
He is my secretary; if I spend time
In private with him, that is the reason. If I
Had not liked him, he would not be my secretary.
As for Lord Bothwell, he has put more strength
Behind what I wished to do than any among you,
And at times when I had despaired. He is my good
    friend.
We were here alone before this conference
And we differed in opinion. To wipe that out
I went to him of myself and kissed his lips.
We had kissed but once before, may not kiss again,
But that 's at my option, not yours.

HUNTLEY

Lassie, ye've been
Too honest for your own good.

MARY

Why, if so much weight
Is placed on a kiss in Scotland, come now, each one
And take your kiss—or if that's no recompense

Come to me then in private, and you shall have,
Each one, one kiss.

MORTON

And after that, there are kisses
Elsewhere—and when you've finished, whether you'll
    marry
Or not may not be the question, but whether we can
    find
A prince who'll have you.

MARY

[Rising and taking a step down]
And having heard that word—
My lords, when you wish to talk with me again
As civilized men, and not barbarians,
You shall have audience. This Scottish kirk of yours
Has misled you as to the meaning of kisses. I am
Unsullied and young, and have my own faith to
    plight
And more to think of than these maunderings
Over pantry gossip. I shall not marry till
I find it wise, nor until I have made quite sure
What effect it will have on my inheritance
Of the throne of England. You come here in high
    conclave
And spend three-farthing's worth of wit to chaffer
Over a kiss in my audience-chamber! The question
Is not to save my name, I hope, nor my throne,
But how best to meet the destiny that has made me
Full heir to all this island.—Scotland is mine,
And England will come to me or to the child

I hope to have. It's this that makes my marriage
A matter of moment.—And this—with your good
   pardon—
Will be the last for today.
    [*She goes into her study*]

MORAY

Morton, I warned you
To leave all speech to Lethington.

MORTON

She sits on that throne
Only so long as we want her there, no longer.

BOTHWELL

If my lord of Morton
Would care to lose those black feathers from his crest
I await his pleasure.
    [*He goes out*]

MORAY

I'm for that, too. Settle it between you,
And may you both win. We'll all be the better for it.
    [LIVINGSTONE *enters from the right*]

LIVINGSTONE

Lord Throgmorton is here from England
With embassies for the queen.

MAITLAND

She's gone to her study.
She'll wish to admit him.

LIVINGSTONE

Yes.

> [*She goes to the queen's study.* MORTON *goes out the other door*]

MAITLAND

We get no further
Today then,

> [*He goes to the door*]

HUNTLEY

No. Erskine, a word with you.

> [ERSKINE *and* HUNTLEY *go out.* THROGMORTON *enters*]

MAITLAND

Come in, Lord Throgmorton. You've been announced within.

THROGMORTON

Greetings, my lord, fair greetings.

MAITLAND

We can have speech later.

THROGMORTON

We shall.

> [MAITLAND *goes out.* THROGMORTON *and* MORAY *are alone*]

Greetings also to my Lord James Stuart,
In fine, the best of greetings.

MORAY

From Elizabeth?

THROGMORTON

I'm burdened with them—and more to you than any.

MORAY

May I know the drift?

THROGMORTON

This is hardly the place for that,
But this much for now: Elizabeth has determined
That you are to reign in Scotland, if not as king,
Then as regent again.

MORAY

Well, that's news.

THROGMORTON

She bids me to tell you
As if from herself, you are not to be disturbed
If her policy seems at variance with her mind.
It's a wide arc of intrigue, but she carries
These schemes in her head like a gambit, and she
    means
To play it to the end. Your sister Mary
Is not acceptable to her.

MORAY

But this scheme of hers?

THROGMORTON

Later, later. You're a silent man, I know.
No word.

MORAY

None.
        [MARY *enters*]

MARY

Lord Throgmorton?

THROGMORTON

Your Majesty.
  [*He kneels. She comes to him and gives him her
  hand to kiss*]
From one great queen to another, happiness.

MARY

A courtier in the grand style.

THROGMORTON

Nay, Majesty,
A plain man of business.

MARY

Let us to business, then.
  [*She motions him to rise, and he does so*]
My brother, did you wish further word with me?

MORAY

No, madame, only that I may see you tomorrow.

MARY

  [*Goes to her chair*]
At your own time.
  [MORAY *bows low and goes out*]
You had more to say?

THROGMORTON

Much more. My poor brain's taxed with remembering.
But to begin, Queen Elizabeth sends her love

To her cousin of Scotland, wishes her well, and a
  reign
Both long and easy, and proffers to that end
Whatever friendship and amity between thrones
Your Majesty will accept.

MARY

Tell Elizabeth
She will not find me niggard of friendship or love.

THROGMORTON

I shall report Your Majesty so. Then, further,
I'm bid to say, what Elizabeth most desires
Is that all briars of discord that have grown
Between this city and England, be wed away,
And leave a path for peace.

MARY

I desire that, too.
Does she put a name to these briars?

THROGMORTON

Your Majesty, I am
Permitted to speak quite frankly?

MARY

I beg you to.

THROGMORTON

You are next heir to the throne of England, and you
Are a Catholic. This is a danger to you
As well as Elizabeth. Were to you turn Protestant
Elizabeth would at once recognize in you
Next heir to her succession.

MARY

I should think she might,
Since I am next heir.

THROGMORTON

Forgive me for speaking plainly.

MARY

Oh, forgive me!

THROGMORTON

If this seems difficult, I am bid to remind you
That Elizabeth was a Catholic, but became
A Protestant for political reasons.

MARY

That
I could never do. Nor do I see that one's faith
Should be touched by politics.

THROGMORTON

Why, not politics,
My gracious queen! God forbid me that I should
    bring
That word into such a context! We know, of course,
How one clings, shall we say for sentimental reasons,
To the rituals of his youth! Aye, and even a prince,
We admit, would rather say his pater nosters
The way he learned them when he was a child. And
    yet
Must we take these childish things so gravely now,
When war or peace hangs on them? There are
    Catholics

In England still. They still plot against our queen.
Were she struck down by one of them you'd take
Her throne and rule us. It follows that your faith
Is a challenge to her—yes, if your Grace will pardon
The word—a defiance.

MARY

You were bid to say this to me?

THROGMORTON

Madame, it was said so smoothly by my queen
There was no offense in it, but I have no gift
Of language. I must say things out.

MARY

Your manner
Is packed with the most magniloquent impudence
That's come my way. Do you or your queenly mis-
tress
Deem me an inferior, to be given orders blithely,
With a high hand?

THROGMORTON

No, madame.

MARY

Say three words more
In this cavalier offensive style of yours
And you'll find yourself in the courtyard.

THROGMORTON

Madame, I—

MARY

Come down to earth, and speak without swaggering.

THROGMORTON

I've been in the wrong.

MARY

That's better.

THROGMORTON

It's true that I'd
Rehearsed my song and dance. Your wit is quicker
Than's been supposed in London.

MARY

Quick enough
To perceive an insult, I hope.

THROGMORTON

Your Majesty,
There was none intended, but I might have spoken
    more wisely
Had I known your mettle. Elizabeth is concerned,
As I have said, with the differences that are certain
To arise over your religion. Further than that,
What arrangements may be made to avert a breach
In the present concord, if we may discuss these
    things
Frankly, and you will make frank replies, I have
No other mission.

MARY

Now you talk sense. And frankly.
I will not change my faith.

THROGMORTON

And, frankly again,
There was little hope that you would. There is some
   hope,
However, that when Your Majesty seeks a consort
You will not do so to bolster up your claim
To the English crown, which is strong enough already
To cause us uneasiness in London.

MARY

That
Had not occurred to me.

THROGMORTON

But surely your choice in marriage
Will imply your attitude?

MARY

I have no intention
Of plighting my troth at once, but if I had
I've received advice already on that point,
A mort of it—and I'm tender.

THROGMORTON

Say no more,
Madame, and I'll say no more.

MARY

Oh, out with it now,
Give the advice. I won't take it.

THROGMORTON

Why, it's only this:
If Your Majesty were to marry a Protestant lord

Of no royal pretensions, it would indicate
That you meant no danger to our Elizabeth.

MARY

She has chosen for me, I daresay? She has some lord
Of the sort in mind?

THROGMORTON

You embarrass me to go on.
She mentioned a name.

MARY

Yes?

THROGMORTON

Madame, the Earl of Leicester.

MARY

I hope her ears burn now. Leicester? Her cast-off!—
Her favorite—the one she's dangled? This is an
    affront—
She named Lord Leicester?

THROGMORTON

Nay, nay—only to show you
What it was she had in mind. The kind of match.

MARY

I would hope so.

THROGMORTON

For, you see, Your Majesty,
She had a fear of this—the young Lord Darnley
Has come north against her will. Why he's here we
    don't know.

Nor whether by invitation, nor what your plans
Might be concerning him.

MARY

I have none.

THROGMORTON

Then, if you will,
Forget what I've said. It was only that this Darnley
Combines to exactness what Elizabeth dreads
In case you marry. After you he's next to her throne,
And he's a Catholic. Should you marry Lord Darnley
And call up Catholic Europe to your back—
Well, we'd be ringed in steel.

MARY

I have offered your queen
My friendship and love. I meant that offer.

THROGMORTON

But even
If there were no quarrel, and you should marry
    Darnley
And have a son by him—he'd be heir to England—
And I think the plain fact is that Elizabeth
Would rather choose her own heir.

MARY

Now God forgive me!—
I am heir to the throne of England, and after me
Whatever children I have—unless by some chance
The virgin queen should bear sons! Is it part of her
    love
To cut me off from my right?

THROGMORTON

It must be remembered
That England is Protestant, and it might come hard
To accept a Romish sovereign. In brief, my queen
Has wished that you might choose Bothwell, or
    perhaps some other
Of Protestant persuasion!

MARY

And that's the message.
We're down to it at last. My lord Throgmorton,
I marry where I please—whether now or later,
And I abate not one jot of my good blood's lien
On the English throne. Nay, knowing now the gist
Of Elizabeth's polity toward that claim, I shall
    rather
Strengthen it if I can. The least worthy sovereign
Has a duty toward his blood, not to weaken it
Nor let it decline in place.

THROGMORTON

This will hardly please.

MARY

I could hardly expect it would. But I too am a power,
And it matters what pleases me. This was all?

THROGMORTON

This was all
I'm commissioned with.

MARY

I shall see to your safe-conduct.

THROGMORTON

I thank your Majesty.
[*He goes out.* MARY *is alone a moment, brooding.*
RIZZIO *enters*]

MARY

Oh, Rizzio, Rizzio,
They make a mock of me! It was as you predicted
To the utter syllable.

RIZZIO

A warning, then.

MARY

We'll expect no friendship from England.
She cuts me off, me and my line.

RIZZIO

May I say that this
Is only her wish, not accomplished?

MARY

Aye, and not to be.
I'd have stood her friend, Rizzio, meant to be her
    friend,
But now—this is not to be borne! Go and find Lord
    Darnley.

RIZZIO

Your Majesty—you have made a decision?

MARY

Yes.

RIZZIO

Now I thank you. Now, God helping us, we'll win.
She'll not stamp you out.

MARY

So I think. And now find him.

RIZZIO

Yes.
[MARY BEATON *comes to the outer door*]

BEATON

Will your Majesty see a gentleman calling himself
Lord Bothwell?
[BOTHWELL *comes to the door*]

MARY

He's in again?

BEATON

There's no keeping him out.

BOTHWELL

[*Entering*]
The doxy invited me in herself. She's a slut,
This Beaton of yours.
[RIZZIO *goes out the outer door*]

MARY

Oh, I know.

BEATON

May I put in a word
For this gentleman, madame? Of all who come calling
on you

He's the most ill-favored. It may be that he's honest,
I hope so, to go with that face. You're not afraid
To be left alone with him?

MARY

You may go, Beaton.

BEATON

Yes, Majesty.
[*She curtseys hurriedly, and goes out*]

BOTHWELL

Now, what an inexperienced queen you are
To surround yourself with such taking bitches!

MARY

My lord,
I have heard from England.

BOTHWELL

Mary, my queen, what you heard
I could have guessed. She's your demon. She bodes
you ill.

MARY

I believe it now.

BOTHWELL

And moreover, between the two,
This cormorant brother of yours, and that English
harpy
They'll have the heart out of you, and share it. Trust
Not one word they say to you, trust not even the
anger
Their words rouse in you. They calculate effects.

MARY

Where is Lord Morton?

BOTHWELL

Lord Morton is not well.
[*He is very serious*]
A sudden indisposition.

MARY

Bothwell, Bothwell—
You've fought with him!

BOTHWELL

A mere puncture. What men think
I cannot punish, nor what they say elsewhere but
when
I hear them, by Christ, they'll learn manners.

MARY

I forbade it.

BOTHWELL

Forbade it! My dear, not God nor the holy angels
Forbid me when I'm angry.

MARY

I say I forbade it
It's I who's responsible for my kingdom—not you—
You were bound to keep the peace!

BOTHWELL

When my lady's slandered?
I'll teach them to hold their peace where you're con-
cerned
Or find their sweet peace in heaven.

MARY

Would God I'd been born
Deep somewhere in the Highlands, and there met
   you—
A maid in your path, and you but a Highland bow-
   man
Who needed me.

BOTHWELL

Why, if you love me, Marie,
You're my maid and I your soldier.

MARY

And it won't be.

BOTHWELL

Aye, it will be.

MARY

For, hear me, my lord of Bothwell.
I too have a will—a will as strong as your own,
And enemies of my own, and my long revenges
To carry through. I will have my way in my time
Though it burn my heart out and yours. The gods
   set us tasks,
My lord, what we must do.

BOTHWELL

Let me understand you.
The gods, supposing there are such, have thrown us
   together
Somewhat, of late.

MARY

Look, Bothwell. I am a sovereign,
And you obey no one. Were I married to you I'd be
Your woman to sleep with. You'd be king here in
   Edinburgh,
And I'd have no mind to your ruling.

BOTHWELL

They'll beat you alone.
Together we could cope them.

MARY

Love you I may—
Love you I have—but not now, and no more. It's for
   me
To rule, not you. I'll deliver up no land
To such a hot-head. If you'd been born to the blood
I'd say, aye, take it, the heavens had a meaning in
   this,
But the royal blood's in me.—It's to me they turn
To keep the peace, patch up old quarrels, bring home
Old exiles, make a truce to anarchy. Escape it I can-
   not.
Delegate it I cannot. The blame's my own
For whatever's done in my name.—I will have no
   master.
   [BOTHWELL *is silent when she pauses*]
Nay, I am jealous of this my Stuart blood.
Jealous of what it has meant in Scotland, jealous
Of what it may mean. They've attacked that blood,
   and I'm angry.
They'll meet more anger than they know.

BOTHWELL

And who
Has angered you? Not I?

MARY

Elizabeth.

BOTHWELL

I thought so.
She's afraid, if I'm half a prophet,
That you'll marry me.

MARY

Her fears run the other way.
She's afraid I'll marry a Catholic and threaten her
  throne!
She threatens disinheritance! Offers me Leicester!
Her leavings!

BOTHWELL

Yes, by God, that's a cold potato.

MARY

And means to choose another heir for her throne!
I may never sit on it, but the Stuart line
Shall not suffer by me!

BOTHWELL

Will you tell me what that means?

MARY

I mean if I have a son he'll govern England.

BOTHWELL

And so he might, if he were mine, too.

MARY

Nay, might—
But it must be!
She dares to threaten my heritage!

BOTHWELL

Does that mean Lord Darnley?
    [*She is silent*]
Aye, lady, will you stoop so low to choose
A weapon? This is not worthy of the girl
I've known. Am I to be ousted by a papejay
Who drinks in the morning and cannot carry his
    drink?
An end of mouldy string? You take too much
On yourself of the future. Think of us, and the hours
Close on us here we might have together. Leave some-
    thing
To the gods in heaven! They look after lovers!

MARY

Oh, what's a little love, a trick of the eyes,
A liking, to be set beside the name
You'll have forever, or your son will have?

BOTHWELL

Well, it's been nibbling at you this long while,
And now it's got you, the blight of Charlemagne—
The itch to conquer.

MARY

I have an itch to conquer?

BOTHWELL

It goes deep, too, that itch. It eats out the brain.

MARY

Well, and my love for you, how worthy is that?
It's my body wants you. Something I've fought
     against
Comes out in me when you're near. You've not held it
     sacred,
You've taken others. I've known. And then come
     wooing.
It would happen again.

BOTHWELL

It's a man's way. I've loved you
None the less.

MARY

You don't offer enough, Lord Bothwell.
You're not true in it, and I'm not true to myself
In what I feel for you.

BOTHWELL

I'm no lute-player,
To languish and write sonnets when my lady
Says me nay. Faith, I've lived rough on the border,
And cut some throats I don't forgive myself
Too easily, when I look back, but I tell you
If I give my pledge to you it's an honest pledge,
And I'll keep it. Yes, and when the tug begins
Around your throne, you'll be lost without me. Try
No threats toward England.—It will tax a hardy
     man
All his time to hold what you have.

MARY

We differ there, too.
What I have I'll defend for myself.

BOTHWELL

If you marry this Darnley
I take away my hand.

MARY

Before God, he believes
He's held me up so far, and I'd fall without him!

BOTHWELL

I believe it, and it's true! Darnley, sweet Christ!
No miracle could make him a king! He's a punk,
And he'll rule like a punk!

MARY

We shall see, Lord Bothwell.

BOTHWELL

Well, I'm sped. My suit's cold. But, dod, lady—
    Darnley—
He sticks in my craw—I can't go him. You'll find
    few that can.
Think twice about that. Let him not cross my way,
Or he'll lose his plumes like Morton!

MARY

Will you learn, Lord Bothwell,
That this is not your palace, but mine? Or must you
Be taught that lesson?

BOTHWELL

There's been a bond between us
We'll find it hard to forget.

MARY

You may. Not I.
I've set my face where I'm going.
    [RIZZIO *enters*. DARNLEY *is seen behind him*]

RIZZIO

Lord Darnley is here,
Your Majesty.

MARY

Let him enter.
    [DARNLEY *enters from the doorway*]

BOTHWELL

Lass, lass, God fend thee.
You've seen the last of me.

MARY

I've given no leave
For departure, Lord Bothwell!

BOTHWELL

I need no leave, nor leave-taking.
You see no more of me.
    [*He goes out.* RIZZIO *bows and follows him.* MARY
    crosses the room away from DARNLEY *and looks
    for a moment in the fire. Then she turns to him*]

MARY

I have sent for you.
Lord Darnley, to tell you your suit has prospered.
   You've asked
My hand in marriage, and I grant it.

DARNLEY

Your Majesty—
I hardly hoped—I haven't dared—this is fortune
To take one's breath!
      [*He comes forward and falls to one knee*]
I shall love you, keep you, defend you!

MARY

We shall face troubled times.

DARNLEY

We'll meet them bravely.
This is some dream—or a jest. It can't be.

MARY

Aye. I feel that.
And yet it's true.

DARNLEY

I'm to hold you in my arms!

MARY

Not yet. And yet, if you like, come, kiss me.

DARNLEY

They say
A kiss seals the bargain!
      [*He rises, staggering slightly*]

MARY

I've heard so.
[*He crosses to her*]
You've drunk too much.

DARNLEY

Nay, only a morning cup. Oh, Lady, lady—
When you're kind the whole world's kind!

MARY

[*She faces him, then draws back a step in repulsion*]
You're a boy, a child

DARNLEY

Older than you, though.
It's a bargain, then?

MARY

Yes.
[*He puts out his arms to her. Her eyes hold him off*]
Let the kissing go. Let it go till the bond's sealed.

DARNLEY

Aye, madame.
[*He drops his arms. They stand looking at each other*]

Curtain

ACT TWO

ACT TWO

SCENE I

SCENE: *The hall in the palace. Evening.* MARY *and the* FOUR
MARY'S-IN-WAITING *are sitting near the fire, listening as*
RIZZIO *sings to his lute.*

RIZZIO

My heart's in the north,
And my life's in the south,
False I've pledged with my hand,
False I've kissed with my mouth.

Oh, would we might lie
Where we lay by the firth,
With one cloak about us,
To keep us from earth,

With hand caught to hand
And the rain driving blind,
As the new years have driven
Old love out of mind.

MARY

What is the line, False I've pledged with my hand?

RIZZIO

False I've pledged with my hand,
False I've kissed with my mouth.

MARY

Where did you come by the song?

RIZZIO

It's one I made.

MARY

I thought so. Well, it's too true—and past time for crying.

BEATON

These poets make much of false pledges and false kisses—but they often turn out quite as well.

MARY

Nay, they turn out badly. If you should love, Beaton, give yourself where you love.

BEATON

There's one of these silly hackbuteers I could have a mind to but I gather he has his penny a day and no more.

MARY

Then if I were you I'd take him.

LIVINGSTONE

And live on a penny a day?

MARY

Or anything.

RIZZIO

My lady, I shall never forgive myself.

MARY

It was my own doing.

RIZZIO

My counsel weighed with you. I favored Darnley
because he was of my faith. And he's our weakness,
not our strength.

MARY

None could have known that.

RIZZIO

I should have known. Bothwell would have been
better.

LIVINGSTONE

Bothwell!

RIZZIO

Aye, Bothwell. He'd have held them off. There's no
trifling with him.

LIVINGSTONE

We do well enough without him.

RIZZIO

Well enough perhaps.

MARY

Let's have no talk of Bothwell.

LIVINGSTONE

He's better away. The country's been much quieter
since he left it. Hasn't it, madame?

MARY

Much quieter.

FLEMING

You will have a child, your Majesty. You will have
an heir, and then you will be happier.

MARY

With Darnley's child?

FLEMING

He will change, too. The man changes when there are
children.

MARY

We must hope so.

SETON

His Majesty will return tomorrow?

MARY

He was to have returned three days since. But the
hunting may have been delayed.

BEATON

The hunting! He does his hunting o' nights.

MARY

Nay, Beaton.

BEATON

Nor do I take much joy in hearing him called His Majesty.

SETON

But it's the correct address. Lord Darnley has been crowned.

BEATON

Is that a reason for giving him any deference among ourselves? He's a baby, and a spoilt one, and it would give me small pain if I never saw his foolish face again.

SETON

I think that's very treacherous talk!

MARY

It is, too.

BEATON

I'm true to my queen, and I'll be true to none else.
[*She goes to* MARY *and leans her head against her knee*]

MARY

Not even your hackbuteer?

BEATON

Not even him.

RIZZIO

Your Majesty, I have a request which you have denied before, but which I must make again. It is necessary for me to leave Scotland.

MARY

David, David!

RIZZIO

I grow lonely for Italy.

MARY

And who will write my letters?

RIZZIO

There are many who could write letters.

MARY

Can you name one—both efficient and to be trusted?

RIZZIO

Maitland.

MARY

Would you trust him?

RIZZIO

I think I should go, Your Majesty.

MARY

We know why, David, and I won't have it. I won't have my friends driven from me.

RIZZIO

I think it's best.

MARY

Has His Majesty spoken to you?

RIZZIO

Only by the way.—I'm not wanted here—you know
that.

MARY

The king is full of these whims and fancies, my dear
Rizzio. If I gave way to one I should have to humor
him in all. You and I know that I am quite innocent
with you, and you with me.—And I can't spare you.

RIZZIO

God knows you are innocent, madame, and I too,
unless it be a crime to love you. I do love you, I can't
deny that.

MARY

Nor do I hold it a crime.

RIZZIO

Majesty, I tell you honestly it's torture to speak of
going away—and yet—oh, I want no harm to come to
you through me!

MARY

And none will. The king is jealous, of everyone, my
Rizzio, everyone I see or have seen. It's a brainsick
notion. I know that he has acted and spoken foolishly
in many such matters. But as for danger, there is
none.

RIZZIO

I hope there is none.
    [*There is a clatter of armor in the hall to the right*]

MARY

Say no more of going.

RIZZIO

My queen, I am too easy to convince in this! Too much of me cries out to stay—and yet—say no more and let me go!

MARY

Why, very well.

RIZZIO

But not angrily—not in anger.

MARY

Not in anger.

RIZZIO

I thank your Majesty.
 [*A* PORTER *comes to the door at the right*]

PORTER

Master Rizzio?

RIZZIO

Yes.

PORTER

Lord Maitland of Lethington and Master John Knox are here.

MARY

They are to come in.
 [RIZZIO *makes a gesture to the Porter, who goes out.*
 The Queen rises. RIZZIO *goes to the door and ushers*

in MAITLAND *and* KNOX, *then goes out.* KNOX
stands at the door]

MAITLAND

Ah, Your Majesty—I was to bring Master Knox—

MARY

Yes, I remember.

MAITLAND

[*Looking about*]
I gather that he wishes to speak with you in private.

MARY

I doubt that we shall find the subject makes it necessary. Master Knox, will you come closer to the fire?

KNOX

I am very well here, I thank your Majesty.

MARY

You come—was it the word?—to make a protest?

KNOX

Would it be convenient that I speak with you alone?

MARY

When we last spoke alone, sir, there was some talk
to the effect that I had used arts on you. I could wish
to avoid a repetition of that.

KNOX

Why, then, I have but one thing to say and I shall
make shift to say it quickly. You are a Catholic
queen in a Protestant land, your Majesty—

MARY

Only in part Protestant.

KNOX

Protestant in great majority—

MARY

Yes.

KNOX

You have taken a Catholic husband and set him on
the throne beside you, giving him what is called in
the courts of this world the crown matrimonial. You
have also set up an altar in this your palace, where
the mass and other idolatrous rites are said for you.
In these ways you encourage Lord Huntley and the
Highland Catholics of the north in their heathenish
practices, and in so doing bring grave dissension
among your people. I come to warn you.

MARY

To warn me of what, Master Knox?

KNOX

That the forms and appurtenances of the Romish
faith cannot be thrust upon us. That this will not be
borne by the defenders of the Lord's word and
church.

MARY

I ask no one to subscribe to my faith, sir. But it has
been mine from a child, and I keep it.

KNOX

You seek to gain it a foothold here, and build it up
about you. I wish no evil to you nor to this kingdom
and I say the celebration of the mass must cease, for
there are those among us to whom it is abhorrent.
And though it cost civil war and the slaughter of
brother by brother it will not be borne.

MARY

And are you among those who will not bear it?

KNOX

I am.

MARY

Do you find it written that all men must worship in
one fashion?

KNOX

There is but one true faith and one true fashion of
worship.

MARY

And would you enforce it with the sword?

KNOX

There is no tolerance for the idolator nor the adulterer. They are to be weeded out—and even now—
before they come to the great pit and are given over
to his unending fire—a fire not to be quenched nor
remedied nor appeased.

MARY

I understand your attitude toward the idolator, Master Knox, but do you consider it apposite to bring adulterers also into this conversation?

KNOX

The idolator, the adulterer, the priests of Baal, they shall be uprooted, seed and seedling, and cast into the burning—

MARY

But Master Knox, Master Knox, let us have a meeting of minds! An idolator is not the same as an adulterer. Confine yourself to some meaning!

KNOX

They come among us in one person—the priests of the flesh and the worshippers of the flesh—

MARY

If you would but leave off prophesying for a moment and speak sense! Who is the idolator here?

KNOX

Have you not set up an altar?

MARY

A very little one, sir. Nothing to what I could wish. And does that make me an idolator?

KNOX

Will you deny it?

MARY

I do deny it. And now tell me who is the adulterer.

KNOX

Let them search in their hearts who came from France.

MARY

I have searched in mine, and find no adultery there. And shall not those who live in Scotland search in their hearts also?

MAITLAND

Your Majesty, I have brought Master Knox here only because I am convinced that he voices an attitude which must be seriously considered.

MARY

But I try to take him seriously and he speaks in parables. I ask him to define his words and he talks of a great fire. To him a priest is a priest of Baal, an idolator is the same as an adulterer, and those who come from France run especial danger of damnation. What can one say to such a man? Master Knox, I believe you mean well, but can you not see that I also mean well, and that there might be more than one opinion concerning the worship of Our Lord?

KNOX

There will be but one opinion held in that last day—when he comes with his armies, and driveth before him those who are not his children!

MARY

Look, what can one say to him? You ask him a question—and he threatens you with the Last

Judgment! You see, Master Knox, you are not the judge who will sit over us in the Last Judgment! You are instead an elderly gentleman of provincial learning and fanatical beliefs, lately married to a niece of your own some forty years your junior, and one who conducts his conversations almost exclusively in quotations from the Old Testament. If you will talk sensibly with me I shall talk sensibly with you, but if you come here to frighten me I shall regard you as a most ridiculous antediluvian figure, and find you very funny. Which shall it be?

KNOX

Well I know you hold the Lord God as a jest and a mockery!

MARY

Do not confuse yourself with Lord God again! There's a difference!

KNOX

I am His spokesman.
   [RIZZIO *comes to the door*]

MARY

Indeed. Will you show me your commission?

KNOX

I call ruin to fall on this house, the shelter of the great beast—!

MARY

And there again! Maitland, can you, by any stretch of the imagination, look upon me as the great beast?

RIZZIO

Your Majesty, Lord Huntley is here.

MARY

Come in, Lord Huntley!
[HUNTLEY *enters*]
Sir, I have just heard myself likened to the great
beast of Revelations. Can you see any similarity
there?

HUNTLEY

Why, lass, I'd say at the least it's an exaggeration.

MAITLAND

If Your Majesty wishes to give audience to Lord
Huntley—
[*He starts to withdraw*]

MARY

Nay, why should you go? And why should John
Knox and Lord Huntley not meet face to face in one
room? I am aware that Master Knox is a Protestant
and that Huntley is a Catholic, but they dwell in
the same small kingdom, and it would be well if
they understood each other.

KNOX

I am loath to say it, but I am of a mind that there
can be no understanding between him and me, no,
nor between myself and Your Majesty, lest I betray
my Lord.

HUNTLEY

Madame, it's my opinion we understand each other dom well. Too dom well.

MARY

But since you must both live in this kingdom and one must be Catholic and one Protestant, surely it were wiser to be amiable over small matters, Maitland?

MAITLAND

Aye, it would be wiser.

KNOX

Not for what you have said to me or of my person, for that unto seventy times seven those who follow him forgive, but because the air of this house is offensive in his nostrils, I call ruin on it! Nor will I commune in it further, neither with those who make their beds here nor with those who come here for counsel! Yea, if there are any here who would avoid the wrath, let them turn now, for it is upon you and your servants!

MARY

Well—it would seem there's little to be done about that. You are dismissed if you wish to go.

[MAITLAND *and* KNOX *turn to leave*]

MAITLAND

I offer my apologies, Your Majesty.

MARY

Oh, surely.

KNOX

Yea, those who breed and take their ease in the places
of the annointed, turn, turn now, before the axe fall
quickly and be followed by silence! For now it is not
too late, but no man knows when he cometh, nor on
the wings of what morning!

> [MAITLAND *and* KNOX *go out.* RIZZIO *rejoins the*
> *group at the fire*]

MARY

You are duly impressed by this talk, sir?

BEATON

Why, the solemn ass! He should have been booted!

HUNTLEY

My dear, you've been too easy with him, and if you
continue to be easy we'll pay for it.

MARY

And in what way, sir?

HUNTLEY

You and I are alone here, Your Majesty, so far as
Catholicism's concerned. My Highlanders are Catholic, it's true, and there's a plenty of them, and they're
tough, but the rest are all against us, every noble
and man of note. They're John Knox's men, and
you heard yourself what he said.

BEATON

He with the persimmon-colored whiskers?

HUNTLEY

Aye, he. And he means it.

MARY

What does he mean?

HUNTLEY

Ruin to this house.

MARY

Is this a house to be blown down with windy talk?

HUNTLEY

My birdie—I canna call you Ye're Majesty and all that—

MARY

You need not.

HUNTLEY

Then, my bird, they draw their nets tight about us. I told you before, and it's coming.

MARY

And who draws the net?

HUNTLEY

[*Looking at the others*]
Lady—

MARY

These five know my secret heart. They'll say nothing.

HUNTLEY

Lady, there's only one defence. Attack them first. And there's but one proper place for John Knox.

He should be in Edinburgh Castle—and all those with him who are of his mind.

MARY

You'd imprison him?

HUNTLEY

He and some twenty others.

MARY

And then?

HUNTLEY

Then you can go to work. You're not safe here and I'm not safe here while a sect of Protestant lords divide your dominion with you. You rule by sufferance only.

MARY

They are here by my sufferance, Huntley.

HUNTLEY

You have heard of the sheep nursed the wolf-pups till they tore her to pieces.

MARY

But we're not sheep and wolves, my lord. There's room for all of us here, and for whatever faiths we may choose to have.

HUNTLEY

Never think it, my bird, never believe it! It's never yet happened that a state survived with two religions in it. Never. Elizabeth knows that. She's behind this

Knox. He'd never dare be so bold if she weren't behind him.

MARY

But it's my thought that in Scotland, though it be the first time in the world, we shall all believe as we please and worship as we list. And Elizabeth may take it as she sees fit.

HUNTLEY

She uses it against you, my dear, and uses John Knox against you. Ladybird, I'm willing to beg it of you, take heed of me now or we're both done!

MARY

Rizzio?

RIZZIO

You know my mind. I'm with Lord Huntley in this.

MARY

But how can I bring myself to imprison men for no wrong they've done, on suspicion only, imprison them for their faith—?

HUNTLEY

It's more than faith. It's works. You heard John Knox!

MARY

It cuts athwart every right instinct I have, my lord! Every fibre I have that's royal shrinks at such penny-wise petty doings! And John Knox—a doddering imbecile, drooling prophecy!

HUNTLEY

He threatened you, lady.

MARY

No, no, I can't. Even if it were wisdom to do it, and
it's not.
  [*The right-hand door opens suddenly and* DARNLEY
  stands in it. MARY *turns toward him*]
My lord!
  [DARNLEY *walks slowly to the middle of the room
  and lays a hand on the table*]

DARNLEY

I'm unexpected, perhaps? Too early? A thought
Too early? I'll retire. Come when I'm wanted.

MARY

No,
My lord, you've been long expected, and more than
  welcome.

DARNLEY

Why, a pretty wife, a huswife with her maids;
A pretty sight, and maybe a cavalier
Or two, for the maids' company. Dod, sit down, all!
Damn me if I'll intrude!

MARY

Will you speak to Lord Huntley?

DARNLEY

  [*Focussing on* HUNTLEY]
Right. That's right. Lord Huntley, give me your
  hand.

I thank you for watching over the pretty wife here.
I've been away.

HUNTLEY

[*Turning*]
Your Majesty, you've a wife
Such as I wish I'd had when I was young.

DARNLEY

Right—You have right. They all say that. I'd say it
myself,
Only I know her better.
[*He turns to the door*]
I know her too well,
And not well enough. She wouldn't care to hear it.
Not from me.

MARY

Darnley.

DARNLEY

She sleeps alone.
At least as far as I know.

HUNTLEY

I'll take my leave,
My lady.

MARY

Yes.

DARNLEY

Stay, stay, I'm going. I only
Tell you she sleeps alone as far as I know.

A pretty wife. These women—they get with child,
You never know how—and then they won't sleep
   with you.
     [HUNTLEY *bows to* MARY, *turns deliberately, and
     goes out the door to the right, closing it*]
What's the matter with him? He's an old married
   man.
He knows these things.

MARY

You're tired, my lord. Will you wish
Some service, something to eat and drink?

DARNLEY

She sends me
Off to bed, you note. You note it, Rizzio?
There's a service she could do me, but I doubt
She'll offer it. And I'm a king, by God, a king,
And you're a clark by office!

MARY

My lord, I hoped
You'd have some other word for me when you
Returned.

DARNLEY

My pink, if I gave you the word you've earned
The room would smell. I've been at the hunting. We
   had
Something to drink. Alban! Alban! Allons!

MARY

You call someone?

DARNLEY

Alban! God's right! St. Andrew! Alban!
I'm drunk, you see.

MARY

I think not.

DARNLEY

Yes, but I am.
Alban! Christ his sonties, am I left
Alone here! God and St. Andrew!
   [*The right hand door opens and* RUTHVEN *enters
   in full armor*]

MARY

What is this?
   [*To* RUTHVEN]
You will retire, sir. Who are you?

DARNLEY

My good friend Ruthven.

MARY

Is this a place for armor? I will receive
Lord Ruthven another time.

DARNLEY

The callant's there,
Ruthven.

RUTHVEN

Aye.

MARY

I had heard that Lord Ruthven was ill,
And thought to go to him, not to see him here.

RUTHVEN

I am ill, and it's mortal, but I've sworn to be mortal
To another first.

MARY

This is my apartment, sir,
And I ask you to go.
          [DOUGLAS *appears behind* RUTHVEN]

MARY

I demand little courtesy,
But that little I must have. Are these your friends?
If so, take them elsewhere.

DARNLEY

Aye, I'm to have my friends
In my apartment—and you're to have yours here.
I say no—they're to mingle.—
          [*He points to* RIZZIO]
You see that grig
With the kinked hair there? He with the lady's hands
And feet? Where does he sleep nights? That's he,
     that's the one
We have in question!

MARY

My lord, when you've been drinking
I have little taste for your company, and tonight
Less, perhaps, than ever.

DARNLEY

He, he, I tell you!
That Italian spawn!

[RIZZIO, *trembling, steps back toward the queen's study*]

MARY

[*Stepping in front of* RIZZIO]
Go into my study.

[LORD MORTON *enters*]

Lord Morton,
Whatever you have in hand here, put no faith
In this king I've crowned and set beside me! His word
Is a paper shield.

DARNLEY

I'm king in this country, mistress—
And I know my rights.

MARY

Beaton, why were these men
Not stopped at my door?

DARNLEY

They came with me.

BEATON

[*Facing* MORTON]
Will you tell me
What you want with the queen?

MORTON

[*His dagger drawn*]
Damme, do you want this bodkin
Through that bodice of yours? .

[*She shrinks back.* RIZZIO, *having reached the study step by step, opens it and reveals a* GUARD, *a drawn claymore in his hand*]

RIZZIO

Let me pass!

THE GUARD

Nay, lad.

FLEMING

Your Majesty,
They've broken into your rooms.
[MARY *turns and sees the guard*]

MARY

Lord Darnley, was that
By your order?

RIZZIO

[*Hardly able to speak for fear*]
Save me, my queen, save me!

MARY

Aye, Rizzio.
[*The five women retreat before the armed men, covering* RIZZIO *from them*]

MORTON

Look to they women-folk, Darnley. We'll care for
him.
[RIZZIO *turns suddenly and leaps behind the heavy drapes of the high window down-stage.* MORTON, DOUGLAS *and* RUTHVEN *follow him,* DOUGLAS *with his dagger raised*]

MARY

Douglas, I'll remember this!
[*A fall is heard behind the curtains, but no cry.*
MARY *runs toward the window, but is met by*
RUTHVEN, *sheathing his dagger*]
You've murdered him!
You pack of filthy cowards!

RUTHVEN

Yea, and done well.

MARY

Done well! Oh, fools and cowards!
[*She runs to the curtain and with* MARY BEATON
pulls it back from RIZZIO, *then bends over him and
draws back again in terror*]
Oh, David, David,
It was I wouldn't let you go!

DARNLEY

[*Looking away*]
You might cover that sight.

MARY

Is he dead, Beaton?

BEATON

Yes, madame.

MARY

Oh, you do well, you do well.
All of you!
[*She conquers her repulsion, and tries to loosen*
RIZZIO'S *ruff.* FLEMING *comes to help her*]

We'll help him if we can,
Fleming.

FLEMING

Yes.

MARY

You were too gentle for them,
David. They couldn't bear it—these boors and
  swine—
Your kerchief, Fleming! He bleeds so—

FLEMING

It's useless, Madame.

MARY

[*Rising*]
Yes.
[*To the lords*]
To take him unarmed, and poniard him—
One who had never hurt you!

RUTHVEN

[*Sinking to a chair*]
Well, the work's done,
And my queen's wiped clear of him.

MARY

Wiped clear! You believed
I was guilty with him!

RUTHVEN

Were you not?

MARY

No!

RUTHVEN

I'd be sorry
If you were not. I struck him down for that.

MARY

I was not guilty. But will you tell me now
Who'll believe me innocent? You've branded me deep
With this murder, and you've killed a guiltless man!
Why do you sit in my presence?

RUTHVEN

Because I'm ill
And dying. I should be sorry if this thing
I've done were in error—for it's the last I'll do.

MARY

You'll stand in my presence! Whose order was it?

RUTHVEN

Why, ask His Majesty that—
And Morton there, and Moray.
    [*He rises with difficulty*]

MARY

Moray too?

RUTHVEN

Yea, your brother. For me—let me go home

MARY

Go. Morton and Douglas, I give you three days
To leave this kingdom.

MORTON

And the king? I have the king's seal
For what I've done.

MARY

Is that true?

DARNLEY

Aye.

MARY

The worse for you.
The worse for you all.

DARNLEY

My lady, this long while past
You've denied me your chamber, and when I've seen
   you there's been
This Rizzio with you.

MARY

Never again while I live
Will you see me alone. I bear your child in me
Or you'd answer for this!

DARNLEY

There'll be no answering!
We know what we know about you!

MARY

I would I knew
In what strange dark chamber of your oafish brain
You found reasons for Rizzio's death. If I saw you
   seldom
Remember how often you drank yourself imbecile
Before you came to me. You've slain your last friend,
   sir.
It was Rizzio's counsel put you where you are

And kept you there. These are not your friends,
    these three,
Nor Moray. They wanted Rizzio out of the way,
And they wanted to drag you down, and drag me
    down,
And you play into their hands. I've never been
Unfaithful to you, but we're at an end, we two.
From this time forward if I touch your hand
May God blight me and my child!

DARNLEY

I wanted you!
You kept away from me, and it drove me mad!

MARY

You won't mend it now. Look, young Rizzio's dead,
You've blackened me, blackened yourself, thrown a
    black doubt
On the child who'll be your heir. The lords look on
And smile, knowing they've trapped you. You'll
    never climb
From the pit where you've fallen, and I may fall
    with you. Lord Moray
Weaves his web round us. You've helped him.

DARNLEY

God knows I wanted
Only my right.

MARY

You pitiful dolt! To think
Such a calf should rule, and at my choosing! God

May forgive you—not I. Nor forgive myself.—And
   Rizzio.—
Take yourselves out! You pollute the dead to stand
   there!
He wanted to go to Italy.

FLEMING

Yes.

MARY

Will you go?
   [MORTON *beckons the guards, and they cross from
   the study to the outer door*]

RUTHVEN

   [*At the door*]
You'll want some help, mayhap.

MARY

None of yours. I've noticed
It's men that kill, but women that wash the corpse
And weep for it. May none ever weep for you.

RUTHVEN

None will. I've been in the wrong.

MARY

I'm sorry, Lord Ruthven.
It's an ill thing to have on your heart when you die.

RUTHVEN

Aye, is it.
   [*He goes out, and the men follow him.* DARNLEY
   *looks back as if he wished to speak to the queen,
   but goes silently*]

MARY

And now we're alone. The lords have shown their
    hand.
Rizzio's gone—and Darnley, what there was to go.
We've been not long in Scotland, but time enough
To show I can lose it, have lost it in their minds
Already. We must lay the poor lad somewhere.
Could we lift him together?

SETON

Oh, madame, I'm afraid!

MARY

Of what?

SETON

I've never seen one dead before.
I've not known it was like this.

MARY

It's poor Rizzio.
No one to hurt us. And you and I will lie
Sometime like this, and folk will be afraid
Because we lie so still. How strange it is
That he should frighten us who wished us well,
And would still if he lived. We must take him up
And lay him on my bed. I'll sleep with Beaton
Tonight.
    [*She takes a step toward* RIZZIO]

BEATON

Madame, the blood will stain your dress.

MARY

If that were all. This will bring more blood after.
Now I see it. Before I reign here clearly
There will be many men lie so for me
Slain in needless quarrel. Slain, and each one
With blood to spill but once, like his. And yet
One steps on into it—steps from life to life
Till there are thousands dead, and goes on still
Till the heart faints and sickens, and still goes on
And must go on.

> [*An iron gate clangs outside.* BEATON *parts the
> curtains to look out*]

I tell you, Fleming, my soul
Is aghast at this blood spilled for me, and yet
It hardens me, too. These are their manners, this
Is the way they go to work. I shall work on them,
And not too lightly. They think of me as a girl,
Afraid of them. They shall see.—And yet my mind
Believes nothing of what I say; I'm weak as grief,
Stripped and wept out before them. They press me
close,
And I have no one to send.

> [*There is a rattle of staves in the courtyard*]

BEATON

> [*Turning back*]

It's the provost, madame,
I heard them call his name.

MARY

He's not to enter.
Let no one enter.

> [BEATON *goes out right*]

No one. In all this kingdom
I can trust only five, and one's myself,
And we're women, all of us.—If they go scot-free
After this indignity I'm no queen. For Ruthven,
He'll pay his own score. He's dying. Morton and
  Douglas
Must die too.

FLEMING

They were under Lord Darnley's orders.

MARY

He was under theirs. It won't save them.

FLEMING

Your Majesty,
They've left the city by now. They should have been
  taken
While they were in your hands.

MARY

I know. It's true.
They've fled to raise troops. When next we find them
  they'll meet us
With culverins.
    [BEATON enters]
He's gone?

BEATON

Yes. But there's one
Below from France—says he has news.

MARY

From France?
Tomorrow, though. I wish I were still in France
And had never seen these stone walls.

LIVINGSTONE

And so do I.

MARY

What is his name?

BEATON

He gave me
This token for you, no name. It's a crow's feather.

MARY

[*Takes the feather, then pauses*]
Tell my Lord Bothwell I have no wish to see him
Now or later.

BEATON

Madame, you'll see him? I brought him
Along with me.

MARY

No. Not now. Not ever.
There's nothing to say between us now.

BEATON

He came
From France to see you.

MARY

Tell him.
[LORD BOTHWELL *is seen standing in the doorway*]

BOTHWELL

Your Majesty,
You've had unwelcome company this hour,
If I've heard aright, and I care not to be another,
But I come to make an offer I made before—
To be your soldier.

MARY

I have no time to talk,
Lord Bothwell. Nor do I wish to see you. The time's
Gone by.

BOTHWELL

My queen, my queen, turn not away
Your friends. You've few enough, too few it seems
To prevent what's happened.

MARY

Go.

BOTHWELL

Does he still lie here?
I'll lay the poor boy away for you at least,
And then I'll go, since you wish it.
    [*He crosses to* RIZZIO]
Aye, they made sure,
Lad—and their dirks were sharp. Shall I place him
    within?

MARY

Yes.
    [BOTHWELL *picks up* RIZZIO *and carries him into
    Mary's chamber*]
Must you betray me, too?

BEATON

I wished only—
If you'd but follow your heart!

MARY

We two must twain,
My Beaton. You take too much on you. Lord Both-
well,
May be your friend, not mine.

BEATON

Forgive me.

MARY

What warrant
Have you been given to vouch for my heart, or judge
Whether I should follow it?

BEATON

None.

MARY

Oh, God, this vice
Of women, crying and tears! To weep, weep now
When I need my anger! Say my farewells for me,
I've gone to my study.
[*She turns.* BOTHWELL *enters*]

BOTHWELL

Goodnight, my queen.

MARY

Goodnight.
I'm not unkind. But I'm cut off from you.
You know that.

BOTHWELL

Yes. There's no need to hide your weeping.
He was over-young to die.

MARY

It's not for him.
No, it's for all I wanted my life to be,
And is not.

BOTHWELL

Majesty, you have a fortunate star.
It will come well yet.

MARY

If I have a star at all
It's an evil one. To violate my room,
Kill my servant before my eyes—How I must be
    hated!

BOTHWELL

They'll pay for that.

MARY

Perhaps.

BOTHWELL

I've taken an oath
They'll pay for it. Your Majesty, I wearied
Of France and exile, wearied of sun and wine,
And looked north over the water, longing for fog
And heather and my own country. Further, the news
Was none too happy from Scotland. They want your
    throne
And plan to have it. But I mean to live in this land

And mean you to be queen of it. The Earl of Both-
well
Is home, and spoiling for a fight. Before
Day dawns they'll hear from me.

MARY

My lord, I thank you—

BOTHWELL

Give me no thanks. I like a fight too well
To pretend it's a virtue. Moreover, if I'm to live here
I'd rather you were my liege than Moray. I'm none
So fond of your half-brother. This night's work
Should show you he's what I knew him, half-bred,
half-faced
And double-tongued.

MARY

You have no army.

BOTHWELL

I have
My border men. Lord Huntley's joined with me
With his Highland kilties. If you'd call your clans
We could drive them to the wall.

MARY

It's a war then.

BOTHWELL

It's war,
Already. They've turned your Darnley against you.
They'll use him

As long as they need his seal. Once they've got you
   out
They'll set Moray up as regent. They fear one chance:
That you and I should league together and balk
   them.
I've come back in time, not too soon.

MARY

I think you have.
My lord, I had no heart to face you. The fault
Was mine when we parted.

BOTHWELL

It's not too late. I've come
Only just in time, but in time.

MARY

It is too late—
For you and me. These faults we commit have lives
Of their own, and bind us to them.

BOTHWELL

[*Pointing toward her bedroom*]
Yon was Darnley's work.
Are you still his?

MARY

Am I not?
   [BEATON *gathers up the three others with a look
   and goes into the queen's study with them silently*]
I'm to bear his child.
I cannot hate my child.

BOTHWELL

It's in the wind
This Darnley's not to live long.

MARY

I'd have no hand
In that—nor you!

BOTHWELL

It happens he's a pawn
In the game the lords are playing. They'll sacrifice
   him
When the time comes. It's no plot of mine.

MARY

But he lives
And I'm his wife, and my babe is his. I must drink
My cup down to the rinse. It was I that filled it,
And if there's grief at the bottom it's mine. I'll name
   you
My officer, but only if you can pledge
No harm will come through you to Darnley.

BOTHWELL

Lady,
I need you, and you need me, but I'll be damned
If Darnley's needed on this earth. I have
No project against him, but I'll give no pledge
To block me if I should have. There be men
Who wear their welcome out in this world early,
And Darnley's one of them.

MARY

You have never yet
Learned how to take an order.

BOTHWELL

And never will—
From man or woman living, sovereign or knave,
Judge or vicegerent. I have not been conquered
And will not be. But I offer you my fealty,
And it's worth the more for that.

MARY

You must make your own terms—
I'm but a beggar here.

BOTHWELL

Nay, nay, it's I
That sue, a beggar for what's impossible,
With this Darnley standing between us.
    [*She pauses again*]

MARY

You shall be
My Lord Admiral, and act for me. Yes, and to that
Let me add how my breath caught when I knew you
    here,
Hoping I know not what, things not to be,
Hopes I must strangle down. Oh, Bothwell, Bothwell!
I was wrong! I loved you all the time, and denied
    you!
Forgive me—even too late!

BOTHWELL

I tell you we
Shall be happy yet.

MARY

No, for I think I've been
At the top of what I'll have, and all the rest
Is going down. It's as if a queen should stand
High up, at the head of a stair—I see this now
As in a dream—and she in her dream should step
From level to level downward, all this while knowing
She should mount and not descend—till at last she walks
An outcast in the courtyard—bayed at by dogs
That were her hunters—walks there in harsh morning
And the dream's done.

BOTHWELL

[*Stepping toward her*]
You're weary. You've borne too much.
They shall pay for this.

MARY

Come no nearer, my lord. It's not ours
To have. Go now.

BOTHWELL

Yes, your Majesty.
    [*He turns*]
Yet
I tell you we shall be happy. And there will be nothing
Not ours to have.
    [*He goes out*]
                    Curtain

ACT TWO

Scene Two

Scene: *Elizabeth's study at Whitehall.* burghley *and* elizabeth *are seated across a table.* a third figure *approaches from the side.*

BURGHLEY

This will be Lord Throgmorton.

ELIZABETH

You're early, sir.

THROGMORTON

Madame, I rode all night.—I've news from the
north.
Darnley's been murdered.

ELIZABETH

How?

THROGMORTON

Kirk o' Field was blown up.
The castle's in ruins.

ELIZABETH

Now that was a waste of powder—
And of castles too. But he's dead—

THROGMORTON

Yes, madame—they found him.
It was no accident. He'd been strangled.

ELIZABETH

So there's no more king in Scotland.
Who took this trouble?

THROGMORTON

Moray, and Morton, no doubt—perhaps Maitland—

ELIZABETH

Not Bothwell?—

THROGMORTON

No—though he must have known of it—

ELIZABETH

And the queen—
The queen weeps for her Darnley?

THROGMORTON

Madame—

ELIZABETH

Ah, yes—
She'll weep and wear black—it becomes her. A second time
She's a widow now. And she's borne a child. She begins
To wear a little, no doubt? She must ponder now
What costumes may become her?

THROGMORTON

Nay, truly, your Grace,
I'd say she charms as ever.

ELIZABETH

Would you say so?
But she weeps and puts on mourning?

THROGMORTON

No, madame, Bothwell
And the queen are friends again—or more than that.
They'd be married already, I think, only Moray's
    against it
And the earls behind him.

ELIZABETH

Now in my day and time
I have known fools and blockheads, but never, I
    swear,
In such numbers as among these Scotch earls.
Moray's against it?
Against the queen's marriage with Bothwell?

BURGHLEY

Your Majesty—
If she were to marry Bothwell—we've opposed that,
    too,
And even prevented it.

ELIZABETH

Aye, times have changed,
And we change along with them. She loves this
    Bothwell?
It's a great love—a queen's love?

THROGMORTON

It is indeed.
A madness, almost.

ELIZABETH

Yes, yes—and it's well sometimes
To be mad with love, and let the world burn down
In your own white flame. One reads this in ro-
    mances—
Such a love smokes with incense; oh, and it's grateful
In the nostrils of the gods! Now who would part
    them
For considerations of earth? Let them have this love
This little while—let them bed and board together—
Drink it deep, be happy—aye—

BURGHLEY

Madame, this Bothwell's
No man to play with. if they marry she'll crown him
    king—

ELIZABETH

You did well to ride fast, Throgmorton! Turn now
And ride as fast back again; you can sleep later
When we're old and the years are empty.—And tell
    my lord Moray
If he'd keep me a friend, let his sister marry Both-
    well—
Tell him to favor it—hurry it.

BURGHLEY

And with Bothwell king
Do you think to conquer Mary?

ELIZABETH

Send next to John Knox,
But do this cleverly, giving Knox evidence

That Bothwell slew Darnley with the queen's con-
nivance
And they bed together in blood. Have you wit
enough
To see this well done?

THROGMORTON

I think so, Majesty.

ELIZABETH

See to it.
Who will deny that Bothwell murdered Darnley
When he lives with the queen, and enjoys the fruits?
Or who
Will credit Bothwell's denial? Your brain, my
Burghley!
Where do you wear it, or what has it hardened into
That you're so easily gulled?

BURGHLEY

But is it wise
To make a false accusation? This project hangs
By a thread. Make but one error and we shall lose
Whatever we've gained.

ELIZABETH

Go and do these things—
They are to marry—we sanction it—let none oppose
it—
She refused him before when he could have saved
her—
She'll take him now when it's fatal—Let her have
this love

This little while—we grant her that—then raise
The winds against them—rouse the clans, cry ven-
    geance
On their guilty sleep and love—I say within
This year at the very farthest, there's no more queen
Than king in Scotland!

Curtain

ACT TWO

Scene Three

SCENE: *A hall in Dunbar Castle. A* SENTINEL *is at his post
    near the outer gate, another at the guard-room door.
    There is a step on the cobbles outside. The* FIRST SEN-
    TINEL *swings round to the gate.*

JAMIE
    [*Outside*]
Drop your point, man. Ye ken me.

FIRST SENTINEL
Eh, Jamie. What is it?

JAMIE
I'm late. It was tough getting through. The queen's
taken prisoner. Her army's gone.

FIRST SENTINEL
Nay! And Bothwell?

JAMIE

Bothwell's free yet. Free and able to fight. We're to put the castle in posture of defense. Where's the sergeant?

FIRST SENTINEL

Call Graeme.

SECOND SENTINEL

Graeme!—I told you this was no lucky battle to be in.

FIRST SENTINEL

Says John Knox!
[GRAEME *enters*]

JAMIE

I've orders for the guard. We're to man the walls and be ready on the gates.

GRAEME

It goes that way?
[BEATON *enters from the stair*]

JAMIE

That way and worse.
[*They turn toward the gate*]

BEATON

Jamie, what brings you?

JAMIE

Orders, lass.

BEATON

Quick, tell me!

JAMIE

It goes badly with us, lass.

[LORD HUNTLEY *enters*]

BEATON

My lord—

HUNTLEY

There's to be a parley here. Make ready for it.

JAMIE

Watch that outer post.

[*The* SENTINELS *go out*]

BEATON

A parley—the battle's over?

HUNTLEY

Aye, over and done. This is Moray's kingdom now.

BEATON

And the queen?

HUNTLEY

The queen's a prisoner, lass. My men have deserted,
her own men turned against her.

BEATON

My lord, you'll forgive me, but how could that be?

HUNTLEY

This was John Knox's battle, lady. The auld limmer
took a stance on a hill some half-mile to windward,

and there he stood haranguing like the angel Gabriel,
swearing Bothwell killed Darnley to have the queen.
And the queen's men listened to him, the psalm-
singing red-beards, and then turned and made her
prisoner and delivered her up to Lord Moray.

GRAEME

Bothwell's returning.

JAMIE

Upstairs with you, lass.
[BEATON *goes up the lower stair*]

GRAEME

Shall I set the guard?

HUNTLEY

Wait a moment.
[BOTHWELL *enters*]

BOTHWELL

We're not through yet, my lord. You'll stand by me?

HUNTLEY

Aye,
If it's any use. One may rally an army flying.
But one that flies toward the enemy and makes
friends—

BOTHWELL

Who spoke of rallying? They won by treachery,
And we'll treat them some of the same!
[*To* JAMIE]
There were ninety men
Left to guard the castle! They're here still?

JAMIE

Aye, sir.

BOTHWELL

They're under
Lord Huntley's orders while this parley's on.
Tell them to be ready. He'll join you.

JAMIE

Aye.
          [*He goes into the guard-room*]

BOTHWELL

Sergeant, take the men you need and guard that
    arch—
Let no one enter but the lords themselves.

GRAEME

Aye, my lord.
          [*He goes out by the arch*]

BOTHWELL

I'll talk with these lords, and if they listen to reason
They may keep their mangy lives, but if they refuse
To release the queen and give her back her kingdom
Then hell's their home! Watch my arm, and hark
For my sword on steel. They're outnumbered three
    to one
In this court.

HUNTLEY

Kill them?

BOTHWELL

Cut their throats
If you like that better.

HUNTLEY

That's plain murder.

BOTHWELL

Right,
And if they say no they've earned it.

HUNTLEY

And we'd die, too.

BOTHWELL

Why, it might be we would. But I'd stake more
On our living long with them dead. If the queen's
    deposed
Then I've lived long enough, and so have you.
Will you gamble with me?

HUNTLEY

I will.
    [*They shake hands. A trumpet sounds outside*]

BOTHWELL

Wait for the signal.
My sword on steel.
    [HUNTLEY *goes into the guard-room. The voices of
    the Lords are heard outside*]

MORTON

    [*Outside*]
Go carefully now. Not too fast.

MORAY

Aye, you're the man to say that.

MORTON

Let Maitland speak.
[*They enter; one or two bow ironically*]

BOTHWELL

You may drop these scrapings. We know what we
think of each other!

MORTON

And that's true too!

MORAY

We have little to gain, Lord Bothwell,
By a conference with you. The battle is ours. The
queen
Is prisoner to us. But to spare ourselves further
bloodshed
And spare you bloodshed, we grant this respite, and
ask
That you surrender without conditions.

BOTHWELL

No.
No, I thank you. Moreover if your tongue's
To be foremost in this council, we'll stop now
And argue the matter outside.

MAITLAND

Be patient, Lord Moray.
We're here to make terms, as you are, Bothwell.
The queen
And you have been defeated. We made war on you

Because you two were married, and because she planned
To make you king.

BOTHWELL

You make war on us
Like the pack of lying hounds you are, by swearing
In public and in court that we killed Darnley
So that we might marry! You know where that guilt lies.

MORAY

Who killed Darnley
We care not. Let the courts decide it.

BOTHWELL

It was you that killed him!
And you fight us bearing false witness!

MORAY

You wanted him dead.

BOTHWELL

I grant it. I wanted him dead. You killed him and managed
To shift the wight on me. You've won with that lie,
May your mouths rot out with it! And now what do you want—
What do you ask of us?

MAITLAND

First, that you leave Scotland.

BOTHWELL

That's easily said;
What else?

MAITLAND

Why, next, that the queen should delegate
Her powers to the lords of the council, those you see
Before you—

BOTHWELL

Aye, I see them.

MAITLAND

And bind herself
To act with our consent only.

BOTHWELL

No more?

MAITLAND

No more.

BOTHWELL

Then here are my conditions; I will leave,
And trouble you no more, if you pledge your word
That the queen's to keep her throne and her power
    intact,
Without prejudice to her rights. But if you dare
Encroach one inch on her sovereignty, guard your
    gates,
For I'll be at them!

MORTON

Aye, you make your terms!

BOTHWELL

Aye, I make mine; defeated, I still make mine—
And you'll do well to heed them. I shall want leave
    also
To see the queen for a moment.

MORAY

You know our answer.

BOTHWELL

Then look to yourselves!
    [*He lays a hand on his sword*]

MAITLAND

Look now, Bothwell.
It's you I rebel against. I'd lend no hand
In this company if the queen were to rule alone,
And I've said as much to Lord Moray.

MORTON

I speak for myself,
And say no to it.

MORAY

And I.

BOTHWELL

You've wanted my earldom,
Lord Moray. Well, you may have it. I'll make it over.
You shall choose a new earl of Bothwell. I'll disband
    my army.
And threaten you no more. But on condition
The queen reigns here as before.

MORAY

We'll make our conditions—
We have no time for yours.

BOTHWELL

My lines are not broken.
I'll try conclusions yet, and you'll not sleep easy
While I'm within these borders!

MAITLAND

Take his terms,
My Moray.

MORAY

Are we to fight a war and win
And toss the spoils away?

BOTHWELL

Find some agreement,
For I'm in haste, and if you say no to me
I've other plans!

ERSKINE

Bothwell's been our one weapon
Against the queen, Lord Moray. I believe it's wisdom
To banish him, but remember the queen's a queen
And it's dangerous to touch her. When he's gone
You'll have no cause against her.

MORAY

Why, damn you all!

MORTON

Let him go, and leave her the throne.

MORAY

And even Morton.

MORTON

Gad, I want no long wars,
I'm a married man. Send him on his way!
He leaves his earldom.

BOTHWELL

Then this sword stays in the scabbard
And lucky for all of you. Do you give your pledge?

MAITLAND

I give my pledge, Lord Bothwell, for all here present.
We have not rebelled against the queen, and will not
If you are banished.

BOTHWELL

Then give me leave to speak
Alone with her.

MAITLAND

With the queen?

BOTHWELL

Aye, for a moment.

MORAY

No.

MAITLAND

There's no harm in that, Moray.

ERSKINE

We'll wait in the courtyard.
It's day and we have orders to give.

MORTON

Gordon and Douglas,
You won't be needed. Intercept Lord Huntley's men
While there's yet time.

MAITLAND

The queen is here, Lord Bothwell,
And will be free to see you.
> [*The Lords go out. After a moment's pause,*
> QUEEN MARY *comes to the door—a soldier on
> either side. The guards retire, leaving* MARY *and*
> BOTHWELL *alone*]

MARY

Thank God you're safe!

BOTHWELL

And you are safe, my queen, safe and set free
And may keep your kingdom.

MARY

At what price?

BOTHWELL

They've made
A bargain with me. God knows whether they'll keep
    it,
But I think they will, for Maitland gave his word,
And he's been honest.

MARY

What bargain? You've sacrificed
Yourself for this. What have you offered?

BOTHWELL

Nothing
To weigh against what you'll keep. I've given my
  earldom—
That's a trifle to what we save.

MARY

You shall have it back,
And more to put with it.

BOTHWELL

No. I've accepted exile.
I'm to leave the kingdom.

MARY

Why, then, I'm exiled too.
I'm your wife and I love you, Bothwell.

BOTHWELL

The bargain's made.
You may keep your crown without me but not with
  me.
Do you abdicate your throne? What's left?

MARY

Call in
The men of your guard, cut our way through and
  ride!
They'll never head us! We can rouse the north,

Ask help from France and England, return with an
  army
They dare not meet!

BOTHWELL

You'd raise no army, Marie.
You forget what a drag I am on you. The north
Is sullen as the south toward you and me.
What's left we must do apart.

MARY

What if we lost?
At the worst we'd have each other.

BOTHWELL

And do you vision the end of that?
A woman who was a queen, a man who was
The earl, her husband, but fugitives, put to it
To ask for food and lodging, enemies
On every road; they weary, heartsick, turning,
At last on each other with reproaches, she saying:
I was a queen, would be one now but for you,
And he, I have lost my earldom.

MARY

I betrayed you once
And betrayed my love, but I learned by that; I
  swear
Though it cost my kingdom, not again!

BOTHWELL

If you wish
To thrive, break that oath, betray me, betray your
  love,

Give me up forever—for you know as I know
We lose together. God knows what we'll ever win
Apart.

MARY

Nothing. Oh, Bothwell, the earth goes empty.
What worse could happen than parting?

BOTHWELL

Can I stay?
This once for the last I can save you from yourself,
And me. There's something wills it. I go alone.
This is your kingdom. Rule it.

MARY

You must not surrender
They'd serve you as they served Darnley.

BOTHWELL

I'll not surrender.
I'll see to my own banishment, find my guard,
Force my way out, and go.

MARY

We must say goodbye?

BOTHWELL

Aye, girl, we've spent what time we had,
And I know not when I'll see you. Let's have no
    pretense
Unworthy of us. It's likely we'll not meet again
On this same star.

MARY

God help me and all women
Here in this world, and all men. Fair fall all chances
The heart can long for—and let all women and men
Drink deep while they can their happiness. It goes
    fast
And never comes again. Mine goes with you,
Youth, and the fund of dreams, and to lie a while
Trusted, in arms you trust. We're alone, alone,
Alone—even while we lie there we're alone,
For it's false. It will end. Each one dies alone.

BOTHWELL

I'll come
If I can. We've loved well, lass, could love better.
We've had but the broken fragment of a year
And whenever I've touched you, something that
    broods above us
Has made that touch disaster. This is not my choice.
Lest I bring you utter ruin we must wait,
Wait better times and luck. I'll come again
If I can.

MARY

Yes, if you can. Aye, among all tides
And driftings of air and water it may be
Some dust that once was mine will touch again
Dust that was yours. I'll not bear it! Oh, God, I'll
    not bear it!
Take me with you! Let us be slaves and pick
Our keep from kitchen middens and leavings! Let us

Quarrel over clouts and fragments, but not apart—
Bothwell, that much we could have!

BOTHWELL

Is there refuge in this world for you
And me together? Go far as we could, is there one
Turfed roof where we'd not be reminded of good days
And end in bitterness? Face these lords like a queen
And rule like a queen. I'd help you if I could
But I'm no help. You must meet them now.

MARY

Yes. I'll meet them
Can you break your way through? They're watching!

BOTHWELL

It's a chance.
Huntley! Huntley!

HUNTLEY

            [*Outside*]
I'm here.

BOTHWELL

We ride at once
For Stirling. Be ready for a fight.

HUNTLEY

We're ready.

BOTHWELL

I must take my moment.

MARY

I know.

BOTHWELL

Goodbye, sweet, but if they wrong you—if you ever
  need me,
Look for me back.

  [*He kisses her, and goes*]

MARY

Goodbye. To our two worlds.

  [*There is a cry beyond the guard-room:* "BOTH-
  WELL, *it's* BOTHWELL!" *The alarm is taken up by
  the men at the gate, who call:* "*On guard there!
  Pistol him! Mount and after him! Ride, you devils!
  On guard! Drop the portcullis! He's gone!*" *There
  is a sound of running feet from the gate to the other
  side of the stage.* MARY *stands facing the guard-
  room door.* GORDON *and* DOUGLAS *run in through
  the arch*]

DOUGLAS

Through the guard-room!

GORDON

He'll be over the wall—

DOUGLAS

Out of the way, madam—

GORDON

Nay, it's the queen—

DOUGLAS

Will you let us pass?

MARY

I guard this door, Lord Douglas.
You'll go the long way round!

GORDON

Your pardon, your majesty.
    [*He bows.* BEATON *appears on the stairway.* LORDS
    MORTON, MORAY *and* MAITLAND *enter*]

MORTON

This was hardly well done, your majesty.

MARY

Take care whom you question, sir.

MORAY

You've sent Bothwell off!
That was your ruse!

MARY

Lord Bothwell will leave Scotland.
That was what you wanted.
    [*Enter* LORD ERSKINE]

MORAY

He's gone?

ERSKINE

Clean away!

MAITLAND

Madame, there was some understanding
You two would remain here.

MARY

None that I know of.

MORTON

Eh, god, he'll wish he had.
    [JOHN KNOX *appears in the archway*]

MARY

Remove that man from my presence! Is every stranger
Free to enter my courts?

KNOX

Though you be a queen
And have faith in thy gods and idols, yet in this day
It will not staunch nor avail! Bid the sea remove
From the castle front, and gnaw it no more, as soon
Will it obey thee. Pluck down the whore! Pluck her down,
This contamination of men!

MARY

Maitland, if there's to be counsel here, send out
This preacher and his ravings!

MAITLAND

He may stay, for me.

MORAY

Madame, collect what necessities you require.
You will change your residence.

MARY

That is at my will, I think.

MORTON

Do you think so?

MAITLAND

You are to be lodged
In Holyroodhouse for the time.

MARY

I am to be lodged—
And your faith? You pledged your faith and word,—
   all of you—
To leave my power untouched, leave me my throne
If Bothwell and I were parted.

MAITLAND

We'll keep it
When Lord Bothwell's surrendered to us.

MARY

Go out and take him!
Take him if you can! But for your queen,
I warn you, never since there were kings and queens
In Scotland, has a liegeman laid his hand
On my line without regret!

MORTON

We'll take care of that.

MARY

My lords, if I go with you, expect no pardon,
No clemency; I have friends, this farce will end.
Once more, then, leave me in peace
I have used you royally. Use me so.

MAITLAND

What you need,
Gather it quickly.

MARY

This is betrayal at once
Of your word and sovereign.

MORTON

We know that.
    [*A pause*]

MARY

I need nothing.
I am a prisoner, Beaton.   Come after me
To Holyroodhouse. I may have my own rooms there,
    perhaps?

MAITLAND

Yes, Madame.

MARY

You show great courtesy. For a liar and traitor.
You lied to us, a black and level lie!
Blackest and craftiest! It was you we believed!

MORAY

Aye, sister. It was that we counted on.

MARY

Aye, brother.
    [MARY *turns from* MAITLAND *to* MORAY, *then walks*
    to the archway and goes out]

Curtain

ACT THREE

ACT THREE

SCENE: *A room in Carlisle Castle, in England. There are two windows at the right, both barred, a door at the rear and another, the hall-door, at the left. It is a prison room, but furnished scantily now for the queen's habitation. It is evening, but still light.*

MARY sits at one of the windows, leaning her head against the bars.

BEATON is leaning over a table where FLEMING has unrolled a map.

FLEMING

We came this way, through Cockermouth, and then took hired horses.

BEATON

If I had a thousand maps I couldna tell you how I came. Jamie's acquent wi' the drovers and all the back ways. Seton and Livingstone, poor things, they're pining away back in Edinburgh Town.

FLEMING

We might be as well off in Edinburgh ourselves, as it turns out. We'd looked forward to England for a free country, and strained toward it till our shoulders

165

ached, trying to help the boat through the water.
And here we are, and there's bars on the windows.

BEATON

But whose prisoners are we, Fleming?

FLEMING

I would I knew. It's been a month now, and all I can
tell you is we're prisoners, for we cannot leave.

BEATON

There's some mistake, Fleming.

FLEMING

Aye, if it was a mistake, like, would it last a month?
It's heartbreaking to escape one jailer and walk into
the arms of another.

MARY

When does the guard change, Fleming?

FLEMING

At ten, madame.

MARY

You're certain Jamie will come?

BEATON

Unless he's taken or dead, Your Majesty. He's true
as one can have in a lad.

MARY

But they may unmask him.

BEATON

It's true, they may.

FLEMING

Ye've more friends than a few in this castle, madame.
They'd let us know if summat went wrong.

MARY

What friends?

FLEMING

The two guards that go on for evening watch.

MARY

I fear they can't help much.

FLEMING

They can always bring us news.

BEATON

And you've more friends than that, Your Majesty.
Here and everywhere. As I came through the back
roads I heard talk of you everywhere. I think they
love their queen better now than before, now that
she's shut away unjustly.

MARY

Do you think so?

BEATON

From what I heard I'd say the lords had worked their
own ruin when they first betrayed you. If they could
hear the buzzing against them they'd sleep badly
there nights. And who rules Scotland now? Moray

has no right to it, and nobody can give him the right save your own self.

MARY

Aye, that's so. He'll come begging yet.

BEATON

And for what he'll never have.

MARY

They've taken my son from me, though. If I have friends I would they'd hurry.
[*She turns toward the window*]
God knows what Elizabeth means.

FLEMING

You'll hear from Bothwell tonight, madame, or hear of him. I'm certain of it.
[*A* WATCHMAN *calls outside*]

WATCHMAN

Ten o'clock, and all well. All well.

BEATON

Ten o'clock and still light.

FLEMING

The days grow longer and longer.

MARY

They've grown so long that each is the whole time between a birth and a death—and yet they go so fast, too, that I catch at them with my hand. So fast that I watch the evening light jealously, like a last candle burning. This is life, too, Beaton, here in this prison, and it goes from us quite as much as though we were free. We shall never see these same days again.

FLEMING

And little will I want to.

MARY

But suppose you were to spend all your life in prisons? Might not one grow to love even prison-days—as better than none?

BEATON

We shall have better, though. These are the worst we shall have, and I think the last of them.
   [*There is a rasping at the door*]
You hear?—the signal—
   [*There is a silence*]

FLEMING

Nay, not yet.
   [*Another pause*]

BEATON

It's ten, and more.

FLEMING

If we must wait again, then we must wait. He'll come at the latest, tomorrow.

MARY

   [*Rising and pacing near her window*]
But what could Elizabeth mean? What could she mean? She is my friend—over and over she writes

she is my friend, I am her dear cousin, her sister sovereign, that she suffers when I suffer, that she would confine me on no pretext if it were not to secure me against my own enemies! Enemies! What enemies have I in her kingdom? What right has she to imprison a sovereign who takes sanctuary in England?

FLEMING

Has anyone ever known Elizabeth's mind on any subject?

MARY

Writes, too, that she will come to see me, writes again to put it off, writes to say she cannot bear the week to pass without reassuring me of her good love.

BEATON

And yet I believe if all else fails Elizabeth will be found a friend and a good one at the end. If only for her own interest.

MARY

It may still be that she goes, in her own muddled and devious way, about the business of aiding me. It still may be.
   [*There is a rasping at the door again*]

BEATON

Yes?
   [*The door opens a crack, a chain clanging*]

JAMIE

   [*Outside*]
I may enter?

BEATON

Aye, come in.
[JAMIE *steps in, closing the door*]

JAMIE

[*Bonnet in hand*]
Your Majesty!

MARY

Good evening, Jamie.

JAMIE

Ye'll forgive me. I was not sure I could jouk in, for
the captain loitered about. However, the lad Mark
keeps a look-out, and warns me if there's footsteps.

BEATON

Was there a messenger through, Jamie?

JAMIE

Aye, I'll be quick, for I must, though a man hates to
be quick wi' ill news. There's been a messenger, true
enough, coming down wi' the drovers, as we cam'- -
and his tale is there was a battle at the Little Minch.
Ma'am, it went badly for Bothwell, if the man says
sooth, for he was defeated and taken.

MARY

Bothwell taken?

JAMIE

Aye, madame. Aye, but there's some good, too.
Kirkaldy of Grange has come over to Your Majesty's
side and makes his threats against Moray.

MARY

But Bothwell, Bothwell was taken? How?

JAMIE

That's the bare sum of it, madame. Just that he was prisoner to the lords. Only Kirkaldy has said Bothwell should be freed, and that he will see to it.

MARY

It's little comfort.

JAMIE

Aye, so I feared. Though Kirkaldy was their best general, and they'll miss him.

MARY

I could have used him once.

JAMIE

And now, if you'll pardon me, I must go. I had little liking to come—it's sore bad manners to leave folk wi' heavy hearts—

MARY

Nay, run no risk—only come again if there's any tidings.

JAMIE

Yes, Your Majesty, and I pray God they be better.
[*He turns*]

BEATON

Jamie.
[*There is a sharp rap at the door*]

JAMIE

Aye?
> [BEATON *goes up to him*]
Nay, lass, it's good just to see thee, but we'll not kiss
afore Her Majesty.
> [*The rap again*]
It's for me. Keep thee, and all here.
> [*He opens the door and goes out, closing it softly.
> The chain clanks. There is silence.*]

MARY

It's this that drives one mad, Beaton, to know
That on one certain day, at a certain hour,
If one had but chosen well, he'd have stood beside me
In a land all mine and his. Choosing wrong, I bring
> him
To fight a long war for me, and lose, bow his shoulders
To a castle keep.

FLEMING

They'll not hold him long.

MARY

And that's
To remember too. He's not a man to hold
Easily, no, nor hold at all. I've seen him
When they thought him trapped, and well caught.
> His face goes cold,
Stern, and morgue under his morion. While he lives
And I live, they'll not jail us two apart,
Nor keep our due from us. Aye, it's something to love,
Even late, even bitterly, where it's deserved. Kirk-
> aldy

Throws his weight on our side. There'll be others, too.
  Oh, Bothwell,
You've been my one hope! Bring me back to mind,
Now, as I bring you back!
    [*The chains of the door are undone, and the door
    opens. A* GUARD *steps in*]

GUARD

Your Majesty,
Lord Ruthven desires to see you.

MARY

Lord Ruthven's in Scotland.

GUARD

No, Madame, he's here.

MARY

Why, I will see Lord Ruthven.
Yes, let him come in.
    [*The door swings wider and* YOUNG RUTHVEN *en-
    ters. He bows*]
Sir, there've been days,
Not so far back when I'd have shifted somehow
To do without your face, or any visage
Among a certain congeries of lords
Of which you're one. Perhaps I'm tamed a trace
Sitting mewed at my window, for I'd accept
Any visitor from Scotland, bailiffs and hang-men
Not excluded, I'm that lonely.

RUTHVEN

Madame,
You hold against me much that was not my own.

I'm of a party, and one must swim or go down
With those of his interest.

MARY

Do you come now to see me
In your own person, then, or as representing
Those sharks you swam with last?

RUTHVEN

Why, Your Majesty,
It may be we're sharks. My mind's not made up. But
    I've come,
If you'll pardon me—and this is more truth, I think,
Than I'm supposed to say—because the lords
Who now hold Scotland had more hope you'd see me
Than any the others.

MARY

That's frank.

RUTHVEN

And I lend myself
To the embassy because, as things drift at home,
We verge on the rocks there. You are still queen of
    Scotland,
Yet you don't rule, and can't rule, being here,
A prisoner—and the upshot is we're not ruled.
There's anarchy in the air. It's necessary
That some approach be made between you and your
    brother
Before there's anarchy in the streets.

BEATON

We were saying
That he'd come begging.

MARY

What does my brother ask—
This good brother of mine?

RUTHVEN

That goes beyond
My mission. To be frank still, I'm sent before
To ask whether you will see him.

MARY

Let him ask my jailers
Whether I may be seen.

RUTHVEN

He has asked already, madame.
The request is granted.

MARY

Lord Moray is with you?

RUTHVEN

He is waiting.

MARY

Why, this is an honor. And others too, no doubt?
A shoal of them?

RUTHVEN

Madame, as you have supposed
They are all here.

MARY

It will please me vastly to view them,
If only to know from them who gave permission
To see me. For I swear, I guess not so far
Whose prisoner I am, or who keeps my jail. I've
     moithered
Over this a good deal.

RUTHVEN

I may call them?

MARY

If you'll be so good.
     [RUTHVEN *bows and goes out past the* GUARD]
Is it you, sir, who chain my door
So assiduously at night?

GUARD

No, madame, the turn-key
Goes the rounds at twelve.

MARY

Will you ask him, then.
To make a thought less jangling if he can?
We try to sleep, you see, and these chimes at mid-
     night
Are not conducive to slumber.

GUARD

He shall be told;
I'm very sorry, Your Majesty.

MARY

Thank you.
> [MORTON *and* MORAY *come in, and behind them*
> MAITLAND *and* DOUGLAS. RUTHVEN *re-enters with*
> THROGMORTON]

Gentlemen,
I greet you. You are all here, I see, the whole
Blood-thirsty race. But we lack John Knox. Now,
> surely,
John Knox should be with you.

MORAY

Have your jest, my sister. For us
We're not here for jesting.

MARY

Oh, I'd have sworn you weren't.
You're no harbinger of merriment, my brother,
Nor of good fortune. The corbies from the wood
Presage more of that. And here's the Lord Throgmor-
> ton
Presses in among you! It should be a good day
When I'm crossed by this constellation!

THROGMORTON

We pray it will,
Your Majesty, and that things may be ironed out
> clean
That have grieved us all.

MARY

Oh, do you know of grief,
You who may take your meals in your own wide halls

And walk in the rainy air? I had thought that griev-
ing
Was something found behind bars.

MAITLAND
This has lasted too long,
This imprisonment, Your Majesty, and was never
To any purpose. We come to offer you
Release, and speedily.

MARY
The diplomat always, Maitland.
Always the secret thought glancing behind
The quick-silver tongue. You come to ask for much
And give little for it, as ever.

MORAY
We come to ask
For what we have.

MARY
There, now it's brutally said,
In my brother's plain-Scotch way, spoken plainly out
of
His plain Scotch face. He comes to ask, he says,
For what he has, and he makes no doubt he'll get it.
What is it you have, dear brother, and if you have it
Why ask for it?

MAITLAND
Will Your Majesty give me leave
To rehearse a brief history that may weary you
Since you know it?

MARY

It will weary me, but go on.

MAITLAND

Forgive me: Your Majesty broke from prison in
    Scotland
And fled to England. This action was tantamount
To abandoning your throne.

MARY

Indeed it was not.
I came here for aid against you.

MAITLAND

We will pass that point.

MARY

Do. There's nothing gives me more pleasure, Lord
    Maitland,
Than passing a point.

MAITLAND

Then am I delighted to render
Your Majesty pleasure. Your wit is sharper than
    mine.
But to proceed: You were taken prisoner in England
    —

MARY

By whom, Lord Maitland—will you tell me that?
Who holds me here?

MAITLAND

That I'm not free to answer.
It remains that you're a prisoner, and that your
    realm
Is governed only by makeshift. Your son, the prince
    James—

MARY

Aye, what of him? My lords, I beg of you,
Whatever you must do, or think you must do,
To secure yourselves, he's but a babe, remember.
I can stand up and fight you for myself,
But use my child more kindly.

MAITLAND

The prince James,
Is well, and well cared for, and will be. The succession
Depends on him. We plan to make him king.
Your absence makes this necessary.

MARY

My absence
Is not permanent, I hope. I am queen of Scotland
And have not abdicated, nor do I intend
To abdicate.

MORTON

Will you tell us what you think
To find, should you return?

MARY

If I return
As I intend, I shall not find you there,
Lord Morton, if you're wise. The country's fickle.

For you, as it was for me. Now they've pushed their
    queen
Aside, they begin to wonder if they were not wrong.
And wonder too if they profit by the exchange,
And give you side-long looks.

MAITLAND

If it's still in your mind
That you might win your throne back, ponder on
    this:
The lord of the isles has given you up, the north
Is solidly with us, Bothwell has broken faith—

MARY

Aye?

MAITLAND

For the good of the kingdom, to secure your son
His right to the throne, we ask you tonight to sign
Your abdication, let us take it back with us.

MARY

Yes,
But I catch you in two lies. Kirkaldy of Grange
Has come over to me; you have taken Bothwell
    prisoner,
But before he fights on your side you'll rot in the
    damp
Under Edinburgh castle, and he'll see you do it!

MAITLAND

Madame,
You've been misinformed.

MARY

I've been lied to and by you
Specifically! Let me rehearse for you
A history you may recall, you that stand before me:
It was you killed Rizzio, and made capital of it
To throw discredit on me. It was you
Killed Darnley, and then threw the weight of that
On Bothwell, saying through John Knox that I lived
With my husband's murderer. It was you that prom-
ised
To give me fealty if Bothwell and I were parted,
And then cast me into prison! I escaped,
As the truth will escape about you, and when it's
known   :
My people will drive you out. What you ask of me
I refuse it, finally! I will not abdicate,
Not to this off-scum that's boiled up around
My throne to dirty me! Not now and not ever!
  [*The Lords are silent for a moment, and then*
  MORAY *nods an assent to* MAITLAND]

MAITLAND

Your Majesty, you asked me a moment since
Who held you prisoner here. I cannot answer
Still, but say there's another and higher judge
Must pass on these charges of yours.

MARY

Nay, I know that.

MAITLAND

Oh, an earthly judge, Your Majesty, and yet
High enough, I think. We wish you goodnight.

MARY

Goodnight.

> [*The Lords go out.* MARY *stands unmoving, watching the door. After a pause the* GUARD *pushes the door back and withdraws.* ELIZABETH *comes to the doorway.* MARY *looks at her questioningly*]

I have seen but a poor likeness, and yet I believe
This is Elizabeth.

ELIZABETH

I am Elizabeth.
May we be alone together?

> [*At a sign from* MARY *the* MAIDS *go out the rear door.* ELIZABETH *enters and the hall-door swings to behind her*]

MARY

I had hoped to see you.
When last you wrote you were not sure.

ELIZABETH

If I've come
So doubtfully and tardigrade, my dear,
And break thus in upon you, it's not for lack
Of thinking of you. Rather because I've thought
Too long, perhaps, and carefully. Then at last
It seemed if I saw you near, and we talked as sisters
Over these poor realms of ours, some light might
   break
That we'd never see apart.

MARY

Have I been so much
A problem?

ELIZABETH

Have you not? When the winds blow down
The houses, and there's a running and arming of men,
And a great cry of praise and blame, and the center
Of all this storm's a queen, she beautiful—
As I see you are—

MARY

Nay—

ELIZABETH

Aye, with the Stuart mouth
And the high forehead and French ways and
    thoughts—
Well, we must look to it.—Not since that Helen
We read of in dead Troy, has a woman's face
Stirred such a confluence of air and waters
To beat against the bastions. I'd thought you taller,
But truly, since that Helen, I think there's been
No queen so fair to look on.

MARY

You flatter me.

ELIZABETH

It's more likely envy. You see this line
Drawn down between my brows? No wash or oint-
    ments
Nor wearing of straight plasters in the night

Will take that line away. Yet I'm not much older
Than you, and had looks, too, once.

MARY

I had wished myself
For a more regal beauty such as yours,
More fitting for a queen.

ELIZABETH

Were there not two verses
In a play I remember:
> Brightness falls from the air;
> Queens have died young and fair—?
They must die young if they'd die fair, my cousin,
Brightness falls from them, but not from you yet;
    believe me,
It's envy, not flattery.

MARY

Can it be—as I've hoped—
Can it be that you come to me as a friend—
Meaning me well?

ELIZABETH

Would you have me an enemy?

MARY

I have plenty to choose among as enemies—
And sometimes, as your word reached out to me
Through embassies, entangled with men's tongues,
It has seemed you judged me harshly, even denying
My right to a place beside you. But now you are here,
And a woman like myself, fearing as I do,

With the little dark fears of a woman, the creeping of
    age
On a young face, I see truer—I think I see truer,
And that this may be someone to whom I can reach a
    hand
And feel a clasp, and trust it. A woman's hand,
Stronger than mine in this hour, willing to help.
If that were so—

ELIZABETH

Aye.

MARY

Of, if that were so,
I have great power to love! Let them buzz forever
Between us, these men with messages and lies,
You'll find me still there, and smiling, and open-
    hearted,
Unchanging while the cusped hills wear down!

ELIZABETH

    [*Smiling*]
Nay, pledge
Not too much, my dear, for in these uncertain times
It's slippery going for all of us. I, who seem now
So firm in my footing, well I know one mis-step
Could make me a most unchancy friend. If you'd
    keep
Your place on this rolling ball, let the mountains slide
And slip to the valleys. Put no hand to them
Or they'll pull you after.

MARY

But does this mean you can lend
No hand to me, or I'll pull you down?

ELIZABETH

I say it
Recalling how I came to my throne as you did,
Some five or six years before, beset as you were
With angry factions—and came there young, loving
    truth,
As you did. This was many centuries since,
Or seems so to me, I'm so old by now
In shuffling tricks and the huckstering of souls
For lands and pensions. I learned to play it young,
Must learn it or die.—It's thus if you would rule;
Give up good faith, the word that goes with the
    heart,
The heart that clings where it loves. Give these up,
    and love
Where your interest lies, and should your interest
    change
Let your love follow it quickly. This is queen's por-
    ridge,
And however little stomach she has for it
A queen must eat it.

MARY

I, too, Elizabeth,
Have read my Machiavelli. His is a text-book
Much studied in the French court. Are you serious
To rede me this lesson?

ELIZABETH

You have too loving a heart,
I fear, and too bright a face to be a queen.

MARY

That's not what's charged against me. When I've lost
So far it's been because my people believed
I was more crafty than I am. I've been
Traduced as a murderess and adulteress
And nothing I could have said, and nothing done
Would have warded the blow. What I seek now is
    only
My freedom, so that I may return and prove
In open court, and before my witnesses,
That I am guiltless. You are the queen of England,
And I am held prisoner in England. Why am I held,
And who is it holds me?

ELIZABETH

It was to my interest, child,
To protect you, lest violence be offered to a princess
And set a precedent. Is there anyone in England
Who could hold you against my will?

MARY

Then I ask as a sovereign,
Speaking to you as an equal, that I be allowed
To go, and fight my own battles.

ELIZABETH

It would be madness.

MARY

May I not judge of that?

ELIZABETH

See, here is our love!

MARY

If you wish my love and good-will you shall have it
   freely
When I am free.

ELIZABETH

You will never govern, Mary. If I let you go
There will be long broils again in Scotland, dangers,
And ripe ones, to my peace at home. To be fair
To my own people, this must not be.

MARY

Now speak once
What your will is, and what behind it! You wish me
   here,
You wish me in prison—have we come to that?

ELIZABETH

It's safer.

MARY

Who do you wish to rule in Scotland,
If not my Stuart line?

ELIZABETH

Have I said, my dear,
That I'd bar the Stuarts from Scotland, or bar your
   reign
If you were there, and reigned there? I say only
You went the left way about it, and since it's so

And has fallen out so, it were better for both our
   kingdoms
If you remained my guest.

MARY

For how long?

ELIZABETH

Until
The world is quieter.

MARY

And who will rule in my place?

ELIZABETH

Why, who rules now? Your brother.

MARY

He rules by stealth—

ELIZABETH

But all this could be arranged,
Or so I'm told, if your son were to be crowned king,
And Moray made regent.

MARY

My son in Moray's hands—
Moray in power—

ELIZABETH

Is there any other way?
   [*A pause*]

MARY

Elizabeth—I have been here a long while
Already—it seems so. If it's your policy

To keep me—shut me up—. I can argue no more—
No—I beg now. There's one I love in the north,
You know that—and my life's there, my throne's
    there, my name
To be defended—and I must lie here darkened
From news and from the sun—lie here impaled
On a brain's agony—wondering even sometimes
If I were what they said me—a carrion-thing
In my desires—can you understand this?—I speak it
Too brokenly to be understood, but I beg you
As you are a woman and I am—and our brightness
    falls
Soon enough at best—let me go, let me have my life
Once more—and my dear health of mind again—
For I rot away here in my mind—in what
I think of myself—some death-tinge falls over one
In prisons—

ELIZABETH

It will grow worse, not better. I've known
Strong men shut up alone for years—it's not
Their hair turns white only; they sicken within
And scourge themselves. If you would think like a
    queen
This is no place for you. The brain taints here
Till all desires are alike. Be advised and sign
The abdication.

MARY

Stay now a moment. I begin to glimpse
Behind this basilisk mask of yours. It was this
You've wanted from the first.

ELIZABETH

This that I wanted?

MARY

It was you sent Lord Throgmorton long ago
When first I'd have married Bothwell. All this while
Some evil's touched my life at every turn.
To cripple what I'd do. And now—why now—
Looking on you—I see it incarnate before me—
It was your hand that touched me. Reaching out
In little ways—here a word, there an action—this
Was what you wanted. I thought perhaps a star—
Wildly I thought it—perhaps a star might ride
Astray—or a crone that burned an image down
In wax—filling the air with curses on me
And slander; the murder of Rizzio, Moray in that
And you behind Moray—the murder of Darnley,
    Throgmorton
Behind that too, you with them—and that winged
    scandal
You threw at us when we were married. Proof I have
    none
But I've felt it—would know it anywhere—in your
    eyes—
There—before me.

ELIZABETH

What may become a queen
Is to rule her kingdom. Had you ruled yours I'd say
She has her ways, I mine. Live and let live
And a merry world for those who have it. But now

I must think this over—sadness has touched your
    brain.
I'm no witch to charm you, make no incantations;
You came here by your own road.

MARY

I see how I came.
Back, back, each step the wrong way, and each sign
    followed
As you'd have me go, till the skein picks up and we
    stand
Face to face here. It was you forced Bothwell from
    me—
You there, and always. Oh, I'm to blame in this, too!
I should have seen your hand!

ELIZABETH

It has not been my use
To speak much or spend my time—

MARY

How could I have been
Mistaken in you for an instant?

ELIZABETH

You were not mistaken.
I am all women I must be. One's a young girl,
Young and harrowed as you are—one who could
    weep
To see you here—and one's a bitterness
At what I have lost and can never have, and one's
The basilisk you saw. This last stands guard
And I obey it. Lady, you came to Scotland

A fixed and subtle enemy, more dangerous
To me than you've ever known. This could not be
  borne,
And I set myself to cull you out and down,
And down you are.

MARY

When was I your enemy?

ELIZABETH

Your life was a threat to mine, your throne to my
  throne,
Your policy a threat.

MARY

How? Why?

ELIZABETH

It was you
Or I. Do you know that? The one of us must win
And I must always win. Suppose one lad
With a knife in his hand, a Romish lad who planted
That knife between my shoulders—my kingdom was
  yours.
It was too easy. You might not have wished it.
But you'd take it if it came.

MARY

And you'd take my life
And love to avoid this threat?

ELIZABETH

Nay, keep your life.
And your love, too. The lords have brought a parch-
  ment
For you to sign. Sign it and live.

MARY

If I sign it
Do I live where I please? Go free?

ELIZABETH

Nay, I would you might,
But you'd go to Bothwell, and between you two
You might be too much for Moray. You'll live with
    me
In London. There are other loves, my dear.
You'll find amusement there in the court. I assure
    you
It's better than a cell.

MARY

And if I will not sign
This abdication?

ELIZABETH

You've tasted prison. Try
A diet of it.

MARY

And so I will.

ELIZABETH

I can wait.

MARY

And I can wait. I can better wait than you.
Bothwell will fight free again. Kirkaldy
Will fight beside him, and others will spring up
From these dragon's teeth you've sown. Each week
    that passes
I'll be stronger, and Moray weaker.

ELIZABETH

And do you fancy
They'll rescue you from an English prison? Why,
Let them try it.

MARY

Even that they may do. I wait for Bothwell—
And wait for him here.

ELIZABETH

Where you will wait, bear in mind,
Is for me to say. Give up Bothwell, give up your
    throne
If you'd have a life worth living.

MARY

I will not.

ELIZABETH

I can wait.

MARY

And will not because you play to lose. This trespass
Against God's right will be known. The nations will
    know it,
Mine and yours. They will see you as I see you
And pull you down.

ELIZABETH

Child, child, I've studied this gambit
Before I play it. I will send each year
This paper to you. Not signing, you will step
From one cell to another, step lower always,

Till you reach the last, forgotten, forgotten of men,
Forgotten among causes, a wraith that cries
To fallen gods in another generation
That's lost your name. Wait then for Bothwell's
   rescue.
It will never come.

MARY

I may never see him?

ELIZABETH

Never.
It would not be wise.

MARY

And suppose indeed you won
Within our life-time, still looking down from the
   heavens
And up from men around us, God's spies that watch
The fall of great and little, they will find you out—
I will wait for that, wait longer than a life,
Till men and the times unscroll you, study the tricks
You play, and laugh, as I shall laugh, being known
Your better, haunted by your demon, driven
To death or exile by you, unjustly. Why,
When all's done, it's my name I care for, my name
   and heart,
To keep them clean. Win now, take your triumph
   now,
For I'll win men's hearts in the end—though the
   sifting takes
This hundred years—or a thousand.

ELIZABETH

Child, child, are you gulled
By what men write in histories, this or that,
And never true? I am careful of my name
As you are, for this day and longer. It's not what hap-
    pens
That matters, no, not even what happens that's
    true,
But what men believe to have happened. They will
    believe
The worst of you, the best of me, and that
Will be true of you and me. I have seen to this.
What will be said about us in after-years
By men to come, I control that, being who I am.
It will be said of me that I governed well,
And wisely, but of you, cousin, that your life,
Shot through will ill-loves, battened on lechery, made
    you
An ensign of evil, that men tore down and trampled.
Shall I call for the lord's parchment?

MARY

This will be said—?
But who will say it? It's a lie—will be known as a lie!

ELIZABETH

You lived with Bothwell before Darnley died,
You and Bothwell murdered Darnley.

MARY

And that's a lie!

ELIZABETH

Your letters, my dear. Your letters to Bothwell prove
    it.
We have those letters.

MARY

Then they're forged and false!
For I never wrote them!

ELIZABETH

It may be they were forged.
But will that matter, Mary, if they're believed?
All history is forged.

MARY

You would do this?

ELIZABETH

It is already done.

MARY

And still I win.
A demon has no children, and you have none,
Will have none, can have none, perhaps. This crooked
    track
You've drawn me on, cover it, let it not be believed
That a woman was a fiend. Yes, cover it deep,
And heap my infamy over it, lest men peer
And catch sight of you as you were and are. In myself
I know you to be an eater of dust. Leave me here
And set me lower this year by year, as you promise,

Till the last is an oubliette, and my name inscribed
On the four winds. Still, STILL I win! I have been
A woman, and I have loved as a woman loves,
Lost as a woman loses. I have borne a son,
And he will rule Scotland—and England. You have
    no heir!
A devil has no children.

ELIZABETH

By God, you shall suffer
For this, but slowly.

MARY

And that I can do. A woman
Can do that. Come, turn the key. I have a hell
For you in mind, where you will burn and feel it,
Live where you like, and softly.

ELIZABETH

Once more I ask you,
And patiently. Give up your throne.

MARY

No, devil.
My pride is stronger than yours, and my heart beats
    blood
Such as yours has never known. And in this dungeon,
I win here, alone.

ELIZABETH

    [*Turning*]
Goodnight, then.

MARY

Aye, goodnight.

[ELIZABETH *goes to the door, which opens before her. She goes out slowly. As the door begins to close upon her* MARY *calls*]

Beaton!

ELIZABETH

[*Turning*]

You will not see your maids again,
I think. It's said they bring you news from the north.

MARY

I thank you for all kindness.

[ELIZABETH *goes out.* MARY *stands for a moment in thought, then walks to the wall and lays her hand against the stone, pushing outward. The stone is cold, and she shudders. Going to the window she sits again in her old place and looks out into the darkness*]

Curtain

PAPAGO WEDDING
A Story

BY MARY AUSTIN

THERE was a Papago woman out of Panták who had a
marriage paper from a white man after she had borne
him five children, and the man himself was in love with another woman. This Shuler was the first to raise cotton for
selling in the Gila Valley—but the Pimas and Papagoes had
raised it long before that—and the girl went with him will-
ingly. As to the writing of marriage, it was not then understood that the white man is not master of his heart, but is
mastered by it, so that if it is not fixed in writing it becomes
unstable like water and is puddled in the lowest place. The
Sisters at San Xavier del Bac had taught her to clean and
cook. Shuler called her Susie, which was nearest to her
Papago name, and was fond of the children. He sent them
to school as they came along, and had carpets in the house.

In all things Susie was a good wife to him, though she had
no writing of marriage and she never wore a hat. This was
a mistake which she learned from the sisters. They, being
holy women, had no notion of the *brujeria* which is worked in
the heart of the white man by a hat. Into the presence of
their God also, without that which passes for a hat, they do
not go. Even after her children were old enough to notice
it, Susie went about the country with a handkerchief tied
over her hair, which was long and smooth on either side of her
face, like the shut wings of a raven.

By the time Susie's children were as tall as their mother,
there were many white ranchers in the Gila country, with their
white wives, who are like Papago women in this, that if they
see a man upstanding and prosperous, they think only that he
might make some woman happy, and if they have a cousin

377

or a friend, that she should be the woman. Also the white ones think it so shameful for a man to take a woman to his house without a writing that they have no scruple to take him away from her.   At Rinconada there was a woman with large breasts, surpassing well looking, and with many hats. She had no husband and was new to the country, and when Shuler drove her about to look at it, she wore each time a different hat.

This the Papagoes observed, and, not having visited Susie when she was happy with her man, they went now in numbers, and by this Susie understood that it was in their hearts that she might have need of them.   For it was well known that the white woman had told Shuler that it was a shame for him to have his children going about with a Papago woman who had only a handkerchief to cover her head.   She said it was keeping Shuler back from being the principal man among the cotton growers of Gila Valley, to have in his house a woman who would come there without a writing.   And when the other white women heard that she had said that, they said the same thing.   Shuler said, "My God, this is the truth, I know it," and the woman said that she would go to Susie and tell her that she ought to go back to her own people and not be a shame to her children and Shuler.   There was a man from Panták on the road, who saw them go, and turned in his tracks and went back, in case Susie should need him, for the Papagoes, when it is their kin against whom there is *brujeria* made, have in-knowing hearts.   Susie sat in the best room with the woman and was polite.   "If you want Shuler," she said, "you can have him, but I stay with my children."   The white woman grew red in the face and went out to Shuler in the field where he was pretending to look after something, and they went away together.

After that Shuler would not go to the ranch except of necessity.   He went around talking to his white friends.   "My God," he kept saying, "what can I do, with my children in the hands of that Papago?"   Then he sent a lawyer to Susie to say that if she would go away and not shame his children with a mother who had no marriage writing and no hat, he would give her money, so much every month.   But the children all came in the room and stood by her, and Susie said, "What I want with money when I got my children and this good ranch?" Then Shuler said "My God!" again, and "What can I do?"

The lawyer said he could tell the Judge that Susie was not a proper person to have care of his children, and the Judge would take them away from Susie and give them to Shuler. But when the day came for Susie to come into court, it was seen that though she had a handkerchief on her hair, her dress was good, and the fringe of her shawl was long and fine. All the five children came also, with new clothes, well looking. "My God!" said Shuler, "I must get those kids away from that Papago and into the hands of a white woman." But the white people who had come to see the children taken away saw that although the five looked like Shuler, they had their mouths shut like Papagoes; so they waited to see how things turned out.

Shuler's lawyer makes a long speech about how Shuler loves his children, and how sorry he is in his heart to see them growing up like Papagoes, and water is coming out of Shuler's eyes. Then the Judge asks Susie if she has anything to say why her children shall not be taken away.

"You want to take these children away and giff them to Shuler?" Susie asks him. "What for you giff them to Shuler?" says Susie, and the white people are listening. She says, "Shuler's not the father of them. Thees children all got different fathers," says Susie. "Shuler——"

Then she makes a sign with her hand. I tell you if a woman makes that sign to a Papago he could laugh himself dead but he would not laugh off that. Some of the white people who have been in the country a long time know that sign and they begin to laugh.

Shuler's lawyer jumps up. . . . "Your Honour, I Object——"

The Judge waves his hand. "I warn you the Court cannot go behind the testimony of the mother in such a case. . . ."

By this time everybody is laughing, so that they do not hear what the lawyer says. Shuler is trying to get out of the side door, and the Judge is shaking hands with Susie.

"You tell Shuler," she says, "if he wants people to think hees the father of thees children he better giff me a writing. Then maybe I think so myself."

"I *will*," said the Judge, and maybe two, three days after that he takes Shuler out to the ranch and makes the marriage writing. Then all the children come around Susie and say, "Now, Mother, you will have to wear a hat." Susie, she says, "Go, children, and ask your father." But it is not known to the Papagoes what happened after that.

THE KILLER
A Short Novel

BY STEWART EDWARD WHITE

THE KILLER

CHAPTER I

I want to state right at the start that I am writing this story twenty years after it happened solely because my wife and Señor Buck Johnson insist on it. Myself, I don't think it a good yarn. It hasn't any love story in it; and there isn't any plot. Things just happened, one thing after the other. There ought to be a yarn in it somehow, and I suppose if a fellow wanted to lie a little he could make a tail-twister out of it. Anyway, here goes; and if you don't like it, you know you can quit at any stage of the game.

It happened when I was a kid and didn't know any better than to do such things. They dared me to go up to Hooper's ranch and stay all night; and as I had no information on either the ranch or its owner, I saddled up and went. It was only twelve miles from our Box Springs ranch—a nice easy ride. I should explain that heretofore I had ridden the Gila end of our range, which is so far away that only vague rumours of Hooper had ever reached me at all. He was reputed a tough old devil with horrid habits; but that meant little to me. The tougher and horrider they came, the better they suited me—so I thought. Just to make everything entirely clear I will add that this was in the year of 1897 and the Soda Springs valley in Arizona.

By these two facts you old timers will gather the setting of my tale. Indian days over; "nester" days with frame houses and vegetable patches not yet here. Still a few guns packed for business purposes; Mexican border handy; no railroad in to Tombstone yet; cattle rustlers lingering in the Galiuros; train hold-ups and homicide yet prevalent but frowned upon; favourite tipple whiskey toddy with sugar; but the old fortified ranches all gone; longhorns crowded out by shorthorn blaze-head Herefords or near-Herefords; some indignation against Alfred Henry Lewis's *Wolfville* as a base libel; and, also but, no gasoline wagons or pumps, no white collars, no tourists pervading the desert, and the Injins still wearing blankets and overalls at their reservations instead of bead work on the railway platforms when the Overland goes through. In other words, we were wild and wooly, but sincerely didn't know it.

While I was saddling up to go take my dare, old Jed Parker came and leaned himself up against the snubbing post of the corral. He watched me for a while, and I kept quiet, knowing well enough that he had something to say.

"Know Hooper?" he asked.

"I've seen him driving by," said I.

I had: a little humped, insignificant figure with close-cropped white hair beneath a huge hat. He drove all hunched up. His buckboard was a rattletrap, old, insulting challenge to every little stone in the road; but there was nothing the matter with the horses or their harness. We never held much with grooming in Arizona, but these beasts shone like bronze. Good sizeable horses, clean built—well, I better not get started talking horse! They're the reason I had never really sized up the old man the few times I'd passed him.

"Well, he's a tough bird," said Jed.

"Looks like a harmless old cuss—but mean," says I.

"About this trip," said Jed, after I'd saddled and coiled my rope—"don't, and say you did."

I didn't answer this, but led my horse to the gate.

"Well, don't say as how I didn't tell you all about it," said Jed, going back to the bunk house.

Miserable old coot! I suppose he thought he *had* told me all about it! Jed was always too loquacious!

But I hadn't racked along more than two miles before a man cantered up who was perfectly able to express himself. He was one of our outfit and was known as Windy Bill. Nuff said!

"Hear you're goin' up to stay the night at Hooper's," said he. "Know Hooper?"

"No, I don't," said I, "are you another of these Sunbirds with glad news?"

"Know about Hooper's boomerang?"

"Boomerang!" I replied, "what's that?"

"That's what they call it. You know how of course we all let each other's strays water at our troughs in this country, and send 'em back to their own range at round up."

"Brother, you interest me," said I, "and would you mind informing me further how you tell the dear little cows apart?"

"Well, old Hooper don't, that's all," went on Windy, without paying me any attention. "He built him a chute leading to the water corrals, and half way down the chute he built a gate that would swing across it and open a hole into a dry corral. And he had a high platform with a handle that ran the gate. When any cattle but those of his own brands came along, he had a man swing the gate and they landed up into the dry corral. By and by he let them out on the range again."

"Without water?"

"Sure! And of course back they came into the chute. And so on. Till they died, or we came along and drove them back home."

"Windy," said I, "you're stuffing me full of tacks."

"I've seen little calves lyin' in heaps against the fence like drifts of tumbleweed," said Windy, soberly; and then added, without apparent passion, "The old——!"

Looking at Windy's face, I knew these words for truth.

"He's a bad *hombre*," resumed Windy Bill after a moment. "He never does no actual killing himself, but he's got a bad lot of oilers* there, especially an old one named Andreas and another one called Ramon, and all he has to do is to lift one eye at a man he don't like and that man is as good as dead—one time or another."

This was going it pretty strong, and I grinned at Windy Bill.

"All right," said Windy, "I'm just telling you."

"Well, what's the matter with you fellows down here?" I challenged. "How is it he's lasted so long? Why hasn't someone shot him? Are you all afraid of him or his Mexicans?"

"No, it ain't that, exactly. I don't know. He drives by

*Oiler = Greaser = Mexican.

all alone, and he don't pack no gun ever, and he's sort of runty—and—I do'no *why* he ain't been shot, but he ain't. And if I was you, I'd stick home."

Windy amused but did not greatly persuade me. By this time I was fairly conversant with the cowboy's sense of humour. Nothing would have tickled them more than to bluff me out of a harmless excursion by means of scareful tales. Shortly Windy Bill turned off to examine a distant bunch of cattle; and so I rode on alone.

It was coming on toward evening. Against the eastern mountains were floating tinted mists; and the cañons were a deep purple. The cattle were moving slowly so that here and there a nimbus of dust caught and reflected the late sunlight into gamboge yellows and mauves. The magic time was near when the fierce, implacable day-genius of the desert would fall asleep and the soft, gentle, beautiful star-eyed night-genius of the desert would arise and move softly. My pony racked along in the desert. The mass that represented Hooper's ranch drew imperceptibly nearer. I made out the green of trees and the white of walls and building.

CHAPTER II

Hooper's ranch proved to be entirely enclosed by a wall of adobe ten feet high and whitewashed. To the outside it presented a blank face. Only corrals and an alfalfa patch were not included. A wide, high gateway, that could be closed by massive doors, let into a stable yard, and seemed to be the only entrance. The buildings within were all immaculate also: evidently Old Man Hooper loved whitewash. Cottonwood trees showed their green heads; and to the right I saw the sloped shingled roof of a larger building. Not a living creature was in sight. I shook myself, saying that the undoubted sinister feeling of utter silence and lifelessness was compounded of my expectations and the time of day. But that did not satisfy me. My aroused mind, casting about, soon struck it: I was missing the swarms of blackbirds, linnets, purple finches, and doves that made our own ranch trees vocal. Here were no birds. Laughing at this simple explanation of my eerie feeling, I passed under the gate and entered the courtyard.

It, too, seemed empty. A stable occupied all one side; the other three were formed by bunk houses and necessary out-buildings. Here, too, dwelt absolute solitude and absolute silence. It was uncanny, as though one walked in a vacuum. Everything was neat and shut up and whitewashed and apparently dead. There were no sounds or signs of occu-

8

pancy. I was as much alone as though I had been in the middle of an ocean. My mind, by now abnormally sensitive and alert, leaped on this idea. For the same reason, it insisted—lack of life: there were no birds here, not even *flies!* Of course, said I, gone to bed in the cool of evening: why should there be? I laughed aloud and hushed suddenly; and then nearly jumped out of my skin. The thin blue curl of smoke had caught my eye; and I became aware of the figure of a man seated on the ground, in the shadow, leaning against the building. The curl of smoke was from his cigarette. He was wrapped in a *serape* which blended well with the cool colour of shadow. My eyes were dazzled with the whitewash—natural enough—yet the impression of solitude had been so complete. It was uncanny, as though he had materialized out of the shadow itself. Silly idea! I ranged my eye along the row of houses, and I saw three other figures I had missed before, all broodingly immobile, all merged in shadow, all watching me, all with the insubstantial air of having as I looked taken body from thin air.

This was too foolish! I dismounted, dropped my horse's reins over his head, and sauntered to the nearest figure. He was lost in the dusk of the building and of his Mexican hat. I saw only the gleam of eyes.

"Where will I find Mr. Hooper?" I asked.

The figure waved a long, slim hand toward a wicket gate in one side of the enclosure. He said no word, nor made another motion; and the other figures sat as though graved from stone.

After a moment's hesitation I pushed open the wicket

gate, and so found myself in a smaller intimate courtyard of most surprising character. Its centre was green grass, and about its border grew tall, bright flowers. A wide verandah ran about three sides. I could see that in the numerous windows hung white lace curtains. Mind you, this was in Arizona of the 'nineties!

I knocked at the nearest door, and after an interval it opened and I stood face to face with Old Man Hooper himself.

He proved to be as small as I had thought, not taller than my own shoulder, with a bent little figure dressed in wrinkled and baggy store clothes of a snuff brown. His bullet head had been cropped so that his hair stood up like a short-bristled white brush. His rather round face was brown and lined. His hands, which grasped the doorposts uncompromisingly to bar the way, were lean and veined and old. But all that I found in my recollections afterward to be utterly unimportant. His eyes were his predominant, his formidable, his compelling characteristic. They were round, the pupils very small, the irises large and of a light flecked blue. From the pupils radiated fine lines. The blank, cold, inscrutable stare of them bored me through to the back of the neck. I suppose the man winked occasionally, but I never got that impression. I've noticed that owls have this same intent, unwinking stare—and wildcats.

"Mr. Hooper," said I, "can you keep me over night?"

It was a usual request in the old cattle country. He continued to stare at me for some moments.

"Where are you from?" he asked at length. His voice was soft and low; rather purring.

I mentioned our headquarters on the Gila: it did not seem worth while to say anything about Box Springs only a dozen miles away. He stared at me for some time more. "Come in," he said, abruptly; and stood aside.

This was a disconcerting surprise. All I had expected was permission to stop, and a direction as to how to find the bunk house. Then a more or less dull evening, and a return the following day to collect on my "dare." I stepped into the dimness of the hallway; and immediately after into a room beyond.

Again I must remind you that this was the Arizona of the 'nineties. All the ranch houses with which I was acquainted, and I knew about all of them, were very crudely done. They comprised generally a half dozen rooms with adobe walls and rough board floors, with only such furnishings as deal tables, benches, homemade chairs, perhaps a battered old washstand or so, and bunks filled with straw. We had no such things as tablecloths and sheets, of course. Everything was on a like scale of simple utility.

All right, get that in your mind. The interior into which I now stepped, with my clanking spurs, my rattling *chaps*, the dust of my sweat-stained garments, was a low-ceilinged, dim abode with faint, musty aromas. Carpets covered the floors; an old-fashioned hat rack flanked the door on one side, a tall clock on the other. I saw in passing framed steel engravings. The room beyond contained easy chairs, a sofa upholstered with hair cloth, an upright piano, a marble fireplace with a mantel, in a corner a triangular what-not filled with objects. It, too, was dim and curtained and faintly aromatic as had been the house of an old maiden aunt of my childhood, who used to give me cookies on the Sabbath. I felt now too large, and too noisy, and altogether mis-dressed and blundering and dirty. The little old man moved without a sound, and the grandfather's clock outside ticked deliberately in a hollow silence.

I sat down, rather gingerly, in the chair he indicated for me.

"I shall be very glad to offer you hospitality for the night," he said, as though there had been no interim. "I feel honoured at the opportunity."

I murmured my thanks, and a suggestion that I should look after my horse.

"Your horse, sir, has been attended to, and your *cantinas** are undoubtedly by now in your room, where, I am sure, you are anxious to repair."

He gave no signal, nor uttered any command, but at his last words a grave, elderly Mexican appeared noiselessly at my elbow. As a matter of fact, he came through an un-noticed door at the back, but he might as well have material-ized from the thin air for the start that he gave me. Hooper instantly arose.

"I trust, sir, you will find all to your liking. If anything is lacking, I trust you will at once indicate the fact. We shall dine in a half hour——"

He seized a small implement consisting of a bit of wire screen attached to the end of a short stick, darted across the room with the most extraordinary agility, thwacked a lone house fly, and returned.

"—and you will undoubtedly be ready for it," he finished

---

* Saddle pockets that fit on the pommel.

his speech, calmly, as though he had not moved from his tracks.

I murmured my acknowledgments. My last impression as I left the room was of the baleful, dead, challenging stare of the man's wildcat eyes.

The Mexican glided before me. We emerged into the court, walked along the verandah, and entered a bedroom. My guide slipped by me and disappeared before I had the chance of a word with him. He may have been dumb for all I know. I sat down and tried to take stock.

CHAPTER III

The room was small, but it was papered, it was rugged, its floor was painted and waxed, its window—opening into the court, by the way—was hung with chintz and net curtains, its bed was garnished with sheets and counterpane, its chairs were upholstered and in perfect repair and polish. It was not Arizona, emphatically not, but rather the sweet and garnished and lavendered respectability of a Connecticut village. My dirty old *cantinas* lay stacked against the washstand. At sight of them I had to grin. Of course I travelled cowboy fashion. They contained a toothbrush, a comb, and a change of underwear. The latter item was sheer, rank pride of caste.

It was all most incongruous and strange. But the strangest part, of course, was the fact that I found myself where I was at that moment. Why was I thus received? Why was I, an ordinary and rather dirty cowpuncher, not sent as usual to the men's bunk house? It could not be possible that Old Man Hooper extended this sort of hospitality to every chance wayfarer. Arizona is a democratic country, Lord knows: none more so! But owners are not likely to invite in strange cowboys unless they themselves mess with their own men. I gave it up, and tried unsuccessfully to shrug it off my mind, and sought distraction in looking about me. There was not much to see. The one door and one window opened into the court. The other side was blank except that near the ceiling ran a curious, long, narrow opening closed by a transom-like sash. I had never seen anything quite like it, but concluded that it must be a sort of loop hole for musketry in the old days. Probably they had some kind of scaffold to stand on.

I pulled off my shirt and took a good wash: shook the dust out of my clothes as well as I could; removed my spurs and *chaps;* knotted my silk handkerchief necktie fashion; slicked down my wet hair, and tried to imagine myself decently turned out for company. I took off my gun belt also; but after some hesitation thrust the revolver inside the waistband of my drawers. Had no reason; simply the border instinct to stick to one's weapon.

Then I sat down to wait. The friendly little noises of my own movements left me. I give you my word, never before nor since have I experienced such stillness. In vain I told myself that with adobe walls two feet thick, a windless evening, and an hour after sunset, stillness was to be expected. That did not satisfy. Silence is made up of a thousand little noises so accustomed that they pass over the consciousness. Somehow these little noises seemed to lack. I sat in an aural vacuum. This analysis has come to me since. At that time I only knew that most uneasily I missed something, and that my ears ached from vain listening.

At the end of the half hour I returned to the parlour. Old Man Hooper was there waiting. A hanging lamp had been lighted. Out of the shadows cast from it a slender figure rose and came forward.

"My daughter, Mr.——" he paused.

"Sanborn," I supplied.

"My dear, Mr. Sanborn has most kindly dropped in to relieve the tedium of our evening with his company—his distinguished company." He pronounced the words suavely, without a trace of sarcastic emphasis, yet somehow I felt my face flush. And all the time he was staring at me blankly with his wide, unblinking, wildcat eyes.

The girl was very pale, with black hair and wide eyes under a fair, wide brow. She was simply dressed in some sort of white stuff. I thought she drooped a little. She did not look at me, nor speak to me; only bowed slightly.

We went at once into a dining room at the end of the little dark hall. It was lighted by a suspended lamp that threw the illumination straight down on a table perfect in its appointments of napery, silver, and glass. I felt very awkward and dusty in my cowboy rig; and rather too large. The same Mexican served us, deftly. We had delightful food, well cooked. I do not remember what it was. My attention was divided between the old man and his daughter. He talked, urbanely, of a wide range of topics, displaying a cosmopolitan taste, employing a choice of words and phrases that was astonishing. The girl, who turned out to be very pretty in a dark, pale, sad way, never raised her eyes from her plate.

It was the cool of the evening, and a light breeze from the open window swung the curtains. From the blackness outside a single frog began to chirp. My host's flow of words eddied, ceased. He raised his head uneasily; then, without apology, slipped from his chair and glided from the room. The Mexican remained, standing bolt upright in the dimness.

For the first time the girl spoke. Her voice was low and sweet, but either I or my aroused imagination detected a strained under quality.

"Ramon," she said in Spanish, "I am chilly. Close the window."

The servant turned his back to obey. With a movement rapid as a snake's dart the girl's hand came from beneath the table, reached across, and thrust into mine a small, folded paper. The next instant she was back in her place, staring down as before in apparent apathy. So amazed was I that I recovered barely soon enough to conceal the paper before Ramon turned back from his errand.

The next five minutes were to me hours of strained and bewildered waiting. I addressed one or two remarks to my companion, but received always monosyllabic answers. Twice I caught the flash of lanterns beyond the darkened window; and a subdued, confused murmur as though several people were walking about stealthily. Except for this the night had again fallen deathly still. Even the cheerful frog had hushed.

At the end of a period my host returned, and without apology or explanation resumed his seat and took up his remarks where he had left them.

The girl disappeared somewhere between the table and the sitting room. Old Man Hooper offered me a cigar, and sat down deliberately to entertain me. I had an uncomfortable feeling that he was also amusing himself, as though I were being played with and covertly sneered at. Hooper's politeness and suavity concealed, and well concealed, a bitter irony. His manner was detached and a little precise. Every few moments he burst into a flurry of activity with the fly whacker, darting here and there as his eyes fell upon one of the insects; but returning always calmly to his discourse with an air of never having moved from his chair. He talked to me of Praxiteles, among other things. What should an Arizona cowboy know of Praxiteles? and why should any one talk to him of that worthy Greek save as a subtle and hidden expression of contempt? That was my feeling. My senses and mental apperceptions were by now a little on the raw.

That, possibly, is why I noticed the very first chirp of another frog outside. It continued, and I found myself watching my host covertly. Sure enough, after a few repetitions I saw subtle signs of uneasiness, of divided attention; and soon, again without apology or explanation, he glided from the room. And at the same instant the old Mexican servitor came and pretended to fuss with the lamps.

My curiosity was now thoroughly aroused, but I could guess no means of satisfying it. Like the bedroom, this parlour gave out only on the interior court. The flash of lanterns against the ceiling above reached me. All I could do was to wander about looking at the objects in the cabinet and the pictures on the walls. There was, I remember, a set of carved ivory chessmen and an engraving of the legal trial of some English worthy of the seventeenth century. But my hearing was alert, and I thought to hear footsteps outside. At any rate, the chirp of the frog came to an abrupt end.

Shortly my host returned and took up his monologue.

It amounted to that. He seemed to delight in choosing unusual subjects and then backing me into a corner with an array of well-considered phrases that allowed me no opening for reply nor even comment. In one of my desperate attempts to gain even a momentary initiative I asked him, apropos of the piano, whether his daughter played.

"Do you like music?" he added, and without waiting for a reply seated himself at the instrument.

He played to me for half an hour. I do not know much about music; but I know he played well and that he played good things. Also that, for the first time, he came out of himself, abandoned himself to feeling. His close-cropped head swayed from side to side; his staring, wildcat eyes half closed——

He slammed shut the piano and arose, more drily precise than ever.

"I imagine all that is rather beyond your apperceptions," he remarked, "and that you are ready for your bed. Here is a short document I would have you take to your room for perusal. Good-night."

He tendered me a small, folded paper which I thrust into the breast pocket of my shirt along with the note handed me earlier in the evening by the girl. Thus dismissed I was only too delighted to repair to my bedroom.

There I first carefully drew together the curtains; then examined the first of the papers I drew from my pocket. It proved to be the one from the girl, and read as follows:

I am here against my will. I am not this man's daughter. For God's sake if you can help me, do so. But be careful for he is a dangerous man. My room is the last one on the left wing of the court. I am constantly guarded. I do not know what you can do. The case is hopeless. I cannot write more. I am watched.

I unfolded the paper Hooper himself had given me. It was similar in appearance to the other, and read:

I am held a prisoner. This man Hooper is not my father but he is vindictive and cruel and dangerous. Beware for yourself. I live in the last room in the left wing. I am watched, so cannot write more.

The handwriting of the two documents was the same. I stared at one paper and then at the other, and for a half hour I thought all the thoughts appropriate to the occasion. They led me nowhere, and would not interest you.

CHAPTER IV

After a time I went to bed, but not to sleep. I placed my gun under my pillow, locked and bolted the door, and arranged a string cunningly across the open window so that an intruder—unless he had extraordinary luck—could not have failed to kick up a devil of a clatter. I was young, bold, without nerves; so that I think I can truthfully say I was not in the least frightened. But I cannot deny I was nervous—or rather the whole situation was on my nerves. I lay on my back staring straight at the ceiling. I caught myself gripping the sheets and listening. Only there was nothing to listen to. The night was absolutely still. There were no frogs, no owls, no crickets even. The firm old adobe walls gave off no creak nor snap of timbers. The world was muffled—I almost said smothered. The psychological effect was that of blank darkness, the black darkness of far underground, although the moon was sailing the heavens.

How long that lasted I could not tell you. But at last the silence was broken by the cheerful chirp of a frog. Never was sound more grateful to the ear! I lay drinking it in as thirstily as water after a day on the desert. It seemed that the world breathed again, was coming alive after syncope. And then beneath that loud and cheerful singing I became aware of duller half-heard movements; and a moment or so later yellow lights began to flicker through the transom high at the blank wall of the room, and to reflect in wavering patches on the ceiling. Evidently somebody was afoot outside with a lantern.

I crept from the bed, moved the table beneath the transom, and climbed atop. The opening was still a foot or so above my head. Being young, strong, and active, I drew myself up by the strength of my arms so I could look— until my muscles gave out!

I saw four men with lanterns moving here and there among some willows that bordered what seemed to be an irrigating ditch with water. They were armed with long clubs. Old Man Hooper, in an overcoat, stood in a commanding position. They seemed to be searching. Suddenly from a clump of bushes one of the men uttered an exclamation of triumph. I saw his long club rise and fall. At that instant my tired fingers slipped from the ledge and I had to let myself drop to the table. When a moment later I regained my vantage point, I found that the whole crew had disappeared.

Nothing more happened that night. At times I dozed in a broken sort of fashion, but never actually fell into sound sleep. The nearest I came to slumber was just at dawn. I really lost all consciousness of my surroundings and circumstances, and was only slowly brought to myself by the sweet singing of innumerable birds in the willows outside the blank wall. I lay in a half stupor enjoying them. Abruptly their music ceased. I heard the soft, flat *spat* of a miniature rifle. The sound was repeated. I climbed back on my table and drew myself again to a position of observation.

THE KILLER

Old Man Hooper, armed with a .22 calibre rifle, was prowling along the willows in which fluttered a small band of migratory birds. He was just drawing bead on a robin. At the report the bird fell. The old man darted forward with the impetuosity of a boy, although the bird was dead. An impulse of contempt curled my lips. The old man was childish! Why should he find pleasure in hunting such harmless creatures? and why should he take on triumph over retrieving such petty game? But when he reached the fallen bird he did not pick it up for a possible pot-pie as I thought he would do. He ground it into the soft earth with the heel cf his boot, stamping on the poor thing again and again. And never have I seen on human countenance such an expression of satisfied malignity!

I went to my door and looked out. You may be sure that the message I had received from the unfortunate young lady had not been forgotten; but Old Man Hooper's cynical delivery of the second paper had rendered me too cautious to undertake anything without proper reconnaissance. The left wing about the courtyard seemed to contain two apartments—at least there were two doors, each with its accompanying window. The window farthest out was heavily barred. My thrill at this discovery was, however, slightly dashed by the further observation that also all the other windows into the courtyard were barred. Still, that was peculiar in itself, and not attributable—as were the walls and remarkable transoms—to former necessities of defence. My first thought was to stroll idly around the courtyard, thus obtaining a closer inspection. But the moment I stepped into the open a Mexican sauntered into

23

view and began to water the flowers. I can say no more than that in his hands that watering pot looked fairly silly. So I turned to the right and passed through the wicket gate and into the stable yard. It was natural enough that I should go to look after my own horse.

The stable yard was for the moment empty; but as I walked across it one of its doors opened and a very little, wizened old man emerged leading a horse. He tied the animal to a ring in the wall and proceeded at once to currying.

I had been in Arizona for ten years. During that time I had seen a great many very fine native horses, for the stock of that country is directly descended from the barbs of the *conquistadores*. But, though often well formed and as tough and useful as horseflesh is made, they were small. And no man thought of refinements in caring for any one of his numerous mounts. They went shaggy or smooth according to the season; and not one of them could have called a curry comb or brush out of its name.

The beast from which the wizened old man stripped a *bona fide* horse blanket was none of these. He stood a good sixteen hands; his head was small and clean cut with large, intelligent eyes and little, well-set ears; his long, muscular shoulders sloped forward as shoulders should; his barrel was long and deep and well ribbed up; his back was flat and straight; his legs were clean and—what was rarely seen in the cow country—well proportioned—the cannon bone shorter than the leg bone, the ankle sloping and long and elastic—in short, a magnificent creature whose points of excellence appeared one by one under close scrutiny.

And the high lights of his glossy coat flashed in the sun like water.

I walked from one side to the other of him marvelling. Not a defect, not even a blemish could I discover. The animal was fairly a perfect specimen of horseflesh. And I could not help speculating as to its use. Old Man Hooper had certainly never appeared with it in public; the fame of such a beast would have spread the breadth of the country.

During my inspection the wizened little man continued his work without even a glance in my direction. He had on riding breeches and leather gaiters, a plaid waistcoat and a peaked cap; which, when you think of it, was to Arizona about as incongruous as the horse. I made several conventional remarks of admiration, to which he paid not the slightest attention. But I know a bait.

"I suppose you claim him as a Morgan," said I.

"Claim, is it!" grunted the little man, contemptuously.

"Well, the Morgan is not a real breed, anyway," I persisted. "A sixty-fourth blood will get one registered. What does that amount to?"

The little man grunted again.

"Besides, though your animal is a good one, he is too short and straight in the pasterns," said I, uttering sheer, rank, wild heresy.

After that we talked; at first heatedly, then argumentatively, then with entire, enthusiastic agreement. I saw to that. Allowing yourself to be converted from an absurd opinion is always a sure way to favour. We ended with antiphonies of praise for this descendant of Justin Morgan.

"You're the only man in all this God-forsaken country

that has the sense of a Shanghai rooster!" cried the little man in a glow. "They ride horses and they know naught of them; and they laugh at a horseman! Your hand, sir!" He shook it. "And is that your horse in number four? I wondered! He's the first animal I've seen here properly shod. They use the rasp, sir, on the outside the hoof, and on the clinches, sir; and they burn a seat for the shoe; and they pare out the sole and trim the frog—bah! You shoe your own horse, I take it. That's right and proper! Your hand again, sir. Your horse has been fed this hour agone."

"I'll water him, then," said I.

But when I led him forth I could find no trough or other facilities until the little man led me to a corner of the corral and showed me a contraption with a close-fitting lid to be lifted.

"It's along of the flies," he explained to me. "They must drink, and we starve them for water here, and they go greedy for their poison yonder." He indicated flat dishes full of liquid set on shelves here and about. "We keep them pretty clear."

I walked over, curiously, to examine. About and in the dishes were literally quarts of dead insects, not only flies, but bees, hornets, and other sorts as well. I now understood the deadly silence that had so impressed me the evening before. This was certainly most ingenious; and I said so.

But at my first remark the old man became obstinately silent, and fell again to grooming the Morgan horse. Then I became aware that he was addressing me in low tones out of the corner of his mouth.

"Go on; look at the horse; say something," he muttered,

busily polishing down the animal's hind legs. "You're a man who *saveys* a horse—the only man I've seen here who does. *Get out!* Don't ask why. You're safe now. You're not safe here another day. Water your horse; eat your breakfast; then *get out!*"

And not another word did I extract. I watered my horse at the covered trough, and rather thoughtfully returned to the courtyard.

I found there Old Man Hooper waiting. He looked as bland and innocent and harmless as the sunlight on his own flagstones—until he gazed up at me, and then I was as usual disconcerted by the blank, veiled, unwinking stare of his eyes.

"Remarkably fine Morgan stallion you have, sir," I greeted him. "I didn't know such a creature existed in this part of the world."

But the little man displayed no gratification.

"He's well enough. I have him more to keep Tim happy than anything else. We'll go in to breakfast."

I cast a cautious eye at the barred window in the left wing. The curtains were still down. At the table I ventured to ask after Miss Hooper. The old man stared at me up to the point of embarrassment, then replied drily that she always breakfasted in her room. The rest of our conversation was on general topics. I am bound to say it was unexpectedly easy. The old man was a good talker, and possessed social ease and a certain charm, which he seemed to be trying to exert. Among other things, I remember, he told me of the Indian councils he used to hold in the old days.

"They were held on the willow flat, outside the east

wall," he said. "I never allowed any of them inside the walls." The suavity of his manner broke fiercely and suddenly. "Everything inside the walls is mine!" he declared with heat. "Mine! mine! mine! Understand? I will not tolerate in here anything that is not mine; that does not obey my will; that does not come when I say come; go when I say go; and fall silent when I say be still!"

A wild and fantastic idea suddenly illuminated my understanding.

"Even the crickets, the flies, the frogs, the birds," I said, audaciously.

He fixed his wildcat eyes upon me without answering.

"And," I went on, deliberately, "who could deny your perfect right to do what you will with your own? And if they did deny that right what more natural than that they should be made to perish—or take their breakfasts in their rooms?"

I was never more aware of the absolute stillness of the house than when I uttered these foolish words. My hand was on the gun in my trouser-band; but even as I spoke a sickening realization came over me that if the old man opposite so willed, I would have no slightest chance to use it. The air behind me seemed full of menace, and the hair crawled on the back of my neck. Hooper stared at me without sign for ten seconds; his right hand hovered above the polished table. Then he let it fall without giving what I am convinced would have been a signal.

"Will you have more coffee—my guest?" he inquired. And he stressed subtly the last word in a manner that somehow made me just a trifle ashamed.

At the close of the meal the Mexican familiar glided into the room. Hooper seemed to understand the man's presence, for he arose at once.

"Your horse is saddled and ready," he told me, briskly. "You will be wishing to start before the heat of the day. Your *cantinas* are ready on the saddle."

He clapped on his hat and we walked together to the corral. There awaited us not only my own horse, but another. The equipment of the latter was magnificently reminiscent of the old California days—gaily-coloured braided hair bridle and reins; silver *conchas;* stock saddle of carved leather with silver horn and cantle; silvered bit bars; gay Navajo blanket as corona; silver corners to skirts, silver *conchas* on the long *tapaderos*. Old Man Hooper, strangely incongruous in his wrinkled "store clothes," swung aboard.

"I will ride with you for a distance," he said.

We jogged forth side by side at the slow Spanish trot. Hooper called my attention to the buildings of Fort Shafter glimmering part way up the slopes of the distant mountains, and talked entertainingly of the Indian days, and how the young officers used to ride down to his ranch for music.

After a half hour thus we came to the long string of wire and the huge, awkward gate that marked the limit of Hooper's "pasture." Of course the open range was his real pasture; but every ranch enclosed a thousand acres or so somewhere near the home station to be used for horses in active service. Before I could anticipate him, he had sidled his horse skillfully alongside the gate and was holding it open for me to pass. I rode through the opening murmuring thanks and an apology. The old man followed me through, and halted me by placing his horse square across the path of mine.

"You are now, sir, outside my land and therefore no longer my guest," he said, and the snap in his voice was like the crackling of electricity. "Don't let me ever see you here again. You are keen and intelligent. You spoke the truth a short time since. You were right. I tolerate nothing in my place that is not my own—no man, no animal, no bird, no insect nor reptile even—that will not obey my lightest order. And these creatures, great or small, who will not—*or even cannot*—obey my orders must go—or die. Understand me clearly?

"You have come here, actuated, I believe, by idle curiosity, but without knowledge. You made yourself—ignorantly—my guest; and a guest is sacred. But now you know my customs and ideas. I am telling you. Never again can you come here in ignorance; therefore never again can you come here as a guest; and never again will you pass freely."

He delivered this drily, precisely, with frost in his tones, staring balefully into my eyes. So taken aback was I by this unleashed hostility that for a moment I had nothing to say.

"Now, if you please, I will take both notes from that poor idiot: the one I handed you and the one she handed you."

I realized suddenly that the two lay together in the breast pocket of my shirt; that though alike in tenor, they differed in phrasing; and that I had no means of telling one from the other.

"The paper you gave me I read and threw away," I

stated, boldly. "It meant nothing to me. As to any other, I do not know what you are talking about."

"You are lying," he said, calmly, as merely stating a fact. "It does not matter. It is my fancy to collect them. I should have liked to add yours. Now get out of this, and don't let me see your face again!"

"Mr. Hooper," said I, "I thank you for your hospitality, which has been complete and generous. You have pointed out the fact that I am no longer your guest. I can, therefore, with propriety, tell you that your ideas and prejudices are noted with interest; your wishes are placed on file for future reference; I don't give a damn for your orders; and you can go to hell!"

"Fine flow of language. Educated cowpuncher," said the old man, drily. "You are warned. Keep off. Don't meddle with what does not concern you. And if the rumour gets back to me that you've been speculating or talking or criticizing——"

"Well?" I challenged.

"I'll have you killed," he said, simply; so simply that I knew he meant it.

"You are foolish to make threats," I rejoined. "Two can play at that game. You drive much alone."

"I do not work alone," he hinted, darkly. "The day my body is found dead of violence, that day marks the doom of a long list of men whom I consider inimical to me—like, perhaps, yourself." He stared me down with his un-winking gaze.

CHAPTER V

I returned to Box Springs at a slow jog trot, thinking things over. Old Man Hooper's warning sobered, but did not act as a deterrent of my intention to continue with the adventure. But how? I could hardly storm the fort single handed and carry off the damsel in distress. On the evidence I possessed I could not even get together a storming party. The cowboy is chivalrous enough, but human. He would not uprise spontaneously to the point of war on the mere statement of incarcerated beauty—especially as ill-treatment was not apparent. I would hardly last long enough to carry out the necessary proselyting campaign. It never occurred to me to doubt that Hooper would fulfill his threat of having me killed, or his ability to do so.

So when the men drifted in two by two at dusk, I said nothing of my real adventures, and answered their chaff in kind.

"He played the piano for me," I told them the literal truth, "and had me in to the parlour and dining room. He gave me a room to myself with a bed and sheets; and he rode out to his pasture gate with me to say good-bye," and thereby I was branded a delicious liar.

"They took me into the bunk house and fed me, all right," said Windy Bill, "and fed my horse. And next morning that old Mexican Joe of his just nat'rally up and kicked me off the premises."

"Wonder you didn't shoot him," I exclaimed.

"Oh, he didn't use his foot. But he sort of let me know that the place was unhealthy to visit more'n once. And somehow I seen he meant it; and I ain't never had no call to go back."

I mulled over the situation all day, and then could stand it no longer. On the dark of the evening I rode to within a couple of miles of Hooper's ranch, tied my horse, and scouted carefully forward afoot. For one thing I wanted to find out whether the system of high transoms extended to all the rooms, including that in the left wing: for another I wanted to determine the "lay of the land" on that blank side of the house. I found my surmise correct as to the transoms. As to the blank side of the house, that looked down on a wide, green, moist patch and the irrigating ditch with its stunted willows. Then painstakingly I went over every inch of the terrain about the ranch; and might just as well have investigated the external economy of a mud turtle. Realizing that nothing was to be gained in this manner, I withdrew to my strategic base where I rolled down and slept until daylight. Then I saddled and returned toward the ranch.

I had not ridden two miles, however, before in the boulder-strewn wash of Arroyo Seco I met Jim Starr, one of our men.

"Look here," he said to me. "Jed sent me up to look at the Elder Springs, but my hoss has done cast a shoe. Cain't you ride up there?"

"I cannot," said I, promptly. "I've been out all night and had no breakfast. But you can have my horse."

So we traded horses and separated, each our own way. They sent me out by Coyote Wells with two other men, and we did not get back until the following evening.

The ranch was buzzing with excitement. Jim Starr had not returned, although the ride to Elder Springs was only a two-hour affair. After a night had elapsed, and still he did not return, two men had been sent. They found him half way to Elder Springs with a bullet hole in his back. The bullet was that of a rifle. Being plainsmen they had done good detective work of its kind, and had determined—by the direction of the bullet's flight as evidenced by the wound—that it had been fired from a point above. The only point above was the low "rim" that ran for miles down the Soda Springs Valley. It was of black lava and showed no tracks. The men, with a true sense of values, had contented themselves with covering Jim Starr with a blanket, and then had ridden the rim for some miles in both directions looking for a trail. None could be discovered. By this they deduced that the murder was not the result of chance encounter, but had been so carefully planned that no trace would be left of the murderer or murderers.

No theory could be imagined save the rather vague one of personal enmity. Jim Starr was comparatively a newcomer with us. Nobody knew anything much about him or his relations. Nobody questioned the only man who could have told anything; and that man did not volunteer to tell what he knew.

I refer to myself. The thing was sickeningly clear to me.

Jim Starr had nothing to do with it. I was the man for whom that bullet from the rim had been intended. I was the unthinking, shortsighted fool who had done Jim Starr to his death. It had never occurred to me that my midnight reconnoitring would leave tracks, that Old Man Hooper's suspicious vigilance would even look for tracks. But given that vigilance, the rest followed plainly enough. A skillful trailer would have found his way to where I had mounted; he would have followed my horse to Arroyo Seco where I had met with Jim Starr. There he would have visualized a rider on a horse without one shoe coming as far as the Arroyo, meeting me, and returning whence he had come; and me at once turning off at right angles. His natural conclusion would be that a messenger had brought me orders and had returned. The fact that we had shifted mounts he could not have read, for the reason—as I only too distinctly remembered—that we had made the change in the boulder and rock stream bed which would show no clear traces.

The thought that poor Jim Starr, whom I had well liked, had been sacrificed for me, rendered my ride home with the convoy more deeply thoughtful than even the tragic circumstances warranted. We laid his body in the small office, pending Buck Johnson's return from town, and ate our belated meal in silence. Then we gathered around the corner fireplace in the bunk house, lit our smokes, and talked it over. Jed Parker joined us. Usually he sat with our owner in the office.

Hardly had we settled ourselves to discussion when the door opened and Buck Johnson came in. We had been so absorbed that no one had heard him ride up. He leaned his forearm against the doorway at the height of his head and surveyed the silenced group rather ironically.

"Lucky I'm not nervous and jumpy by nature," he observed. "I've seen dead men before. Still, next time you want to leave one in my office after dark, I wish you'd put a light with him, or tack up a sign, or even leave somebody to tell me about it. I'm sorry it's Starr and not that thoughtful old horned toad in the corner."

Jed looked foolish, but said nothing. Buck came in, closed the door, and took a chair square in front of the fireplace. The glow of the leaping flames was full upon him. His strong face and bulky figure were revealed, while the other men sat in half shadow. He at once took charge of the discussion.

"How was he killed?" he inquired, "bucked off?"

"Shot," replied Jed Parker.

Buck's eyebrows came together.

"Who?" he asked.

He was told the circumstances as far as they were known, but declined to listen to any of the various deductions and surmises.

"Deliberate murder and not a chance quarrel," he concluded. "He wasn't even within hollering distance of that rim-rock. Anybody know anything about Starr?"

"He's been with us about five weeks," proffered Jed, as foreman. "Said he came from Texas."

"He was a Texican," corroborated one of the other men. "I rode with him considerable."

"What enemies did he have?" asked Buck.

But it developed that, as far as these men knew, Jim Starr had had no enemies. He was a quiet sort of a fellow. He had been to town once or twice. Of course he might have made an enemy, but it was not likely; he had always behaved himself. Somebody would have known of any trouble——

"Maybe somebody followed him from Texas."

"More likely the usual local work," Buck interrupted. "This man Starr ever met up with Old Man Hooper or Hooper's men?"

But here was another impasse. Starr had been over on the Slick Rock ever since his arrival. I could have thrown some light on the matter, perhaps, but new thoughts were coming to me and I kept silence.

Shortly Buck Johnson went out. His departure loosened tongues, among them mine.

"I don't see why you stand for this old *hombre* if he's as bad as you say," I broke in. "Why don't some of you brave young warriors just naturally pot him?"

And that started a new line of discussion that left me even more thoughtful than before. I knew these men intimately. There was not a coward among them. They had been tried and hardened and tempered in the fierceness of the desert. Any one of them would have twisted the tail of the devil himself; but they were off Old Man Hooper. They did not make that admission in so many words; far from it. And I valued my hide enough to refrain from pointing the fact. But that fact remained: they were off Old Man Hooper. Furthermore, by the time they had finished recounting in intimate detail some scores of anecdotes dealing with what happened when Old Man Hooper winked his wildcat eye, I began in spite of myself to share some of their sentiments. For no matter how flagrant the killing, nor how certain morally the origin, never had the most brilliant nor the most painstaking effort been able to connect with the slayers nor their instigator. He worked in the dark by hidden hands; but the death from the hands was as certain as the rattlesnake's. Certain of his victims, by luck or cleverness, seemed to have escaped sometimes as many as three or four attempts but in the end the old man's Killers got them.

A Jew drummer who had grossly insulted Hooper in the Lone Star Emporium had, on learning the enormity of his crime, fled to San Francisco. Three months later Soda Springs awoke to find pasted by an unknown hand on the window of the Emporium a newspaper account of that Jew drummer's taking off. The newspaper could offer no theory and merely recited the fact that the man suffered from a heavy-calibred bullet. But always the talk turned back at last to that crowning atrocity, the Boomerang, with its windrows of little calves, starved for water, lying against the fence.

"Yes," someone unexpectedly answered my first question at last, "someone could just naturally pot him easy enough. But I got a hunch that he couldn't get fur enough away to feel safe afterward. The fellow with a hankering for a good *useful* kind of suicide could get it right there. Any candidates? You-all been looking kinda mournful lately, Windy; s'pose you be the human benefactor and rid the world of this yere reptile."

"Me?" said Windy with vast surprise, "me mournful? Why, I sing at my work like a little dicky bird. I'm so plumb cheerful bull frogs ain't in it. You ain't talking to me!"

But I wanted one more point of information before the conversation veered.

"Does his daughter ever ride out?" I asked.

"Daughter?" they echoed in surprise.

"Or niece, or whoever she is," I supplemented impatiently.

"There's no woman there; not even a Mex," said one, and "Did you see any sign of any woman?" keenly from Windy Bill.

But I was not minded to be drawn.

"Somebody told me about a daughter, or niece, or something," I said, vaguely.

CHAPTER VI

I lay in my bunk and cast things up in my mind. The patch of moonlight from the window moved slowly across the floor. One of the men was snoring, but with regularity, so he did not annoy me. The outside silence was softly musical with all the little voices that at Hooper's had so disconcertingly lacked. There were crickets—I had forgotten about them—and frogs, and a hoot owl, and various such matters, beneath whose influence customarily my consciousness merged into sleep so sweetly that I never knew when I had lost them. But I was never wider awake than now, and never had I done more concentrated thinking.

For the moment, and for the moment, only, I was safe. Old Man Hooper thought he had put me out of the way. How long would he continue to think so? How long before his men would bring true word of the mistake that had been made? Perhaps the following day would inform him that Jim Starr and not myself had been reached by his killer's bullet. Then, I had no doubt, a second attempt would be made on my life. Therefore, whatever I was going to do must be done quickly.

I had the choice of war or retreat. Would it do me any good to retreat? There was the Jew drummer who was killed in San Francisco; and others whose fates I have not detailed. But why should he particularly desire my extinction? What had I done or what knowledge did I possess that had not been equally done and known by any chance visitor to the ranch? I remembered the notes in my shirt pocket; and, at the risk of awakening some of my comrades, I lit a candle and studied them. They were undoubtedly written by the same hand. To whom had the other been smuggled? and by what means had it come into Old Man Hooper's possession? The answer hit me so suddenly, and seemed intrinsically so absurd, that I blew out the candle and lay again on my back to study it.

And the more I studied it, the less absurd it seemed, not by the light of reason, but by the feeling of pure intuition. I knew it as sanely as I knew that the moon made that patch of light through the window. The man to whom that other note had been surreptitiously conveyed by the sad-eyed, beautiful girl of the iron-barred chamber was dead; and he was dead because Old Man Hooper had so willed. And the former owners of the other notes of the "Collection" concerning which the old man had spoken were dead, too— dead for the same reason and by the same hidden hands.

Why? Because they knew about the girl? Unlikely. Without doubt Hooper had, as in my case, himself made possible that knowledge. But I remembered many things; and I knew that my flash of intuition, absurd as it might seem at first sight, was true. I recalled the swift, darting onslaughts with the fly whackers, the fierce, vindictive slaughter of the frogs, his early-morning pursuit of the flock of migrating birds. Especially came clear to my recollection the words spoken at breakfast:

"Everything inside the walls is mine! Mine! Mine!

Understand? I will not tolerate anything that is not mine; that does not obey my will; that does not come when I say come; go when I say go; and fall silent when I say be still!"

My crime, the crime of these men from whose dead hands the girl's appeals had been taken for the "Collection," was that of curiosity! The old man would within his own domain reign supreme, in the mental as in the physical world. The chance cowboy, genuinely desirous only of a resting place for the night, rode away unscathed; but he whom the old man convicted of a prying spirit committed a lese-majesty that could not be forgiven. And I had made many tracks during my night reconnaissance.

And the same flash of insight showed me that I would be followed wherever I went; and the thing that convinced my intuitions—not my reason—of this was the recollection of the old man stamping the remains of the poor little bird into the mud by the willows. I saw again the insane rage of his face; and I felt cold fingers touching my spine.

On this I went abruptly and unexpectedly to sleep, after the fashion of youth, and did not stir until Sing, the cook, routed us out before dawn. We were not to ride the range that day because of Jim Starr, but Sing was a person of fixed habits. I plunged my head into the face of the dawn with a new and light-hearted confidence. It was one of those clear, nile-green sunrises whose lucent depths go back a million miles or so; and my spirit followed on wings. Gone were at once my fine-spun theories and my forebodings of the night. Life was clean and clear and simple. Jim Starr had probably some personal enemy. Old Man Hooper was undoubtedly a mean old lunatic, and dangerous; very likely he would attempt to do me harm, as he said, if I bothered him again, but as for following me to the ends of the earth——

The girl was a different matter. She required thought. So, as I was hungry and the day sparkling, I postponed her and went in to breakfast.

CHAPTER VII.

By the time the coroner's inquest and the funeral in town were over it was three o'clock of the afternoon. As I only occasionally managed Soda Springs I felt no inclination to hurry on the return journey. My intention was to watch the Overland through, to make some small purchases at the Lone Star Emporium, to hoist one or two at McGrue's, and to dine sumptuously at the best—and only—hotel. A programme simple in theme but susceptible to variations.

The latter began early. After posing kiddishly as a rough, woolly, romantic cowboy before the passengers of the Overland, I found myself chaperoning a visitor to our midst. By sheer accident the visitor had singled me out for an inquiry.

"Can you tell me how to get to Hooper's ranch?" he asked.

So I annexed him promptly in hope of developments.

He was certainly no prize package, for he was small, pale, nervous, shifty, and rat-like; and neither his hands nor his eyes were still for an instant. Further to set him apart he wore a hard-boiled hat, a flaming tie, a checked vest, a coat cut too tight for even his emaciated little figure, and long toothpick shoes of patent leather. A fairer mark for cowboy humour would be difficult to find; but I had a personal interest and a determined character so the gang took a look at me and bided their time.

But immediately I discovered I was going to have my hands full. It seemed that the little, shifty, rat-faced man had been possessed of a small handbag which the negro porter had failed to put off the train; and which was of tremendous importance. At the discovery it was lacking my new friend went into hysterics. He ran a few feet after the disappearing train; he called upon high heaven to destroy utterly the race of negro porters; he threatened terrible reprisals against a delinquent railroad company; he seized upon a bewildered station agent over whom he poured his troubles in one gush; and he lifted up his voice and wept— literally wept! This to the vast enjoyment of my friends.

"What ails the small party?" asked Windy Bill coming up. "He's lost the family jewels!" "The papers are missing." "Sandy here (meaning me) won't give him his bottle and it's past feeding time." "Sandy's took away his stick of candy and won't give it back." "The little son-of-a-gun's just remembered that he give the nigger porter two bits," were some of the replies he got.

On the general principle of "never start anything you can't finish," I managed to quell the disturbance; I got a description of the bag, and arranged to have it wired for at the next station. On receiving the news that it could not possibly be returned before the following morning, my protégé showed signs of another outburst. To prevent it I took him firmly by the arm and led him across to McGrue's. He was shivering as though from a violent chill.

The multitude trailed interestedly after; but I took my man into one of McGrue's private rooms and firmly closed the door.

"Put that under your belt," I invited, pouring him a half tumbler of McGrue's best, "and pull yourself together."

He smelled it.

"It's only whiskey," he observed. mournfully. "That won't help much."

"You don't know this stuff," I encouraged.

He took off the half tumbler without a blink, shook his head, and poured himself another. In spite of his scepticism I thought his nervousness became less marked.

"Now," said I, "if you don't mind, why do you descend on a peaceful community and stir it all up because of the derelictions of an absent coon? And why do you set such store by your travelling bag? And why do you weep in the face of high heaven and outraged manhood? And why do you want to find Hooper's ranch? And why are you and your vaudeville make up?"

But he proved singularly embarrassed and nervous and uncommunicative, darting his glance here and there about him, twisting his hands, never by any chance meeting my eye. I leaned back and surveyed him in considerable disgust.

"Look here, brother," I pointed out to him. "You don't seem to realize. A man like you can't get away with himself in this country except behind footlights—and there ain't any footlights. All I got to do is to throw open yonder door and withdraw my beneficent protection and you will be set upon by a pack of ravening wolves with their own ideas of humour, among whom I especially mention one Windy Bill. I'm about the only thing that looks like a friend you've got."

He caught at the last sentence only.

"You my friend?" he said, breathlessly, "then tell me: is there a doctor around here?"

"No," said I, looking at him closely, "not this side of Tucson. Are you sick?"

"Is there a drug store in town, then?"

"Nary drug store."

He jumped to his feet, knocking over his chair as he did so.

"My God!" he cried in uncontrollable excitement, "I've got to get my bag! How far is it to the next station where they're going to put it off? Ain't there some way of getting there? I got to get to my bag."

"It's near to forty miles," I replied, leaning back.

"And there's no drug store here? What kind of a bum tank town is this, anyhow?"

"They keep a few patent medicines and such over at the Lone Star Emporium——" I started to tell him. I never had a chance to finish my sentence. He darted around the table, grabbed me by the arm, and urged me to my feet.

"Show me!" he panted.

We sailed through the bar room under full head of steam, leaving the gang staring after us open-mouthed. I could feel we were exciting considerable public interest. At the Lone Star Emporium the little freak looked wildly about him until his eyes fell on the bottle shelves. Then he rushed right in behind the counter and began to paw them over. I headed off Sol Levi, who was coming front making war medicine.

"*Loco,*" says I to him. "If there's any damage, I'll settle."

It looked like there was going to be damage all right, the way he snatched up one bottle after the other, read the labels, and thrust them one side. At last he uttered a crow of delight, just like a kid.

"How many you got of these?" he demanded, holding up a bottle of soothing syrup.

"You only take a tablespoon of that stuff——" began Sol.

"How many you got—how much are they?" interrupted the stranger.

"Six—three dollars a bottle," says Sol, boosting the price.

The little man peeled a twenty off a roll of bills and threw it down.

"Keep the other five bottles for me!" he cried in a shaky voice, and ran out, with me after him, forgetting his change and to shut the door behind us.

Back through McGrue's bar we trailed like one of these moving-picture chases and into the back room.

"Well, here we are home again," said I.

The stranger grabbed a glass and filled it half full of soothing syrup.

"Here, you aren't going to drink that!" I yelled at him. "Didn't you hear Sol tell you the dose is a spoonful?"

But he didn't pay me any attention. His hand was shaking so he could hardly connect with his own mouth, and he was panting as though he'd run a race.

"Well, no accounting for tastes," I said. "Where do you want me to ship your remains?"

He drank her down, shut his eyes a few minutes, and held still. He had quit his shaking, and he looked me square in the face.

"What's it *to* you?" he demanded. "Huh? Ain't you never seen a guy hit the hop before?"

He stared at me so truculently that I was moved to righteous wrath; and I answered him back. I told him what I thought of him and his clothes and his conduct at quite some length. When I had finished he seemed to have gained a new attitude of aggravating wise superiority.

"That's all right, kid; that's all right," he assured me; "keep your hair on. I ain't such a bad scout; but you gotta get used to me. Give me my hop and I'm all right. Now about this Hooper; you say you know him?"

"None better," I rejoined. "But what's that to you? That's a fair question."

He bored me with his beady rat eyes for several seconds.

"Friend of yours?" he asked, briefly.

Something in the intonations of his voice induced me to frankness.

"I have good cause to think he's trying to kill me," I replied.

He produced a pocketbook, fumbled in it for a moment, and laid before me a clipping. It was from the Want column of a newspaper, and read as follows:

A.A.B.—Will deal with you on your terms. H.H.

"A.A.B. that's me—Artie Brower. And H.H.—that's him—Henry Hooper," he explained. "And that lil' piece of paper means that's he's caved, come off, war's over. Means I'm rich, that I can have my own ponies if I want to, 'stead of touting somebody else's old dogs. It means that I got old H.H.—Henry Hooper—where the hair is short, and he's got to come my way!"

His eyes were glittering restlessly, and the pupils seemed

to be unduly dilated. The whiskey and opium together—probably an unaccustomed combination—were too much for his ill-balanced control. Every indication of his face and his narrow eyes was for secrecy and craft; yet for the moment he was opening up to me, a stranger, like an oyster. Even my inexperience could see that much, and I eagerly took advantage of my chance.

"You are a horseman, then?" I suggested.

"Me a horseman? Say, kid, you didn't get my name. Brower—Artie Brower. Why, I've ridden more winning races than any other man on the Pacific Coast. That's how I got onto old H.H. I rode for him. He knows a good horse all right—the old skunk. Used to have a pretty string."

"He's got at least one good Morgan stallion now," said I. "I've seen him at Hooper's ranch."

"I know the old crock—trotter," scorned the true riding jockey. "Probably old Tim Westmore is hanging around, too. He's in love with that horse."

"Is he in love with Hooper, too?" I asked.

"Just like I am," said the jockey with a leer.

"So you're going to be rich," said I. "How's that?"

He leered at me again, going foxy.

"Don't you wish you knew! But I'll tell you this: old H.H. is going to give me all I want—just because I ask him to."

I took another tack, affecting incredulity.

"The hell he is! He'll hand you over to Ramon and that will be the last of a certain jockey."

"No, he won't do no such trick. I've fixed that; and he

50

knows it. If he kills me, he'll lose *all* he's got 'stead of only part."

"You're drunk or dreaming," said I. "If you bother him, he'll just plain have you killed. That's a little way of his."

"And if he does a friend of mine will just go to a certain place and get certain papers and give 'em to a certain lawyer —and then where's old H.H.? And he knows it, damn well. And he's going to be good to Artie and give him what he wants. We'll get along fine. Took him a long time to come to it; but I didn't take no chances while he was making up his mind; you can bet on that."

"Blackmail, eh?" I said, with just enough of a sneer to fire him.

"Blackmail nothing!" he shouted. "It ain't blackmail to take away what don't belong to a man at all!"

"What don't belong to him?"

"Nothing. Not a damn thing except his money. This ranch. The oil wells in California. The cattle. Not a damn thing. That was the agreement with his pardner when they split. And I've got the agreement! Now what you got to say?"

"Say? Why its *loco!* Why doesn't the pardner raise a row?"

"He's dead."

"His heirs then?"

"He hasn't got but one heir—his daughter." My heart skipped a beat in the amazement of a half idea. "And she knew nothing about the agreement. Nobody knows but old H.H.—and me." He sat back, visibly gloating over me. But his mood was passing. His earlier exhilaration had died, and with it was dying the expansiveness of his confidence. The triumph of his last speech savoured he slipped again into his normal self. He looked at me suspiciously, and raised his whiskey to cover his confusion.

"What's it to yuh, anyway?" he muttered into his glass darkly. His eyes were again shifting here and there; and his lips were snarled back malevolently to show his teeth.

At this precise moment the lords of chance willed Windy Bill and others to intrude on our privacy by opening the door and hurling several whiskey-flavoured sarcasms at the pair of us. The jockey seemed to explode after the fashion of an over-inflated ball. He squeaked like a rat, leaped to his feet, hurled the chair on which he had been sitting crash against the door from which Windy Bill *et al* had withdrawn hastily, and ended by producing a small wicked-looking automatic—then a new and strange weapon—and rushing out into the main saloon. There he announced that he was known to the cognoscenti as Art the Blood and was a city gunman in comparison with which these plain, so-called bad men were as sucking doves to the untamed eagle. Thence he glanced briefly at their ancestry as far as known; and ended by rushing forth in the general direction of McCloud's hotel.

"Suffering giraffes!" gasped Windy Bill after the whirlwind had passed. "Was that the scared little rabbit that wept all them salt tears over at the depot? What brand of licker did you feed him, Sandy?"

I silently handed him the bottle.

"Soothing syrup—my God!" said Windy in hushed tones.

CHAPTER VIII

At that epoch I prided myself on being a man of resource; and I proceeded to prove it in a fashion that even now fills me with satisfaction. I annexed the remainder of that bottle of soothing syrup; I went to Sol Levi and easily procured delivery of the other five. Then I strolled peacefully to supper over at McCloud's hotel. Pathological knowledge of dope fiends was outside my ken—I could not guess how soon my man would need another dose of his "hop," but I was positively sure that another would be needed. Inquiry of McCloud elicited the fact that the ex-jockey had swallowed a hasty meal and had immediately retired to Room 4. I found Room 4 unlocked, and Brower lying fully clothed sound asleep across the bed. I did not disturb him, except that I robbed him of his pistol. All looked safe for awhile; but just to be certain I took Room 6, across the narrow hall, and left both doors open. McCloud's hotel never did much of a room business. By midnight the cowboys would be on their way for the ranches. Brower and myself were the only occupants of the second floor.

For two hours I smoked and read. The ex-jockey did not move a muscle. Then I went to bed and to a sound sleep; but I set my mind like an alarm clock, so that the slightest move from the other room would have fetched me broad awake. City-bred people may not know that this

53

can be done by most outdoor men. I have listened subconsciously to horsebells for so many nights, for example. that even on stormy nights the cessation of that faint twinkle will awaken me, while the crash of the elements or even the fall of a tree would not in the slightest disturb my tired slumbers. So now, although the songs and stamping and racket of the revellers below stairs in McCloud's bar did not for one second prevent my falling into deep and dreamless sleep, Brower's softest tread would have reached my consciousness.

However, he slept right through the night, and was still dead to the world when I slipped out at six o'clock to meet the east-bound train. The bag—a small black Gladstone—was aboard in charge of the baggageman. I had no great difficulty in getting it from my friend, the station agent. Had he not seen me herding the locoed stranger? I secreted the black bag with the five full bottles of soothing syrup, slipped the half-emptied bottle in my pocket, and returned to the hotel. There I ate breakfast, and sat down for a comfortable chat with McCloud while awaiting results.

Got them very promptly. About eight o'clock Brower came downstairs. He passed through the office, nodding curtly to McCloud and me, and into the dining room where he drank several cups of coffee. Thence he passed down the street toward Sol Levi's. He emerged rather hurriedly and slanted across to the station.

"In about two minutes," I observed to McCloud, "you're going to observe yon butterfly turn into a stinging lizard. He's going to head in this direction; and he'll probably aim to climb my hump. Such being the case, and the affair

54

beingprivate, you'll do me a favour by supervising something in some remote corner of the premises."

"Sure," said McCloud, "I'll go twist that Chink washee-man. Been intending to for a week." And he stumped out on his wooden foot.

The comet hit at precisely 7:42 by McCloud's big clock. Its head was Brower at high speed and tension; and its tail was the light alkali dust of Arizona mingled with the station agent. No irresistible force and immovable body proposition in mine; I gave to the impact.

"Why, sure, I got 'em for you," I answered. "You left your dope lying around loose so I took care of it for you. As for your bag; you seemed to set such store by it that I got that for you, too."

Which deflated that particular enterprise for the moment, anyway. The station agent, too mad to spit, departed before he should be tempted beyond his strength to resist homicide.

"I suppose you're taking care of my gun for me, too," said Brower; but his irony was weak. He was evidently off the boil.

"Your gun?" I echoed. "Have you lost your gun?"

He passed his hand across his eyes. His super-excitement had passed, leaving him weak and nervous. Now was the time for my counter-attack.

"Here's your gun," said I, "didn't want to collect any lead while you were excited, and I've got your dope," I repeated, "in a safe place." I added, "and you'll not see. any of it again until you answer me a few questions, and answer them straight."

"If you think you can roll me for blackmail," he came back with some decision, "you're left a mile."

"I don't want a cent; but I do want a talk."

"Shoot," said he.

"How often do you have to have this dope—for the best results; and how much of it at a shot?'

He stared at me for a moment, then laughed.

"What's it to yuh?" he repeated his formula.

"I want to know."

"I get to needing it about once a day. Three grains will carry me by."

"All right; that's what I want to know. Now listen to me. I'm custodian of this dope, and you'll get your regular ration as long as you stick with me."

"I can always hop a train. This ain't the only hamlet on the map," he reminded me.

"That's always what you can do if you find we can't work together. That's where you've got me if my proposition doesn't sound good."

"What is your proposition?" he asked after a moment.

"Before I tell you, I'm going to give you a few pointers on what you're up against. I don't know how much you know about Old Man Hooper, but I'll bet there's plenty you *don't* know about."

I proceeded to tell him something of the old man's methods, from the "boomerang" to vicarious murder.

"And he gets away with it?" asked Brower when I had finished.

"He certainly does," said I. "Now," I continued, "you may be solid as a brick church, and your plans may be water-tight, and old Hooper may kill the fatted four-year-old, for all I know. But if I were you, I wouldn't go sasshaying all alone out to Hooper's ranch. It's altogether *too* blame confiding and innocent."

"If anything happens to me, I've left directions for those contracts to be recorded," he pointed out. "Old Hooper knows that."

"Oh, sure!" I replied, "just like that! But one day your trustworthy friend back yonder will get a letter in your well-known hand-write that will say that all is well and the goose hangs high, that the old man is a prince and has come through, and that in accordance with the nice, friendly agreement you have reached he—your friend—will hand over the contract to a very respectable lawyer herein named, and so forth and so on, ending with your equally well-known John Hancock."

"Well, that's all right."

"I hadn't finished the picture. In the meantime, you will be getting out of it just one good swift kick, and that is all."

"I shouldn't write any such letter. Not 'till I felt the feel of the dough."

"Not at first you wouldn't," I said, softly. "Certainly not at first. But after a while you would. These renegade Mexicans—like Hooper's Ramon, for example—know a lot of rotten little tricks. They drive pitch-pine splinters into your legs and set fire to them, for one thing. Or make small cuts in you with a knife, and load them up with powder squibs in oiled paper—so the blood won't wet them—and touch them off. And so on. When you've been shown about ten per cent. of what old Ramon knows about such things, you'll write most any kind of a letter."

"My God!" he muttered, thrusting the ridiculous derby to the back of his head.

"So you see you'd look sweet walking trustfully into Hooper's claws. That's what that newspaper ad was meant for. And when the respectable lawyer wrote that the contract had been delivered, do you know what would happen to you?"

The ex-jockey shuddered.

"But you've only told me part of what I want to know," I pursued. "You got me side-tracked. This daughter of the dead pardner—this girl, what about her? Where is she now?"

"Europe, I believe."

"When did she go?"

"About three months ago."

"Any other relatives?"

"Not that I know of."

"H'm," I pondered. "What does she look like?"

"She's about medium height, dark, good figure, good-looking all right. She's got eyes wide apart and a wide forehead. That's the best I can do. Why?"

"Anybody heard from her since she went to Europe?"

"How should I know?" rejoined Brower, impatiently. "What you driving at?"

"I think I've seen her. I believe she's not in Europe at all. I believe she's a prisoner at the ranch."

"My aunt!" ejaculated Brower. His nervousness was increasing—the symptoms I was to recognize so well. "Why the hell don't you just shoot him from behind a bush? I'll do it, if you won't."

"He's too smooth for that." And I told him what Hooper had told me. "His hold on these Mexicans is remarkable. I don't doubt that fifty of the best killers in the southwest have lists of the men Old Man Hooper thinks might lay him out. And every man on that list would get his within a year—without any doubt. I don't doubt that partner's daughter would go first of all. You, too, of course."

"My aunt!" groaned the jockey again.

"He's a killer," I went on, "by nature, and by interest— a bad combination. He ought to be tramped out like a rattlesnake. But this is a new country, and it's near the border. I expect he's got me marked. If I have to I'll kill him just like I would a rattlesnake; but that wouldn't do me a whole lot of good and would probably get a bunch assassinated. I'd like to figure something different. So you see you'd better come on in while the coming is good."

"I see," said the ex-jockey, very much subdued. "What's your idea? What do you want me to do?"

That stumped me. To tell the truth I had no idea at all what to do.

"I don't want you to go out to Hooper's ranch alone," said I.

"Trust me!" he rejoined, fervently.

"I reckon the first best thing is to get along out of town," I suggested. "That black bag all the plunder you got?"

"That's it."

"Then we'll go out a-horseback."

We had lunch and a smoke and settled up with McCloud. About mid-afternoon we went on down to the livery corral. I knew the keeper pretty well, of course, so I borrowed a horse and saddle for Brower. The latter looked with extreme disfavour on both.

"This is no race meet," I reminded him. "This is a means of transportation."

"Sorry I ain't got nothing better," apologized Meigs, to whom I had confided my companion's profession—I had to account for such a figure somehow. "All my saddle hosses went off with a mine outfit yesterday."

"What's the matter with that chestnut in the shed?"

"He's all right; fine beast. Only it ain't mine. It belongs to Ramon."

"Ramon from Hooper's?"

"Yeah."

"I'd let you ride my horse and take Meigs's old skate myself," I said to Brower, "but when you first get on him this bronc of mine is a rip-humming tail twister. Ain't he, Meigs?"

"He's a bad *caballo*," corroborated Meigs.

"Does he buck?" queried Brower, indifferently.

"Every known fashion. Bites, scratches, gouges, and paws. Want to try him?"

"I got a headache," replied Brower, grouchily. "Bring out your old dog."

When I came back from roping and blindfolding the twisted dynamite I was engaged in "gentling," I found that Brower was saddling the mournful creature with my saddle. My expostulation found him very snappy and very arbitrary. His opium-irritated nerves were beginning to react. I realized that he was not far short of explosive obstinacy. So I conceded the point; although, as every rider knows, a cowboy's saddle and a cowboy's gun are like unto a toothbrush when it comes to lending. Also it involved changing the stirrup length on the livery saddle. I needed things just right to ride Tiger through the first five minutes.

When I had completed this latter operation, Brower had just finished drawing tight the cinch. His horse stood dejectedly. When Brower had made fast the latigo, the horse—as such dispirited animals often do—heaved a deep sigh. Something snapped beneath the slight strain of the indrawn breath.

"Dogged if your cinch ain't busted!" cried Meigs with a loud laugh. "Lucky for you your friend did borrow your saddle! If you'd clumb Tiger with that outfit you could just naturally have begun pickin' out the likely-looking she-angels."

I dropped the stirrup and went over to examine the damage. Both of the quarter straps on the off side had given way. I found that they had been cut nearly through with a sharp knife. My eye strayed to Ramon's chestnut horse standing under the shed.

CHAPTER IX

We jogged out to Box Springs by way of the lower alkali flats. It is about three miles farther that way; but one can see for miles in every direction. I did not one bit fancy the cañons, the mesquite patches, and the open ground of the usual route.

I beguiled the distance watching Brower. The animal he rode was a hammer-headed, ewe-necked beast with a disconsolate eye and a half-shed winter coat. The ex-jockey was not accustomed to a stock saddle. He had shortened his stirrups beyond all reason so that his knees and his pointed shoes and his elbows stuck out at all angles. He had thrust his derby hat far down over his ears, and buttoned his inadequate coat tightly. In addition, he was nourishing a very considerable grouch, attributable, I suppose, to the fact that his customary dose was just about due. Tiger could not be blamed for dancing wide. Evening was falling, the evening of the desert when mysterious things seem to swell and draw imminent out of unguessed distances. I could not help wondering what these gods of the desert could be thinking of us.

However, as we drew imperceptibly nearer the tiny patch of cottonwoods that marked Box Springs, I began to realize that it would be more to the point to wonder what that gang of hoodlums in the bunk house was going to think of us.

The matter had been fairly well carried off up to that moment, but I could not hope for a successful repetition. No man could continue to lug around with him so delicious a vaudeville sketch without some concession to curiosity. Nor could any mortal for long wear such clothes in the face of Arizona without being required to show cause. He had got away with it last night, by surprise; but that would be about all.

At my fiftieth attempt to enter into conversation with him, I unexpectedly succeeded. I believe I was indicating the points of interest. You can see farther in Arizona than any place I know, so there was no difficulty about that. I'd pointed out the range of the Chiracahuas, and Cochise's Stronghold, and the peaks of the Galiuros and other natural sceneries; I had showed him mesquite and yucca, and mescal and soapweed, and sage, and sacatone and niggerheads and all the other known vegetables of the region. Also I'd indicated prairie dogs and squinch owls and Gambel's quail and road runners and a couple of coyotes and lizards and other miscellaneous fauna. Not to speak of naming painstakingly the ranches indicated by the clumps of trees that you could just make out as little spots in the distance—Box Springs, the O. T., the Double H, Fort Shafter, and Hooper's. He waked up and paid a little attention at this; and I thought I might get a little friendly talk out of him. A cowboy rides around alone so much he sort of likes to josh when he has anybody with him. This "strong silent" stuff doesn't go until you've used around with a man quite some time.

I got the talk, all right, but it didn't have a thing to do

with topography or natural history. Unless you call the skate he was riding natural history. That was the burden of his song. He didn't like that horse, and he didn't care who knew it. It was an uncomfortable horse to ride on, it required exertion to keep in motion, and it hurt his feelings. Especially the last. He was a horseman, a jockey, he'd ridden the best blood in the equine world; and here he was condemned through no fault of his own to straddle a cross between a llama and a woolly toy sheep. It hurt his pride. He felt bitterly about it. Indeed, he fairly harped on the subject.

"Is that horse of yours through bucking for the day?" he asked at last.

"Certain thing. Tiger never pitches but the once."

"Let me ride him a ways. I'd like to feel a real horse to get the taste of this kangaroo out of my system."

I could see he was jumpy, so I thought I'd humour him.

"Swing on all at once and you're all right," I advised him. "Tiger don't like fumbling in getting aboard."

He grunted scornfully.

"Those stirrups are longer than the ones you've been using. Want to shorten them?"

He did not bother to answer, but mounted in a decisive manner that proved he was indeed a horseman, and a good one. I climbed old crow bait and let my legs hang.

The jockey gathered the reins and touched Tiger with his heels. I kicked my animal with my stock spurs and managed to extract a lumbering sort of gallop.

"Hey, slow up!" I called after a few moments. "I can't keep up with you."

Brower did not turn his head, nor did Tiger slow up. After twenty seconds I realized that he intended to do neither. I ceased urging on my animal, there was no use tiring us both; evidently the jockey was enjoying to the full the exhilaration of a good horse, and we would catch up at Box Springs. I only hoped the boys wouldn't do anything drastic to him before my arrival.

So I jogged along at the little running walk possessed by even the most humble cattle horse, and enjoyed the evening. It was going on toward dusk and pools of twilight were in the bottomlands. For the moment the world had grown smaller, more intimate, as the skies expanded. The dust from Brower's going did not so much recede as grow littler, more toy-like. I watched idly his progress.

At a point perhaps a mile this side the Box Springs ranch the road divides: the right-hand fork leading to the ranch house, the left on up the valley. After a moment I noticed that the dust was on the left-hand fork. I swore aloud.

"The damn fool has taken the wrong road!" and then after a moment, with dismay: "He's headed straight for Hooper's ranch!"

I envisaged the full joy and rapture of this thought for perhaps half a minute. It sure complicated matters, what with old Hooper gunning on my trail, and this partner's daughter shut up behind bars. Me, I expected to last about two days unless I did something mighty sudden. Brower I expected might last approximately half that time, depending on how soon Ramon *et al* got busy. The girl I didn't know anything about, nor did I want to at that moment. I was plenty worried about my own precious hide just then. And if you think you are going to get a love story out of this, I warn you again to quit right now; you are not.

Brower was going to walk into that gray old spider's web like a nice fat fly. And he was going to land without even the aid and comfort of his own particular brand of Dutch courage. For safety's sake, and because of Tiger's playful tendencies when first mounted, we had tied the famous black bag—which now for convenience contained also the soothing syrup—behind the cantle of Meigs's old nag. Which said nag I now possessed together with all appurtenances and attachments thereunto appertaining I tried to speculate on the reactions of Old Man Hooper, Ramon, Brower and no dope, but it was too much for me. My head was getting tired thinking about all these complicated things, anyhow. I was accustomed to nice, simple jobs with my head, like figuring on the shrinkage of beef cattle, or the inner running of a two-card draw. All this annoyed me. I began to get mad. When I got mad enough I cussed and came to a decision: which was to go after Old Man Hooper and all his works that very night. Next day wouldn't do; I wanted action right off quick. Naturally I had no plans, nor even a glimmering of what I was going to do about it; but you bet you I was going to do something! As soon as it was dark I was going right on up there. Frontal attack, you understand. As to details, those would take care of themselves as the affair developed. Having come to which sapient decision I shoved the whole irritating mess over the edge of my mind and rode on quite happy. I told you at the start of this yarn that I was a kid.

My mind being now quite easy as to my future actions, I gave thought to the first step. That was supper. There seemed to me no adequate reason, with a fine, long night before me, why I shouldn't use a little of the shank end of it to stoke up for the rest. So I turned at the right-hand fork and jogged slowly toward our own ranch.

Of course I had the rotten luck to find most of the boys still at the water corral. When they saw who was the lone horseman approaching through the dusk of the spring twilight, and got a good fair look at the ensemble, they dropped everything and came over to see about it, headed naturally by those mournful blights, Windy Bill and Wooden. In solemn silence they examined my outfit, paying not the slightest attention to me. At the end of a full minute they looked at each other.

"What do you think, Sam?" asked Windy.

"My opinion is not quite formed, suh," replied Wooden, who was a Texican. "But my first examination inclines me to the belief that it is a hoss."

"Yo're wrong, Sam," denied Windy, sadly; "yo're judgment is confused by the fact that the critter carries a saddle. Look at the animile itself."

"I have done it," continued Sam Wooden; "at first glance I should agree with you. Look carefully, Windy. Examine the details; never mind the *toot enscramble*. It's got hoofs."

"So's a cow, a goat, a burro, a camel, a hippypottamus, and the devil," pointed out Windy.

"Of course I may be wrong," acknowledged Wooden. "On second examination I probably am wrong. But if it ain't a hoss, then what is it? Do you know?"

"It's a genuine royal gyasticutus," esserted Windy Bill, positively. "I seen one once. It has one peculiarity that you can't never fail to identify it by."

"What's that?"

"It invariably travels around with a congenital idiot."

Wooden promptly conceded that, but claimed the identification not complete as he doubted whether, strictly speaking, I could be classified as a congenital idiot. Windy pointed out that evidently I had traded Tiger for the gyasticutus. Wooden admitted that this proved me an idiot, but not necessarily a congenital idiot.

This colloquy—and more like it—went on with entire gravity. The other men were hanging about relishing the situation, but without a symptom of mirth. I was unsaddling methodically, paying no attention to anybody, and apparently deaf to all that was being said. If the two old fools had succeeded in eliciting a word from me they would have been entirely happy; but I knew that fact, and shut my lips.

I hung my saddle on the rack and was just about to lead the old skate to water when we all heard the sound of a horse galloping on the road.

"It's a light hoss," said somebody after a moment, meaning a horse without a burden.

We nodded and resumed our occupation. A stray horse coming in to water was nothing strange or unusual. But an instant later, stirrups swinging, reins flapping, up dashed my own horse, Tiger.

CHAPTER X

All this being beyond me, and then some, I proceeded methodically to carry out my complicated plan; which was, it will be remembered, to eat supper and then to go and see about it in person. I performed the first part of this to my entire satisfaction but not to that of the rest. They accused me of unbecoming secrecy; only they expressed it differently. That did not worry me, and in due time I made my escape. At the corral I picked out a good horse, one that I had brought from the Gila, that would stay tied indefinitely without impatience. Then I lighted me a cigarette and jogged up the road. I carried with me a little grub, my six-gun, the famous black bag, and an entirely empty head.

The night was only moderately dark, for while there was no moon there were plenty of those candle-like desert stars. The little twinkling lights of the Box Springs dropped astern like lamps on a shore. By and by I turned off the road and made a wide détour down the sacatone bottoms, for I had still some sense; and roads were a little too obvious. The reception committee that had taken charge of my little friend might be expecting another visitor—me. This brought my approach to the blank side of the ranch where were the willow trees and the irrigating ditch. I rode up as close as I thought I ought to. Then I tied my horse to a

69

prominent lone Joshua-tree that would be easy to find, unstrapped the black bag, and started off. The black bag, however, bothered me; so after some thought I broke the lock with a stone and investigated the contents, mainly by feel. There were a lot of clothes and toilet articles and such junk, and a number of undetermined hard things like round wooden boxes. Finally I withdrew to the shelter of a *barranca* where I could light matches. Then I had no difficulty in identifying a nice compact little hypodermic outfit, which I slipped into a pocket. I then deposited the bag in a safe place where I could find it easily.

Leaving my horse I approached the ranch under cover of the willows. Yes, I remembered this time that I left tracks, but I did not care. My idea was to get some sort of decisive action before morning. Once through the willows I crept up close to the walls. They were twelve or fifteen feet high, absolutely smooth; and with one exception broken only by the long, narrow loopholes or transoms I have mentioned before. The one exception was a small wicket gate or door. I remembered the various sorties with torches after the chirping frogs, and knew that by this opening the hunting party had emerged. This and the big main gate were the only entrances to the enclosure.

I retired to the vicinity of the willows and uttered the cry of the barred owl. After ten seconds I repeated it, and so continued. My only regret was that I could not chirp convincingly like a frog. I saw a shadow shift suddenly through one of the transoms, and at once glided to the wall near the little door. After a moment or so it opened to emit Old Man Hooper and another bulkier figure which

I imagined to be that of Ramon. Both were armed with shotguns. Suddenly it came to me that I was lucky not to have been able to chirp convincingly like a frog. They hunted frogs with torches and in a crowd. Those two carried no light and they were so intent on making a sneak on the willows and the supposititious owl that I, flattened in the shadow of the wall, easily escaped their notice. I slipped inside the doorway.

This brought me into a narrow passage between two buildings. The other end looked into the interior court. A careful reconnaissance showed no one in sight, so I walked boldly along the verandah in the direction of the girl's room. Her note had said she was constantly guarded; but I could see no one in sight, and I had to take a chance somewhere. Two seconds' talk would do me: I wanted to know in which of the numerous rooms the old man slept. I had a hunch it would be a good idea to share that room with him. What to do then I left to the hunch.

But when I was half way down the verandah I heard the wicket door slammed shut. The owl hunters had returned more quickly than I had anticipated. Running as lightly as possible I darted down the verandah and around the corner of the left wing. This brought me into a narrow little garden strip between the main house and the wall dividing the court from the corrals and stable yards. Footsteps followed me but stopped. A hand tried the door knob to the corner room.

"Nothing," I heard Hooper's voice replying to a question. "Nothing at all. Go to sleep."

The fragrant smell of Mexican tobacco reached my nostrils. After a moment Ramon—it was he—resumed a conversation in Spanish:

"I do not know, señor, who the man was. I could but listen; it was not well to inquire nor to show too much interest. His name, yes; Jim Starr, but who he is——" I could imagine the shrug. "It is of no importance."

"It is of importance that the other man still lives," broke in Hooper's harsher voice. "I will not have it, I say! Are you sure of it?"

"I saw him. And I saw his horse at the Señor Meigs. It was the brown that bucks badly, so I cut the quarter straps of his saddle. It might be that we have luck; I do not count on it. But rest your mind easy, señor, it shall be arranged."

"It better be."

"But there is more, señor. The señor will remember a man who rode in races for him many years ago, one named Artie——"

"Brower!" broke in Hooper. "What about him?"

"He is in town. He arrived yesterday afternoon."

Hooper ejaculated something.

"And more, he is all day and all night with this Sanborn."

Hooper swore fluently in English.

"Look, Ramon!" he ordered, vehemently. "It is necessary to finish this Sanborn at once, without delay."

"*Bueno*, señor."

"It must not go over a single day."

"Haste makes risk, señor."

"The risk must be run."

"*Bueno*, señor. And also this Artie?"

72

"No! no! no!" hastened Hooper. "Guard him as your life! But send a trusty man for him to-morrow with the buckboard. He comes to see me, in answer to my invitation."

"And if he will not come, señor?" inquired Ramon's quiet voice.

"Why should he not come?"

"He has been much with Sanborn."

"It's necessary that he come," replied Hooper, emphasizing each word.

"*Bueno*, señor."

"Who is to be on guard?"

"Cortinez, señor."

"I will send him at once. Do me the kindness to watch for a moment until I send him. Here is the key; give it to him. It shall be but a moment."

"*Bueno*, señor," replied Ramon.

He leaned against the corner of the house. I could see the half of his figure against the sky and the dim white of the walls.

The night was very still, as always at this ranch. There was not even a breeze to create a rustle in the leaves. I was obliged to hold rigidly motionless, almost to hush my breathing, while the figure bulked large against the whitewashed wall. But my eyes, wide to the dimness, took in every detail of my surroundings. Near me stood a water barrel. If I could get a spring from that water barrel I could catch one of the heavy projecting beams of the roof.

After an apparently interminable interval the sound of footsteps became audible, and a moment later Ramon moved to meet his relief. I seized the opportunity of their conversation and ascended to the roof. It proved to be easy, although the dried-out old beam to which for a moment I swung creaked outrageously. Probably it sounded louder to me than the actual fact. I took off my boots and moved cautiously to where I could look down into the court. Ramon and his companion were still talking under the verandah, so I could not see them; but I waited until I heard one of them move away. Then I went to seat myself on the low parapet and think things over.

The man below me had the key to the girl's room. If I could get the key I could accomplish the first step of my plan—indeed the only step I had determined upon. The exact method of getting the key would have to develop. In the meantime, I gave passing wonder to the fact, as developed by the conversation between Hooper and Ramon, that Brower was not at the ranch and had not been heard of at the ranch. Where had Tiger dumped him, and where now was he lying? I keenly regretted the loss of a possible ally; and, much to my astonishment, I found within myself a little regret for the man himself.

The thought of the transom occurred to me. I tiptoed over to that side and looked down. The opening was about five feet below the parapet. After a moment's thought I tied a bit of stone from the coping in the end of my silk bandana and lowered it at arm's length. By swinging it gently back and forth I determined that the transom was open. With the stub of the pencil every cowboy carried to tally with I scribbled a few words on an envelope which I wrapped about the bit of coping. Something to the effect that I was there, and expected to gain entrance to her room later, and to be prepared. Then I lowered my contraption, caused it to tap gently a dozen times on the edge of the transom, and finally swung it with a rather nice accuracy to fly, bandana and all, through the opening. After a short interval of suspense I saw the reflection of a light and so knew my message had been received.

There was nothing to do now but return to a point of observation. On my way I stubbed my stockinged foot against a stone *metate* or mortar in which Indians and Mexicans make their flour. The heavy pestle was there. I annexed it. Dropped accurately from the height of the roof it would make a very pretty weapon. The trouble, of course, lay in that word "accurately."

But I soon found the fates playing into my hands. At the end of a quarter hour the sentry emerged from under the verandah, looked up at the sky, yawned, stretched, and finally sat down with his back against the wall of the building opposite. Inside of ten minutes he was sound asleep and snoring gently.

I wanted nothing better than that. The descent was a little difficult to accomplish noiselessly, as I had to drop some feet, but I managed it. After crouching for a moment to see if the slight sounds had aroused him, I crept along the wall to where he sat. The stone pestle of the *metate* I had been forced to leave behind me, but I had the heavy barrel of my gun, and I was going to take no chances. I had no compunctions as to what I did to any one of this pack of mad dogs. Cautiously I drew it from its holster and poised it to strike. At that instant I was seized and pinioned from behind.

CHAPTER XI

I did not struggle. I would have done so if I had been able, but I was caught in a grip so skillful that the smallest move gave me the most exquisite pain. At that time I had not even heard the words *jiu jitsu*, but I have looked them up since. Cortinez, the sleepy sentry, without changing his position, had opened his eyes and was grinning at me.

I was forced to my feet and marched to the open door of the corner room. There I was released, and turned around to face Hooper himself. The old man's face was twisted in a sardonic half-snarl that might pass for a grin; but there was no smile in his unblinking wildcat eyes. There seemed to be trace neither of the girl nor the girl's occupation.

"Thank you for your warning of your intended visit," said Hooper in silky tones, indicating my bandana which lay on the table. "And now may I inquire to what I owe the honour of this call? Or it may be that the visit was not intended for me at all. Mistake in the rooms, perhaps. I often shift and change my quarters, and those of my household; especially if I suspect I have some reason for doing so. It adds interest to an otherwise uneventful life."

He was eying me sardonically, evidently gloating over the situation as he found it.

"How did you get on that roof? Who let you inside the walls?" he demanded, abruptly.

I merely smiled at him.

"That we can determine later," he observed, resuming command of himself.

I measured my chances, and found them at present a minus quantity. The old man was separated from me by a table, and he held my own revolver ready for instant use. So I stood tight and waited.

The room was an almost exact replica of the one in which I had spent the night so short a time before; the same long narrow transom near the ceiling, the same barred windows opening on the court, the same closet against the blank wall. Hooper had evidently inhabited it for some days, for it was filled with his personal belongings. Indeed he must have moved in *en bloc* when his ward had been moved out, for none of the furnishings showed the feminine touch, and several articles could have belonged only to the old man personally. Of such was a small iron safe in one corner and a tall old-fashioned desk crammed with papers.

But if I decided overt action unwise at this moment, I decidedly went into action the next. Hooper whistled and four Mexicans appeared with ropes. Somehow I knew if they once hog-tied me I would never get another chance. Better dead now than helpless in the morning, for what that old buzzard might want of me.

One of them tossed a loop at me. I struck it aside and sailed in.

It had always been my profound and contemptuous belief that I could lick any four Mexicans. Now I had to take that back. I could not. But I gave the man argument, and by the time they had my elbows lashed behind me and my legs tied to the legs of one of those big solid chairs they like to name as "Mission style," I had marked them up and torn their pretty clothes and smashed a lot of junk around the place and generally got them so mad they would have knifed me in a holy second if it had not been for Old Man Hooper. The latter held up the lamp where it wouldn't get smashed and admonished them in no uncertain terms that he wanted me alive and comparatively undamaged. Oh, sure! they mussed me up, too. I wasn't very pretty, either.

The bravos withdrew muttering curses, as the story books say; and after Hooper had righted the table and stuck the lamp on it, and taken a good look at my bonds, he withdrew also.

Most of my time until the next thing occurred was occupied in figuring on all the things that might happen to me. One thing I acknowledged to myself right off the reel: the Mexicans had sure trussed me up for further orders! I could move my hands, but I knew enough of ropes and ties to realize that my chances of getting free were exactly nothing. My plans had gone perfectly up to this moment. I had schemed to get inside the ranch and into Old Man Hooper's room; and here I was! What more could a man ask?

The next thing occurred so soon, however, that I hadn't had time to think of more than ten per cent. of the things that might happen to me. The outside door opened to admit Hooper, followed by the girl. He stood aside in the most courtly fashion.

"My dear," he said, "here is Mr. Sanborn, who has come

to call on you. You remember Mr. Sanborn, I am sure. You met him at dinner; and besides, I believe you had some correspondence with him, did you not? He has taken so much trouble, so very much trouble to see you that I think it a great pity his wish should not be fulfilled. Won't you sit down here, my dear?"

She was staring at me, her eyes gone wide with wonder and horror. Half thinking she took her seat as indicated. Instantly the old man had bound her elbows at the back and had lashed her to the chair. After the first start of surprise she made no resistance.

"There," said Hooper, straightening up after the accomplishment of this task; "now I'm going to leave you to your visit. You can talk it all over. Tell him all you please, my dear. And you, sir, tell her all you know. I think I can arrange so your confidences will go no further."

For the first time I heard him laugh, a high, uncertain cackle. The girl said nothing, but she stared at him with level, blazing eyes. Also for the first time I began to take an interest in her.

"Do you object to smoking?" I asked her, suddenly.

She blinked and recovered.

"Not at all," she answered.

"Well then, old man, be a sport. Give me the makings. I can get my hands to my mouth."

The old man transferred his baleful eyes on me. Then without saying a word he placed in my hands a box of tailor-made cigarettes and a dozen matches.

"Until morning," he observed, his hand on the door knob. He inclined in a most courteous fashion, first to the one of us, then to the other, and went out. He did not lock the door after him, and I could hear him addressing Cortinez outside. The girl started to speak, but I waved my shackled hand at her for silence. By straining my ears I could just make out what was said.

"I am going to bed," Hooper said. "It is not necessary to stand guard. You may get your blankets and sleep on the verandah."

After the old man's footsteps had died, I turned back to the girl opposite me and looked her over carefully. My first impression of meekness I revised. She did not look to be one bit meek. Her lips were compressed, her nostrils wide, her level eyes unsubdued. A person of sense, I said to myself, well balanced, who has learned when it is useless to kick against the pricks, but who has not necessarily on that account forever renounced all kicking. It occurred to me that she must have had to be pretty thoroughly convinced before she had come to this frame of mind. When she saw that I had heard all I wanted of the movements outside, she spoke hurriedly in her low, sweet voice:

"Oh, I am so distressed! This is all my doing! I should have known better——"

"Now," I interrupted her, decisively, "let's get down to cases. You had nothing to do with this; nothing whatever. I visited this ranch the first time out of curiosity, and to-night because I knew that I'd have to hit first to save my own life. You had no influence on me in either case."

"You thought this was my room—I wrote you it was," she countered, swiftly.

"I wanted to see you solely and simply that I might find

out how to get at Hooper. This is all my fault; and we're going to cut out the self-accusations and get down to cases."

I afterward realized that all this was somewhat inconsiderate and ungallant and slightly humiliating; I should have taken the part of the knight-errant rescuing the damsel in distress, but at that moment only the direct essentials entered my mind.

"Very well," she assented in her repressed tones.

"Do you think he is listening to what we say; or has somebody listening?"

"I am positive not."

"Why?"

"I lived in this room for two months, and I know every inch of it."

"He might have some sort of a concealed listening hole somewhere, just the same."

"I am certain he has not. The walls are two feet thick."

"All right; let it go at that. Now let's see where we stand. In the first place, how do you dope this out?"

"What do you mean?"

"What does he intend to do with us?"

She looked at me straight, eye to eye.

"In the morning he will kill you—unless you can contrive something."

"Cheering thought."

"There is no sense in not facing situations squarely. If there is a way out, that is the only method by which it may be found."

"True," I agreed, my admiration growing. "And yourself; will he kill you, too?"

"He will not. He does not dare!" she cried, proudly, with a flash of the eyes.

I was not so sure of that, but there was no object in saying so.

"Why has he tied you in that chair, then, along with the condemned?" I asked.

"You will understand better if I tell you who I am."

"You are his deceased partner's daughter; and everybody thinks you are in Europe," I stated.

"How in the world did you know that? But no matter; it is true. I embarked three months ago on the Limited for New York intending, as you say, to go on a long trip to Europe. My father and I had been alone in the world. We were very fond of each other. I took no companion, nor did I intend to. I felt quite independent and able to take care of myself. At the last moment Mr. Hooper boarded the train. That was quite unexpected. He was on his way to the ranch. He persuaded me to stop over for a few days to decide some matters. You know, since my father's death I am half owner."

"Whole owner," I murmured.

"What did you say?"

"Nothing. Go ahead. Sure you don't mind my smoking?" I lit one of the tailor-mades and settled back. Even my inexperienced youth recognized the necessity of relief this long-continued stubborn repression must feel. My companion had as yet told me nothing I did not already know or guess; but I knew it would do her good to talk, and I might learn something valuable.

"We came out to the ranch, and talked matters over

quite normally; but when it came time for my departure, I was not permitted to leave. For some unexplained reason I was a prisoner, confined absolutely to the four walls of this enclosure. I was guarded night and day; and I soon found I was to be permitted conversation with two men only, Mexicans named Ramon and Andreas."

"They are his right and left hand," I commented.

"So I found. You may imagine I did not submit to this until I found I had to. Then I made up my mind that the only possible thing to do was to acquiesce, to observe, and to wait my chance."

"You were right enough there. Why do you figure he did this?"

"I don't know!" she cried with a flash of thwarted despair. "I have racked my brains, but I can find no motive. He has not asked me for a thing; he has not even asked me a question. Unless he's stark crazy, I cannot make it out!"

"He may be that," I suggested.

"He may be; and yet I doubt it somehow. I don't know why; but I *feel* that he is sane enough. He is inconceivably cruel and domineering. He will not tolerate a living thing about the place that will not or cannot take orders from him. He kills the flies, the bees, the birds, the frogs, because they are not his. I believe he would kill a man as quickly who stood out even for a second against him here. To that extent I believe he is crazy: a sort of monomania. But not otherwise. That is why I say he will kill you; I really believe he would do it."

"So do I," I agreed, grimly. "However, let's drop that

83

for right now. Do you know a man named Brower, Artie Brower?"

"I don't think I ever heard of him. Why?"

"Never mind for a minute. I've just had a great thought strike me. Just let me alone a few moments while I work it out."

I lighted a second cigarette from the butt of the first and fell into a study. Cortinez breathed heavily outside. Otherwise the silence was as dead as the blackness of the night. The smoke from my cigarettes floated lazily until it reached the influence of the hot air from the lamp; then it shot upward toward the ceiling. The girl watched me from under her level brows, always with that air of controlled restraint I found so admirable.

"I've got it," I said at last, "—or at least I think I have. Now listen to me, and believe what I've got to say. Here are the facts: first, your father and Hooper split partnership a while back. Hooper took his share entirely in cash; your father took his probably part in cash, but certainly all of the ranch and cattle. Get that clear? Hooper owns no part of the ranch and cattle. All right. Your father dies before the papers relating to this agreement are recorded. Nobody knew of those papers except your father and Hooper. So if Hooper were to destroy those papers, he'd still have the cash that had been paid him, and an equal share in the property. That plain?"

"Perfectly," she replied, composedly. "Why didn't he destroy them?"

"Because they had been stolen by this man Brower I asked you about—an ex-jockey of Hooper's. Brower held them for blackmail. Unless Hooper came through Brower would record the papers."

"Where do I come in?"

"Easy. I'm coming to that. But answer me this: who would be your heir in case you died?"

"Why—I don't know!"

"Have you any kin?"

"Not a soul!"

"Did you ever make a will?"

"I never thought of such a thing!"

"Well, I'll tell you. If you were to die your interest in this property would go to Hooper."

"What makes you think so? I thought it would go to the state."

"I'm guessing," I acknowledged, "but I believe I'm guessing straight. A lot of these old Arizona partnerships were made just that way. Life was uncertain out here. I'll bet the old original partnership between your father and Hooper provides that in case of the extinction of one line, the other will inherit. It's a very common form of partnership in a new country like this. You can see for yourself it's a sensible thing to provide."

"You may be right," she commented. "Go on."

"You told me a while ago it was best to face any situation squarely. Now brace up and face this. You said a while ago that Hooper would not dare kill you. That is true for the moment. But there is no doubt in my mind that he has intended from the first to kill you, because by that he would get possession of the whole property."

"I cannot believe it!" she cried.

"Isn't the incentive enough? Think carefully, and answer honestly: don't you think him capable of it?"

"Yes—I suppose so," she admitted, reluctantly, after a moment. She gathered herself as after a shock. "Why hasn't he done so? Why has he waited?"

I told her of the situation as it concerned Brower. While the dissolution of partnership papers still existed and might still be recorded, such a murder would be useless. For naturally the dissolution abrogated the old partnership agreement. The girl's share of the property would, at her demise intestate, go to the state. That is, provided the new papers were ever recorded.

"Then I am safe until——?" she began.

"Until he negotiates or otherwise settles with Brower. Until he has destroyed all evidence."

"Then everything seems to depend on this Brower," she said, knitting her brows anxiously. "Where is he?"

I did not answer this last question. My eyes were riveted on the door knob which was slowly, almost imperceptibly, turning. Cortinez continued to breathe heavily in sleep outside. The intruder was evidently at great pains not to awaken the guard. A fraction of an inch at a time the door opened. A wild-haired, wild-eyed head inserted itself cautiously through the crack. The girl's eyes widened in surprise and, I imagine, a little in fear. I began to laugh, silently, so as not to disturb Cortinez. Mirth overcame me; the tears ran down my cheeks.

"It's so darn complete!" I gasped, answering the girl's horrified look of inquiry. "Miss Emory, allow me to present Mr. Artie Brower!"

CHAPTER XII

Brower entered the room quickly but very quietly, and at once came to me. His eyes were staring, his eyelids twitched, his hands shook. I recognized the symptoms.

"Have you got it? Have you got it with you?" he whispered, feverishly.

"It's all right. I can fix you up. Untie me first," I replied.

He began to fumble with the knots of my bonds too hastily and impatiently for effectiveness. I was trying to stoop over far enough to see what he was doing when my eye caught the shadow of a moving figure outside. An instant later Tim Westmore, the English groom attached to the Morgan stallion, came cautiously through the door, which he closed behind him. I attempted unobtrusively to warn Brower, but he only looked up, nodded vaguely, and continued his fumbling efforts to free me. Westmore glanced at us all curiously, but went at once to the big windows, which he proceeded to swing shut. Then he came over to us, pushed Brower one side, and most expeditiously untied the knots. I stood up stretching in the luxury of freedom, then turned to perform a like office for Miss Emory. But Brower was by now frantic. He seized my arm and fairly shook me, big as I was, in the urgence of his desire. He was rapidly losing all control and caution.

"Let him have it, sir," urged Westmore in a whisper. "I'll free the young lady."

I gave Brower the hypodermic case. He ran to the wash bowl for water. During the process of preparation he uttered little animal sounds under his breath. When the needle had sunk home he lay back in a chair and closed his eyes.

In the meantime, I had been holding a whispered colloquy with Westmore.

"He sneaked in on me at dark, sir," he told me, "on foot. I don't know how he got in without being seen. They'd have found his tracks anyway in the morning. I don't think he knew quite what he wanted to do. Him and me were old pals, and he wanted to ask me about things. He didn't expect to stay, I fancy. He told me he had left his horse tied a mile or so down the road. Then a while back orders came to close down, air tight. We're used to such orders. Nobody can go out or come in, you understand. And there are guards placed. That made him uneasy. He told me then he was a hop fiend. I've seen them before, and I got uneasy, too. If he came to the worst I might have to tie and gag him. I know how they are."

"Go ahead," I urged. He had stopped to listen.

"I don't like that Cortinez being so handy like out there," he confessed.

"Hooper told him he could sleep. He's not likely to pay attention to us. Miss Emory and I have been talking aloud."

"I hope not. Well, then, Ramon came by and stopped to talk to me for a minute. I had to hide Artie in a box-stall and hope to God he kept quiet. He wasn't as bad as he is now. Ramon told me about you being caught, and went on. After that nothing must do but find you. He thought you might have his dope. He'd have gone into the jaws of hell after it. So I came along to keep him out of mischief."

"What are you going to do now?" asked the girl, who had kicked off her slippers and had been walking a few paces to and fro.

"I don't know, ma'am. We've got to get away."

"We?"

"You mean me, too? Yes, ma'am! I have stood with the doings of this place as long as I can stand them. Artie has told me some other things. Are you here of your free will, ma'am?" he asked, abruptly.

"No," she replied.

"I suspected as much. I'm through with the whole lot of them."

Brower opened his eyes. He was now quite calm.

"Hooper sold the Morgan stallion," he whispered, smiled sardonically, and closed his eyes again.

"Without telling me a word of it!" added Tim with heat. "He ain't delivered him yet."

"Well, I don't blame you. Now you'd better quietly sneak back to your quarters. There is likely to be trouble before we get through. You, too, Brower. Nobody knows you are here."

Brower opened his eyes again.

"I can get out of this place now I've had me hop," said he, decidedly. "Come on, let's go."

"We'll all go," I agreed; "but let's see what we can find here first. There may be some paper—or something——"

"What do you mean? What sort of papers? Hadn't we better go at once?"

"It is supposed to be well known that the reason Hooper isn't assassinated from behind a bush is because in that case his killers are in turn to assassinate a long list of his enemies. Only nobody is sure: just as nobody is really sure that he has killers at all. You can't get action on an uncertainty."

She nodded. "I can understand that."

"If we could get proof positive it would be no trick at all to raise the country."

"What sort of proof?"

"Well, I mentioned a list. I don't doubt his head man—Ramon, I suppose, the one he'd trust with carrying out such a job—must have a list of some sort. He wouldn't trust to memory."

"And he wouldn't trust it to Ramon until after he was dead!" said the girl with sudden intuition. "If it exists we'll find it here."

She started toward the paper-stuffed desk, but I stopped her.

"More likely the safe," said I.

Tim, who was standing near it, tried the handle.

"It's locked," he whispered.

I fell on my knees and began to fiddle with the dial, of course in vain. Miss Emory, with more practical decision of character, began to run through the innumerable bundles and loose papers in the desk, tossing them aside as they proved unimportant or not germane to the issue. I had not the slightest knowledge of the constructions of safes but whirled the knob hopelessly in one direction or another trying to listen for clicks, as somewhere I had read was the thing to do. As may be imagined, I arrived nowhere. Nor did the girl. We looked at each other in chagrin at last.

"There is nothing here but ranch bills and accounts and business letters," she confessed.

I merely shook my head.

At this moment Brower, whom I had supposed to be sound asleep, opened his eyes.

"Want that safe open?" he asked, drowsily.

He arose, stretched, and took his place beside me on the floor. His head cocked one side, he slowly turned the dials with the tips of fingers I for the first time noticed were long and slim and sensitive. Twice after extended, delicate manipulations he whirled the knob impatiently and took a fresh start. On the proverbial third trial he turned the handle and the door swung open. He arose rather stiffly from his knees, resumed his place in the arm-chair, and again closed his eyes.

It was a small safe, with few pigeon holes. A number of blue-covered contracts took small time for examination. There were the usual number of mine certificates not valuable enough for a safe deposit, some confidential memoranda and accounts having to do with the ranch.

"Ah, here is something!" I breathed to the eager audience over my shoulder. I held in my hands a heavy manila envelope, sealed, inscribed "Ramon. (To be destroyed unopened.)"

"Evidently we were right: Ramon has the combination and is to be executor," I commented.

I tore open the envelope and extracted from it another of the blue-covered documents.

"It's a copy, unsigned, of that last agreement with your father," I said, after a disappointed glance. "It's worth keeping," and I thrust it inside my shirt.

But this particular pigeon hole proved to be a mine. In it were several more of the same sort of envelope, all sealed, all addressed to Ramon. One was labelled as the Last Will, one as Inventory, and one simply as Directions. This last had a further warning that it was to be opened only by the one addressed. I determined by hasty examination that the first two were only what they purported to be, and turned hopefully to a perusal of the last. It was in Spanish, and dealt at great length with the disposition and management of Hooper's extensive interests. I append a translation of the portion of this remarkable document, having to do with our case.

"These are my directions," it began, "as to the matter of which we have many times spoken together. I have many enemies, and many who think they have cause to wish my death. They are cowards and soft and I do not think they will ever be sure enough to do me harm. I do not fear them. But it may be that one or some of them will find it in their souls to do a deed against me. In that case I shall be content, for neither do I fear the devil. But I shall be content only if you follow my orders. I add here a list of my enemies and of those who have cause to wish me ill. If I am killed, it is probable that some one of these will have done the deed. Therefore they must all die. You must see to it, following them if necessary to the ends of the earth. You will know how; and what means to employ. When all these are gone, then go you to the highest rock on the southerly pinnacle of Cochise's Stronghold. Ten paces northwest is a gray, flat slab. If you lift this slab there will be found a copper box. In the box is the name of a man. You will go to this man and give him the copper box and in return he will give to you one hundred thousand dollars. I know well, my Ramon, that your honesty would not permit you to seek the copper box before the last of my enemies is dead. Nevertheless, that you may admire my recourse, I have made an arrangement. If the gray slab on Cochise's Stronghold is ever disturbed before the whole toll is paid, you will die very suddenly and unpleasantly. I know well that you, my Ramon, would not disturb it; and I hope for your sake that nobody else will do so. It is not likely. No one is fool enough to climb Cochise's Stronghold for pleasure; and this gray slab is one among many."

At this time I did not read carefully the above cheerful document. My Spanish was good enough, but took time in the translating. I dipped into it enough to determine that it was what we wanted, and flipped the pages to come to the list of prospective victims. It covered two sheets, and a glance down the columns showed me that about every permanent inhabitant of the Soda Springs Valley was included. I found my own name in quite fresh ink toward the last.

"This is what we want," I said in satisfaction, rising to my feet. I sketched in a few words the purport of the document.

"Let me see it," said the girl.

I handed it to her. She began to examine carefully the

list of names, her face turning paler as she read. Tim Westmore looked anxiously over her shoulder. Suddenly I saw his face congest and his eyes bulge.

"Why! why!" he gasped, "I'm there! What've I ever done, I ask you that? The old——" he choked, at a loss and groping. Then his anger flared up. "I've always served him faithful and done what I was told," he muttered, fiercely. "I'll do him in for this!"

"I am here," observed Miss Emory.

"Yes, and that sot in the chair!" whispered Tim, fiercely. Again Brower proved he was not asleep by opening one eye.

"Thanks for them kind words," said he.

"We've got to get out of here," stated Tim with conviction.

"That idea just got through your thick British skull?" queried Artie, rousing again.

"I wish we had some way to carry the young lady— she can't walk," said Westmore, paying no attention.

"I have my horse tied out by the lone Joshua-tree," I answered him.

"I'm going to take a look at that Cortinez," said the little Englishman, nodding his satisfaction at my news as to the horse. "I'm not easy about him."

"He'll sleep like a log until morning," Miss Emory reassured me. "I've often stepped right over him where he has been on guard and walked all around the garden."

"Just the same I'm going to take a look," persisted Westmore.

He tiptoed to the door, softly turned the knob and opened it. He found himself face to face with Cortinez.

CHAPTER XIII

I had not thought of the English groom as a man of re-source, but his action in this emergency proved him. He cast a fleeting glance over his shoulder. Artie Brower was huddled down in his armchair practically out of sight; Miss Emory and I had reseated ourselves in the only other two chairs in the room, so that we were in the same relative positions as when we had been bound and left. Only the confusion of the papers on the floor and the open safe would have struck an observant eye.

"It is well that you come," said Tim to Cortinez in Spanish. "The señor sent me to conduct these two to the East Room and I like not the job alone. Enter."

He held the door with one hand and fairly dragged Cortinez through with the other. Instantly he closed the door and cast himself on Cortinez's back. I had already launched myself at the Mexican's throat.

The struggle was violent but brief. Fortunately I had not missed my spring at our enemy's windpipe, so he had been unable to shout. The noise of our scuffle sounded loud enough within the walls of the room; but those walls were two feet thick, and the door and windows closed.

"Get something to gag him with, and the cords," panted Tim to the girl.

Brower opened his eyes again.

"I can beat that," he announced.

He produced his hypodermic and proceeded to mix a gunful of the dope.

"This'll fix him," he observed, turning back the Mexican's sleeve. "You can lay him outside and if anybody comes along they'll think he's asleep—as usual."

This we did when the dope had worked.

It was now high time to think of our next move. For weapons we had the gun and knife taken from Cortinez and the miserable little automatic belonging to Brower. That was all. It was perfectly evident that we could not get out through the regular doorways, as, by Tim's statement, they were all closed and guarded. On my representation it was decided to try the roof.

We therefore knotted together the cord that had bound me and two sheets from the bed, and sneaked cautiously out on the verandah, around the corner to the water barrel, and so to the vantage point of the roof.

The chill of the night was come, and the stars hung cold in the sky. It seemed that the air would snap and crackle were some little resolving element to be dropped into its suspended hush. Not a sound was to be heard except a slow drip of water from somewhere in the courtyard.

It was agreed that I, as the heaviest, should descend first. I landed easily enough and steadied the rope for Miss Emory who came next. While I was waiting I distinctly heard, from the direction of the willows, the hooting of an owl. Furthermore, it was a great horned owl, and he seemed to have a lot to say. You remember what I told you about setting your mind so that only one sort of noise will arouse

it, but that one instantly? I knew perfectly well that Old
Man Hooper's mind was set to all these smaller harmless
noises that most people never notice at all, waking or sleeping—frogs, crickets, owls. And therefore I was convinced
that sooner or later that old man and his foolish ideas and
his shotgun would come projecting right across our well-
planned getaway. Which was just what happened, and
almost at once. Probably that great horned owl had
been hooting for some time, but we had been too busy to
notice. I heard the wicket door turning on its hinges, and
ventured a warning hiss to Brower and Tim Westmore,
who had not yet descended. An instant later I could make
out shadowy forms stealing toward the willows. Evidently
those who served Old Man Hooper were accustomed to
broken rest.

We kept very quiet, straining our eyes at the willows.
After an interval a long stab of light pierced the dusk and
the round detonation of old-fashioned black powder shook
the silence. There came to us the babbling of voices released. At the same instant the newly risen moon plas-
tered us against that whitewashed wall like insects pinned
in a cork-lined case. The moonlight must have been visibly
creeping down to us for some few minutes, but so absorbed
had I been in the doings of the party in the willows, and
so chuckleheaded were the two on the roof, that actually
none of us had noticed!

I dropped flat and dragged the girl down with me. But
there remained that ridiculous, plainly visible rope; and anyway a shout relieved me of any doubt as to whether we had
been seen. Brower came tumbling down on us, and with

one accord we three doubled to the right around the walls
of the ranch. A revolver shot sang by us, but we were not
immediately pursued. Our antagonists were too few and
too uncertain of our numbers and arms.

It was up to us to utilize the few minutes before the ranch
should be aroused. We doubled back through the willows
and across the mesquite flat toward the lone Joshua-tree
where I had left my horse. I held the girl's hand to help
her when she stumbled, while Brower scuttled along with
surprising endurance for a dope wreck. Nobody said anything, but saved their wind.

"Where's Tim?" I asked at a check when we had to
scramble across a *barranca*.

"He went back into the ranch the way we came," replied
Artie with some bitterness.

It was, nevertheless, the wisest thing he could have done.
He had not been identified with this outfit except by Cortinez, and Cortinez was safe for twelve hours.

We found the Joshua-tree without difficulty.

"Now," said I, "here is the plan. You are to take these
papers to Señor Buck Johnson, at the Box Springs ranch.
That's the next ranch on the fork of the road. Do you remember it?"

"Yes," said Brower, who had waked up and seemed quite
sober and responsible. "I can get to it."

"Wake him up. Show him these papers. Make him
read them. Tell him that Miss Emory and I are in the
Bat-eye Tunnel. Remember that?"

"The Bat-eye Tunnel," repeated Artie.

"Why don't *you* go?" inquired the girl, anxiously.

"I ride too heavy; and I know where the tunnel is," I replied. "If anybody else was to go, it would be you. But Artie rides light and sure, and he'll have to ride like hell. Here, put these papers inside your shirt. Be off!"

Lights were flickering at the ranch as men ran to and fro with lanterns. It would not take these skilled *vaqueros* long to catch their horses and saddle up. At any moment I expected to see the massive doors swing open to let loose the wolf pack.

Brower ran to my horse—a fool proceeding, especially for an experienced horseman—and jerked loose the tie rope. Badger is a good reliable cow horse, but he's not a million years old, and he's got some natural equine suspicions. I kind of lay a good deal of it to that fool hard-boiled hat. At any rate, he snorted and sagged back on the rope, hit a yucca point, whirled and made off. Artie was game. He hung on until he was drug into a bunch of *chollas*, and then he had to let go. Badger departed into the distance, tail up and snorting.

"Well, you've done it now!" I observed to Brower, who, crying with nervous rage and chagrin, and undoubtedly considerably stuck up with *cholla* spines, was crawling to his feet.

"Can't we catch him? Won't he stop?" asked Miss Emory. "If he gets to the ranch, won't they look for you?"

"He's one of my range ponies: he won't stop short of the Gila."

I cast over the chances in my mind, weighing my knowledge of the country against the probabilities of search. The proportion was small. Most of my riding experience had been farther north and to the west. Such obvious hole-ups as the one I had suggested—the Bat-eye Tunnel—were of course familiar to our pursuers. My indecision must have seemed long, for the girl broke in anxiously on my meditations.

"Oughtn't we to be moving?"

"As well here as anywhere," I replied. "We are under good cover; and afoot we could not much better ourselves as against mounted men. We must hide."

"But they may find the trampled ground where your horse has been tied."

"I hope they do."

"You hope they do!"

"Sure. They'll figure that we must sure have moved away. They'll never guess we'd hide near at hand. At least that's what I hope."

"How about tracks?"

"Not at night. By daylight maybe."

"But then to-morrow morning they can——"

"To-morrow morning is a long way off."

"Look!" cried Brower.

The big gates of the ranch had been thrown open. The glare of a light—probably a locomotive headlight—poured out. Mounted figures galloped forth and swerved to right or left, spreading in a circle about the enclosure. The horsemen reined to a trot and began methodically to quarter the ground, weaving back and forth. Four detached themselves and rode off at a swift gallop to the points of the compass. The mounted men were working fast for fear, I suppose, that we may have possessed horses. Another contingent, afoot and with lanterns, followed more slowly, going over the ground for indications. I could not but admire the skill and thoroughness of the plan.

"Our only chance is in the shadow from the moon," I told my companions. "If we can slip through the riders, and get in their rear, we may be able to follow the *barranca* down. Any of those big rocks will do. Lay low, and after a rider has gone over a spot, try to get to that spot without being seen."

We were not to be kept long in suspense. Out of all the three hundred and sixty degrees of the circle one of the swift outriders selected precisely our direction! Straight as an arrow he came for us, at full gallop. I could see the toss of his horse's mane against the light from the opened door. There was no time to move. All we could do was to cower beneath our rock, muscles tense, and hope to be able to glide around the shadow as he passed.

But he did not pass. Down into the shallow *barranca* he slid with a tinkle of shale, and drew rein within ten feet of our lurking place.

We could hear the soft snorting of his mount above the thumping of our hearts. I managed to get into a position to steal a glimpse. It was difficult, but at length I made out the statuesque lines of the horse, and the rider himself, standing in his stirrups and leaning slightly forward, peering intently about him. The figures were in silhouette against the sky, but nobody ever fooled me as to a horse. It was the Morgan stallion, and the rider was Tim Westmore. Just as the realization came to me, Tim uttered a low, impatient whistle.

It's always a good idea to take a chance. I arose into view—but I kept my gun handy.

"Thank God!" cried Tim, fervently, under his breath. "I remembered you'd left your horse by this Joshua: it's the only landmark in the dark. Saints!" he ejaculated in dismay as he saw us all. "Where's your horse?"

"Gone."

"We can't all ride this stallion——"

"Listen," I cut in, and I gave him the same directions I had previously given Brower. He heard me attentively.

"I can beat that," he cut me off. He dismounted. "Get on here, Artie. Ride down the *barranca* two hundred yards and you'll come to an alkali flat. Get out on that flat and ride like hell for Box Springs."

"Why don't you do it?"

"I'm going back and tell 'em how I was slugged and robbed of my horse."

"They'll kill you if they suspect; dare you go back?"

"I've been back once," he pointed out. He was helping Brower aboard.

"Where did you get that bag?" he asked.

"Found it by the rock where we were hiding: it's mine," replied Brower.

Westmore tried to get him to leave it, but the little jockey was obstinate. He kicked his horse and, bending low, rode away.

"You're right: I beg your pardon," I answered Westmore's remark to me. "You don't look slugged."

"That's easy fixed," said Tim, calmly. He removed his hat and hit his forehead a very solid blow against a projection of the conglomerate boulder. The girl screamed slightly.

"Hush!" warned Tim in a fierce whisper. He raised his hand toward the approaching horsemen, who were now very near. Without attention to the blood streaming from his brow he bent his head to listen to the faint clinking of steel against rock that marked the stallion's progress toward the alkali flat. The searchers were by now dangerously close, and Tim uttered a smothered oath of impatience. But at last we distinctly heard the faint, soft thud of galloping hoofs.

The searchers heard it, too, and reined up to listen. Tim thrust into my hand the 30-30 Winchester he was carrying together with a box of cartridges. Then with a leap like a tiger he gained the rim of the *barranca*. Once there, however, his forces seemed to desert him. He staggered forward calling in a weak voice. I could hear the volley of rapid questions shot at him by the men who immediately surrounded him; and his replies. Then somebody fired a revolver thrice in rapid succession and the whole cavalcade swept away with a mighty crackling of brush. Immediately after Tim rejoined us. I had not expected this.

Relieved for the moment we hurried Miss Emory rapidly up the bed of the shallow wash. The tunnel mentioned was part of an old mine operation, undertaken at some remote period before the cattle days. It entered the base of one of those isolated conical hills, lying like islands in the plain, so common in Arizona. From where we had hidden it lay about three miles to the northeast. It was a natural and obvious hide out, and I had no expectation of remaining unmolested.   My hope lay in rescue.

We picked our way under cover of the ravine as long as we could, then struck boldly across the plain.   Nobody seemed to be following us.   A wild hope entered my heart that perhaps they might believe we had all made our escape to Box Springs.

As we proceeded the conviction was borne in on me that the stratagem had at least saved us from immediate capture. Like most men who ride I had very sketchy ideas of what three miles afoot is like—at night—in high heels.   The latter affliction was common to both Miss Emory and myself. She had on a sort of bedroom slipper, and I wore the usual cowboy boots.   We began to go footsore about the same time, and the little rolling volcanic rocks among the bunches of *sacatone* did not help us a bit.   Tim made good time, curse him.   Or rather, bless him; for as I just said, if he had not tolled away our mounted pursuit we would have been caught as sure as God made little green apples.   He seemed as lively as a cricket, in spite of the dried blood across his face.

The moon was now sailing well above the horizon, throwing the world into silver and black velvet.   When we moved in the open we showed up like a train of cars; but, on the other hand, the shadow was a cloak.   It was by now nearly one o'clock in the morning.

Miss Emory's nerve did not belie the clear, steadfast look of her eye; but she was about all in when we reached the foot of Bat-eye Butte.   Tim and I had discussed the procedure as we walked.   I was for lying in wait outside; but Tim pointed out that the tunnel entrance was well down in the boulders, that even the sharpest outlook could not be sure of detecting an approach through the shadows, and that from the shelter of the roof props and against the light we should be able to hold off a large force almost indefinitely. In any case, we would have to gamble on Brower's winning through, and having sense enough in his opium-saturated mind to make a convincing yarn of it. So after a drink at the *tenaja* below the mine we entered the black square of the tunnel.

The work was old, but it had been well done. They must have dragged the timbers down from the White Mountains. Indeed a number of unused beams, both trunks of trees and squared, still lay around outside. From time to time, since the original operations, some locoed prospector comes projecting along and does a little work in hopes he may find something the other fellow had missed. So the passage was crazy with props and supports, new and old, placed to brace the ageing overhead timbers. Going in they were a confounded nuisance against the bumped head; but looking back toward the square of light they made fine protections behind which to crouch. In this part of the country any tunnel would be dry. It ran straight for about a hundred and fifty feet.

We groped our way about seventy-five feet, which was as far as we could make out the opening distinctly, and sat down to wait. I still had the rest of the tailor-made cigarettes, which I shared with Tim. We did not talk, for we wished to listen for sounds outside. To judge by her breathing, I think Miss Emory dozed, or even went to sleep.

About an hour later I thought to hear a single tinkle of shale. Tim heard it, too, for he nudged me. Our straining ears caught nothing further, however; and I, for one, had relaxed from my tension when the square of light was darkened by a figure. I was nearest, so I raised Cortinez's gun and fired. The girl uttered a scream, and the figure disappeared. I don't know yet whether I hit him or not; we never found any blood.

We made Miss Emory lie down behind a little slide of rock, and disposed ourselves under shelter.

"We can take them as fast as they come," exulted Tim.

"I don't believe there are more than two or three of them," I observed. "It would be only a scouting party. They will go for help."

As there was no longer reason for concealment, we talked aloud and freely.

Now ensued a long waiting interim. We could hear various sounds outside as of moving to and fro. The enemy had likewise no reason for further concealment.

"Look!" suddenly cried Tim. "Something crawling."

He raised the 30-30 and fired. Before the flash and the fumes had blinded me I, too, had seen indistinctly something low and prone gliding around the corner of the entrance. That was all we could make out of it, for as you can imagine the light was almost non-existent. The thing glided steadily, untouched or unmindful of the shots we threw at it. When it came to the first of the crazy uprights supporting the roof timbers it seemed to hesitate gropingly. Then it drew slowly back a foot or so, and darted forward.

The ensuing thud enlightened us. The thing was one of the long, squared timbers we had noted outside; and it was being used as a battering ram.

"They'll bring the whole mountain down on us!" cried Tim, springing forward.

But even as he spoke, and before he had moved two feet, that catastrophe seemed at least to have begun. The prop gave way: the light at the entrance was at once blotted out; the air was filled with terrifying roaring echoes. There followed a succession of crashes, the rolling of rocks over each other, the grinding slide of avalanches great and small. We could scarcely breathe for the dust. Our danger was that now the thing was started it would not stop: that the antique and inadequate supports would all give way, one bringing down the other in succession until we were buried. Would the forces of equilibrium establish themselves through the successive slight resistances of these rotted, worm-eaten old timbers before the constricted space in which we crouched should be entirely eaten away?

After the first great crash there ensued a moment's hesitation. Then a second span succumbed. There followed a series of minor chutes with short intervening silences. At last so long an interval of calm ensued that we plucked up courage to believe it all over. A single stone rolled a few feet and hit the rock floor with a bang. Then, immediately after, the first deafening thunder was repeated as evidently another span gave way. It sounded as though the whole mountain had moved. I was almost afraid to stretch out my hand for fear it would encounter the wall of débris. The roar ceased as abruptly as it had begun. Followed then a long silence. Then a little cascading tinkle of shale. And another dead silence.

"I believe it's over," ventured Miss Emory, after a long time.

"I'm going to find out how bad it is," I asserted.

I moved forward cautiously, my arms extended before me, feeling my way with my feet. Foot after foot I went, encountering nothing but the props. Expecting as I did to meet an obstruction within a few paces at most, I soon lost my sense of distance; after a few moments it seemed to me that I must have gone much farther than the original length of the tunnel. At last I stumbled over a fragment, and so found my fingers against a rough mass of débris.

"Why, this is fine!" I cried to the others, "I don't believe more than a span or so has gone!"

I struck one of my few remaining matches to make sure. While of course I had no very accurate mental image of the original state of things, still it seemed to me there was an awful lot of tunnel left. As the whole significance of our situation came to me, I laughed aloud.

"Well," said I, cheerfully, "they couldn't have done us a better favour! It's a half hour's job to dig us out, and in the meantime we are safe as a covered bridge. We don't even have to keep watch."

"Provided Brower gets through," the girl reminded us.

"He'll get through," assented Tim, positively. "There's nothing on four legs can catch that Morgan stallion."

I opened my watch crystal and felt of the hands. Half-past two.

"Four or five hours before they can get here," I announced.

"We'd better go to sleep, I think," said Miss Emory.

"Good idea," I approved. "Just pick your rocks and go to it."

I sat down and leaned against one of the uprights, expecting fully to wait with what patience I might the march of events. Sleep was the farthest thing from my thoughts. When I came to I found myself doubled on my side with a short piece of ore sticking in my ribs and eighteen or twenty assorted cramp-pains in various parts of me. This was all my consciousness had room to attend to for a few moments. Then I became dully aware of faint tinkling sounds and muffled shoutings from the outer end of the tunnel. I shouted in return and made my way as rapidly as possible toward the late entrance.

A half hour later we crawled cautiously through a precarious opening and stood blinking at the sunlight.

CHAPTER XIV

A group of about twenty men greeted our appearance with a wild cowboy yell. Some of the men of our outfit were there, but not all; and I recognized others from as far south as the Chiracahuas. Windy Bill was there with Jed Parker; but Señor Johnson's bulky figure was nowhere to be seen. The other men were all riders—nobody of any particular standing or authority. The sun made it about three o'clock of the afternoon. Our adventures had certainly brought us a good sleep!

After we had satisfied our thirst from a canteen we began to ask and answer questions. Artie Brower had made the ranch without mishap, had told his story, and had promptly fallen asleep. Buck Johnson, in his usual deliberate manner, read all the papers through twice; pondered for some time while the more excited Jed and Windy fidgeted impatiently; and then, his mind made up, acted with his customary decision. Three men he sent to reconnoitre in the direction of the Bat-eye Tunnel with instructions to keep out of trouble and to report promptly. His other riders he dispatched with an insistent summons to all the leading cattlemen as far south as the Chiracahua Range, as far east as Grant's Pass, as far west as Madrona. Such was Buck Johnson's reputation for level-headedness that without hesitation these men saddled and rode at their best speed. By noon the weightiest of the Soda Spring Valley had gathered in conclave.

"That's where we faded out," said Jed Parker. "They sent us up to see about you-all. The scouts from up here come back with their little Wild West story about knocking down this yere mountain on top of you. We had to believe them because they brought back a little proof with them. Mex guns and spurs and such plunder looted off'n the deceased on the field of battle. Bill here can tell you."

"They was only two of them," said Windy Bill, diffident for the first time in his life, "and we managed to catch one of 'em foul. We been digging here for too long. We ain't no prairie dogs to go delving into the bosom of the earth. We thought you must be plumb deceased anyhow: we couldn't get a peep out of you. I was in favour of leavin' you lay myself. This yere butte seemed like a first-rate imposing tomb; and I was willing myself to carve a few choice sentiments on some selected rock. Sure I can carve! But Jed here allowed that you owed him ten dollars and maybe had some money in your pocket——"

"Shut up, Windy," I broke in. "Can't you see the young lady——"

Windy whirled all contrition and apologies.

"Don't you mind me, ma'am," he begged. "They call me Windy Bill, and I reckon that's about right. I don't mean nothing. And we'd have dug all through this butte before——"

"I know that. It isn't your talk," interrupted Miss Emory, "but the sun is hot—and—haven't you anything at all to eat?"

"Suffering giraffes!" cried Windy above the chorus of dismay. "Lunkheads! chumps! Of all the idiot plays ever made in this territory!" He turned to the dismayed group. "Ain't any one of you boys had sense enough to bring any grub?"

But nobody had. The old-fashioned Arizona cowboy ate only twice a day. It would never occur to him to carry a lunch for noon. Still, they might have considered a rescue party's probable needs.

We mounted and started for the Box Springs ranch. They had at least known enough to bring extra horses.

"Old Hooper knows the cat is out of the bag now," I suggested as we rode along.

"He sure does."

"Do you think he'll stick or will he get out?"

"He'll stick."

"I don't know——" I argued, doubtfully.

"I do," with great positiveness.

"Why are you so sure?"

"There are men in the brush all around his ranch to see that he does."

"For heaven's sake how many have you got together?" I cried, astonished.

"About three hundred." said Jed.

"What's the plan?"

"I don't know. They were chewing over it when I left. But I'll bet something's going to pop. There's a bunch of 'em on that sweet little list you-all dug up."

We rode slowly. It was near five o'clock when we pulled down the lane toward the big corrals. The latter were full of riding horses, and the fences were topped with neatly arranged saddles. Men were everywhere, seated in rows on top rails, gathered in groups, leaning idly against the ranch buildings. There was a feeling of waiting.

We were discovered and acclaimed with a wild yell that brought everybody running. Immediately we were surrounded. Escorted by a clamouring multitude we moved slowly down the lane and into the enclosure.

There awaited us a dozen men headed by Buck Johnson. They emerged from the office as we drew up. At sight of them the cowboys stopped, and we moved forward alone. For here were the substantial men of this part of the territory, the old timers, who had come in the early days and who had persisted through the Indian wars, the border forays, the cattle rustlings, through drought and enmity and bad years. A grim, elderly, four-square, unsmiling little band of granite-faced pioneers, their very appearance carried a conviction of direct and, if necessary, ruthless action. At sight of them my heart leaped. Twenty-four hours previous my case had seemed none too joyful. Now, mainly by my own efforts, after all, I was no longer alone.

They did not waste time in vain congratulations or query. The occasion was too grave for such side issues. Buck Johnson said something very brief to the effect that he was glad to see us safe.

"If this young lady will come in first," he suggested.

But I was emboldened to speak up.

"This young lady has not had a bite to eat since last night," I interposed.

The señor bent on me his grave look.

"Thank you," said he. "Sing!" he roared, and then to the Chinaman who showed up in a nervous hover: "Give this lady grub, savvy? If you'll go with him, ma'am, he'll get you up something. Then we'd like to see you."

"I can perfectly well wait——" she began.

"I'd rather not, ma'am," said Buck with such grave finality that she merely bowed and followed the cook.

CHAPTER XV

They had no tender feelings about me, however. Nobody cared whether I ever ate or not. I was led into the little ranch office and catechized to a fare-ye-well. They sat and roosted and squatted about, emitting solemn puffs of smoke and speaking never a word; and the sun went down in shafts of light through the murk, and the old shadows of former days crept from the corners. When I had finished my story it was dusk.

And on the heels of my recital came the sound of hoofs in a hurry; and presently loomed in the doorway the gigantic figure of Tom Thorne, the sheriff. He peered, seeing nothing through the smoke and the twilight; and the old timers sat tight and smoked.

"Buck Johnson here?" asked Thorne in his big voice.

"Here," replied the señor.

"I am told," said Thorne, directly, "that there is here an assembly for unlawful purposes. If so, I call on you in the name of the law to keep the peace."

"Tom," rejoined Buck Johnson, "I want you to make me your deputy."

"For what purpose?"

"There is a dispossession notice to be served hereabouts; a trespasser who must be put off from property that is not his."

"You men are after Hooper, and I know it. Now you can't run your neighbours' quarrels with a gun, not any more. This is a country of law now."

"Tom," repeated Buck in a reasoning tone, "come in. Strike a light if you want to: and take a look around. There's a lot of your friends here. There's Jim Carson over in the corner, and Donald Macomber, and Marcus Malley, and Dan Watkins."

At this slow telling of the most prominent names in the southwest cattle industry Tom Thorne took a step into the room and lighted a match. The little flame, held high above his head, burned down to his fingers while he stared at the impassive faces surrounding him. Probably he had thought to interfere dutifully in a local affair of considerable seriousness; and there is no doubt that Tom Thorne was never afraid of his duty. But here was Arizona itself gathered for purposes of its own. He hardly noticed when the flame scorched his fingers.

"Tom," said Buck Johnson after a moment, "I heerd tell of a desperate criminal headed for Grant's Pass, and I figure you can just about catch up with him if you start right now and keep on riding. Only you'd better make me your deputy first. It'll sort of leave things in good legal responsible hands, as you can always easy point out if asked."

Tom gulped.

"Raise your right hand," he commanded, curtly, and administered the oath. "Now I leave it in your hands to preserve the peace," he concluded. "I call you all to witness."

"That's all right, Tom," said Buck, still in his crooning

tones, taking the big sheriff by the elbow and gently propelling him toward the door, "now as to this yere criminal over toward Grant's Pass, he was a little bit of a runt about six foot three tall; heavy set, weight about a hundred and ten; light complected with black hair and eyes. You can't help but find him. Tom's a good sort," he observed, coming back, "but he's young. He don't realize yet that when things get real serious this sheriff foolishness just nat'rally bogs down. Now I reckon we'd better talk to the girl."

I made a beeline for the cook house while they did that and filled up for three. By the time I had finished, the conference was raised, and men were catching and saddling their mounts. I did not intend to get left out, you may be sure, so I rustled around and borrowed me a saddle and a horse, and was ready to start with the rest.

We jogged up the road in a rough sort of column, the old timers riding ahead in a group of their own. No injunction had been laid as to keeping quiet; nevertheless, conversation was sparse and low voiced. The men mostly rode in silence smoking their cigarettes. About half way the leaders summoned me, and I trotted up to join them.

They wanted to know about the situation of the ranch as I had observed it. I could not encourage them much. My recollection made of the place a thoroughly protected walled fortress, capable of resisting a considerable assault.

"Of course with this gang we could sail right over them," observed Buck, thoughtfully, "but we'd lose a considerable of men doing it."

"Ain't no chance of sneaking somebody inside?" suggested Watkins.

"Got to give Old Man Hooper credit for some sense," replied the señor, shortly.

"We can starve 'em out," suggested somebody.

"Unless I miss the old man a mile he's already got a messenger headed for the troops at Fort Huachuca," interposed Macomber. "He ain't fool enough to take chances on a local sheriff."

"You're tooting he ain't," approved Buck Johnson. "It's got to be quick work."

"Burn him out," said Watkins.

"It's the young lady's property," hesitated my boss. "I kind of hate to destroy it unless we have to."

At this moment the Morgan stallion, which I had not noticed before, was reined back to join our little group. Atop him rode the diminutive form of Artie Brower whom I had thought down and out. He had evidently had his evening's dose of hop and under the excitation of the first effect had joined the party. His derby hat was flattened down to his ears. Somehow it exasperated me.

"For heaven's sake why don't you get you a decent hat!" I muttered, but to myself. He was carrying that precious black bag.

"Blow a hole in his old walls!" he suggested, cheerfully. "That old fort was built against Injins. A man could sneak up in the shadow and set her off. It wouldn't take but a dash of soup to stick a hole you could ride through a-horseback."

"Soup?" echoed Buck.

"Nitroglycerine," explained Watkins, who had once been a miner.

"Oh, sure!" agreed Buck, sarcastically. "And where'd we get it?"

"I always carry a little with me just for emergencies," asserted Brower, calmly, and patted his black bag.

There was a sudden and unanimous edging away.

"For the love of Pete!" I cried. "Was there some of that stuff in there all the time I've been carrying it around?"

"It's packed good: it can't go off," Artie reassured us. "I know my biz."

"What in God's name do you want such stuff for!" cried Judson.

"Oh, just emergencies," answered Brower, vaguely, but I remembered his uncanny skill in opening the combination of the safe. Possibly that contract between Emory and Hooper had come into his hands through professional activities. However, that did not matter.

"I can make a drop of soup go farther than other men a pint," boasted Artie. "I'll show you: and I'll show that old——"

"You'll probably get shot," observed Buck, watching him closely.

"W'at t'hell," observed Artie with an airy gesture.

"It's the dope he takes," I told Johnson aside. "It only lasts about so long. Get him going before it dies on him."

"I see. Trot right along," Buck commanded.

Taking this as permission Brower clapped heels to the stallion and shot away like an arrow.

"Hold on! Stop! Oh, damn!" ejaculated the señor. "He'll gum the whole game!" He spurred forward in pursuit, realized the hopelessness of trying to catch the Morgan,

and reined down again to a brisk travelling canter. We surmounted the long, slow rise this side of Hooper's in time to
see a man stand out in the brush, evidently for the purpose
of challenging the horseman. Artie paid him not the slightest attention, but swept by magnificently, the great stallion
leaping high in his restrained vitality. The outpost
promptly levelled his rifle. We saw the vivid flash in the
half light. Brower reeled in his saddle, half fell, caught
himself by the stallion's mane and clung, swinging to and
fro. The horse, freed of control, tossed his head, laid back
his ears, and ran straight as an arrow for the great doors
of the ranch.

We uttered a simultaneous groan of dismay. Then with
one accord we struck spurs and charged at full speed, grimly
and silently. Against the gathering hush of evening rose
only the drum-roll of our horses' hoofs and the dust cloud
of their going. Except that Buck Johnson, rising in his stirrups, let off three shots in the air; and at the signal from all
points around the beleagured ranch men arose from the
brush and mounted concealed horses, and rode out into the
open with rifles poised.

The stallion thundered on; and the little jockey managed
to cling to the saddle, though how he did it none of us could
tell. In the bottomland near the ranch he ran out of the
deeper dusk into a band of the strange, luminous after-glow
that follows erratically sunset in wide spaces. Then we
could see that he was not only holding his seat, but was
trying to do something, just what we could not make out.
The reins were flying free, so there was no question of re-
gaining control.

THE KILLER

A shot flashed at him from the ranch; then a second; after which, as though at command, the firing ceased. Probably the condition of affairs had been recognized.

All this we saw from a distance. The immensity of the Arizona country, especially at dusk when the mountains withdraw behind their veils and mystery flows into the bottomlands, has always a panoramic quality that throws small any human-sized activities. The ranch houses and their attendant trees look like toys; the bands of cattle and the men working them are as though viewed through the reverse lenses of a glass; and the very details of mesquite or *sacatone* flats, of alkali shallow or of oak grove are blended into broad washes of tone. But now the distant, galloping horse with its swaying mannikin charging on the ranch seemed to fill our world. The great forces of portent that hover aloof in the dusk of the desert stooped as with a rush of wings. The peaceful, wide spaces and the veiled hills and the brooding skies were swept clear. Crisis filled our souls: crisis laid her hand on every living moving thing in the world, stopping it in its tracks so that the very infinities for a brief, wierd period seemed poised over the running horse and the swaying, fumbling man.

At least that is the way it affected me; and subsequent talk leads me to believe that that it is how it affected every man jack of us. We all had different ways of expressing it. Windy Bill subsequently remarked: "I felt like some old Injun He-God had just told me to crawl in my hole and give them that knew how a chanct."

But I know we all stopped short, frozen in our tracks, and stared, and I don't believe man, *or* horse, drew a deep breath.

THE KILLER

Nearer and nearer the stallion drew to the ranch. Now he was within a few yards. In another moment he would crash head on, at tremendous speed, into the closed massive doors. The rider seemed to have regained somewhat of his strength. He was sitting straight in the saddle, was no longer clinging. But apparently he was making no effort to regain control. His head was bent and he was still fumbling at something. The distance was too great for us to make out what, but that much we could see.

On flew the stallion at undiminished speed. He was running blind; and seemingly nothing could save him from a crash. But at almost the last moment the great doors swung back. Those within had indeed realized the situation and were meeting it. At the same instant Brower rose in his stirrups and brought his arm forward in a wide, free swing. A blinding glare flashed across the world. We felt the thud and heave of a tremendous explosion. Dust obliterated everything.

"Charge, you coyotes! Charge!" shrieked Buck Johnson.

And at full speed, shrieking like fiends, we swept across flats.

CHAPTER XVI

There was no general resistance. We tumbled pell mell through the breach into the courtyard, encountering only terror-stricken wretches who cowered still dazed by the unexpectedness and force of the explosion. In the excitement order and command were temporarily lost. The men swarmed through the ranch buildings like locusts. Señor Buck Johnson and the other old timers let them go; but I noticed they themselves scattered here and there keeping a restraining eye on activities. There was to be no looting: and that was early made plain.

But before matters had a chance to go very far we were brought up all standing by the sound of shots outside. A rush started in that direction: but immediately Buck Johnson asserted his authority and took command. He did not intend to have his men shot unnecessarily.

By now it was pitch dark. A reconnaissance disclosed a little battle going on down toward the water corrals. Two of our men, straying in that direction, had been fired upon. They had promptly gone down on their bellies and were shooting back.

"I think they've got down behind the water troughs," one of these men told me as I crawled up alongside. "Cain't say how many there is. They shore do spit fire considerable. I'm just cuttin' loose where I see the flash. When

123

I shoot, you prepare to move and move lively. One of those horned toads can sure shoot some; and it ain't healthy to linger none behind your own flash."

The boys, when I crawled back with my report, were eager to pile in and rush the enemy.

"Just put us a hoss-back, señor," pleaded Windy Bill, "and we'll run right over them like a Shanghai rooster over a little green snake. They can't hit nothing moving fast in the dark."

"You'll do just what I say," rejoined Buck Johnson, fiercely. "Cow hands are scarce, and I don't aim to lose one except in the line of business. If any man gets shot to-night, he's out of luck. He'd better get shot good and dead; or he'll wish he had been. That goes! There can't be but a few of those renegades out there, and we'll tend to them in due order. Watkins," he addressed that old timer, "you tend to this. Feel around cautious. Fill up the place full of lead. Work your men around through the brush until you get them surrounded, and then just squat and shoot and wait for morning."

Watkins sent out a dozen of the nearest men to circle the water troughs in order to cut off further retreat, if that were projected. Then he went about methodically selecting others to whom he assigned various stations.

"Now you get a-plenty of catteridges," he told them, "and you lay low and shoot 'em off. And if any of you gets shot I'll sure skin him alive!"

In the meantime, the locomotive lantern had been lit so that the interior of the courtyard was thrown into brilliant light. Needless to say the opening blown in the walls did *not* face toward the water corrals. Of Artie Brower and the Morgan stallion we found hardly a trace. They had been literally blown to pieces. Not one of us who had known him but felt in his heart a kindly sorrow for the strange little man. The sentry who had fired at him and who had thus, indirectly, precipitated the catastrophe, was especially downcast.

"I told him to stop, and he kep' right on a-going, so I shot at him," he explained. "What else was I to do? How was I to know he didn't belong to that gang? He acted like it."

But when you think of it how could it have come out better? Poor, weak, vice-ridden, likeable little beggar, what could the future have held for him? And it is probable that his death saved many lives.

The prisoners were brought in—some forty of them, for Old Man Hooper maintained only the home ranch and all his cow hands as well as his personal bravos were gathered here. Buck Johnson separated apart seven of them, and ordered the others into the stables under guard.

"Bad *hombres*, all of them," he observed to Jed Parker. "We'll just nat'rally ship them across the line very *pronto*. But these seven are worse than bad *hombres*. We'll have to see about them."

But neither Andreas, Ramon, nor Old Man Hooper himself were among those present.

"Maybe they slipped out through our guards; but I doubt it," said Buck. "I believe we've identified that peevish lot by the water troughs."

The firing went on quite briskly for a while; then slackened, and finally died to an occasioned burst, mainly from our own side. Under our leader's direction the men fed their horses and made themselves comfortable. I was summoned to the living quarters to explain on the spot the events that had gone before. Here we examined more carefully and in detail the various documents—the extraordinary directions to Ramon; the list of prospective victims to be offered at the tomb, so to speak, of Old Man Hooper; and the copy of the agreement between Emory and Hooper. The latter, as I had surmised, stated in so many words that it superceded and nullified an old partnership agreement. This started us on a further search which was at last rewarded by the discovery of that original partnership. It contained, again as I had surmised, the not-uncommon clause that in case of the death of one or the other of the partners without direct heirs the common property should revert to the other. I felt very stuck on myself for a good guesser. The only trouble was that the original of the second agreement was lacking: we had only a copy, and of course without signatures. It will be remembered that Brower said he had deposited it with a third party, and that third party was to us unknown. We could not even guess in what city he lived. Of course we could advertise. But Windy Bill who—leaning his long figure against the wall—had been listening in silence—a pretty fair young miracle in itself—had a good idea, which was the real miracle, in my estimation.

"Look here," he broke in, "if I've been following the plot of this yere dime novel correctly, it's plumb easy. Just catch Jud—Jud—you know, the editor of the *Cochise*

Branding Iron, and get him to telegraph a piece to the other papers that Artie Brower, celebrated jockey et ceterer, has met a violent death at Hooper's ranch, details as yet unknown. That's the catch-word, as I *savey* it. When this yere third party sees that, he goes and records the paper, and there you are!"

Windy leaned back dramatically and looked exceedingly pleased with himself.

"Yes, that's it," approved Buck, briefly, which disappointed Windy, who was looking for high encomium.

At this moment a messenger came in from the firing party to report that apparently all opposition had ceased. At least there had been for some time no shooting from the direction of the water troughs; a fact concealed from us by the thickness of the ranch walls. Buck Johnson immediately went out to confer with Watkins.

"I kind of think we've got 'em all," was the latter's opinion. "We haven't had a sound out of 'em for a half hour. It may be a trick, of course."

"Sure they haven't slipped by you?" suggested the señor.

"Pretty certain. We've got a close circle."

"Well, I wouldn't take chances in the dark. Just lay low 'till morning."

We returned to the ranch house where, after a little further discussion, I bedded down and immediately fell into a deep sleep. This was more and longer continued excitement than I was used to.

I was afoot with the first stirrings of dawn, you may be sure, and out to join the party that moved with infinite

precaution on the water troughs as soon as it was light
enough to see clearly. We found them riddled with bullets
and the water all run out. Gleaming brass cartridges scattered, catching the first rays of the sun, attested the vigour
of the defence. Four bodies lay huddled on the ground
under the partial shelter of the troughs. I saw Ramon,
his face frowning and sinister even in death, his right hand
still grasping tenaciously the stock of his Winchester; and
Andreas flat on his face; and two others whom I did not
recognize. Ramon had been hit at least four times. But
of Hooper himself was no hide nor hair! So certain had we
been that he had escaped to this spot with his familiars
that we were completely taken aback at his absence.

"We got just about as much sense as a bunch of sheep-
men!" cried Buck Johnson, exasperated. "He's probably
been hiding out somewhere about the place. God knows
where he is by now!"

But just as we were about to return to the ranch house we
were arrested by a shout from one of the cowboys who had
been projecting around the neighbourhood. He came
running to us. In his hand he held a blade of *sacatone* on
which he pointed out a single dark spot about the size of
the head of a pin. Buck seized it and examined it closely.

"Blood, all right," he said at last. "Where did you get
this, son?"

The man, a Chiracahua hand named Curley something-
or-other, indicated a *sacatone* bottom a hundred yards to the
west.

"You got good eyes, son," Buck complimented him.
"Think you can make out the trail?"

"Do'no," said Curley. "Used to do a considerable of tracking."

"Horses!" commanded Buck.

We followed Curley afoot while several men went to saddle up. On the edge of the two-foot jump-off we grouped ourselves waiting while Curley, his brows knit tensely, quartered here and there like a setter dog. He was a good trailer, you could see that in a minute. He went at it right. After quite a spell he picked up a rock and came back to show it. I should never have noticed anything—merely another tiny black spot among other spots—but Buck nodded instantly he saw it.

"It's about ten rods west of whar I found the grass," said Curley. "Looks like he's headed for that water in Cockeye Basin. From thar he could easy make Cochise when he got rested."

"Looks likely," agreed Buck. "Can't you find no footprints?"

"Too much tramped up by cowboys and other jack-asses," said Curley. "It'll come easier when we get outside this yere battlefield."

He stood erect, sizing up the situation through half-squinted eyes.

"You-all wait here," he decided. "Chances are he kept right on up the broad wash."

He mounted one of the horses that had now arrived and rode at a lope to a point nearly half a mile west. There he dismounted and tied his horse to the ground. After rather a prolonged search he raised his hand over his head and described several small horizontal circles in the air.

"Been in the army, have you?" muttered Buck; "well, I will say you're a handy sort of leather-leg to have around. He gave the soldier signal for 'assemble'," he answered Jed Parker's question.

We rode over to join Curley.

"It's all right; he came this way," said the latter; but he did not trouble to show us indications. I am a pretty fair game trailer myself, but I could make out nothing.

We proceeded slowly, Curley afoot leading his horse. The direction continued to be toward Cockeye. Sometimes we could all see plain footprints; again the trail was, at least as far as I was concerned, a total loss. Three times we found blood, once in quite a splash. Occasionally even Curley was at fault for a few moments; but in general he moved forward at a rapid walk.

"This Curley person is all right," observed Windy Bill after a while, "I was brung up to find my way about, and I can puzzle out most anywhere a critter has gone and left a sign; but this yere Curley can track a humming bird acrost a granite boulder!"

After a little while Curley stopped for us to catch up.

"Seems to me no manner of doubt but what he's headed for Cockeye," he said. "There ain't no other place for him to go out this way. I reckon I can pick up enough of this trail just riding along. If we don't find no sign at Cockeye, we can just naturally back track and pick up where he turned off. We'll save time that-away, and he's had plenty of time to get thar and back again."

So Curley mounted and we rode on at a walk on the horse

trail that led up the broad, shallow wash that came out of Cockeye.

Curley led, of course. Then rode Buck Johnson and Watkins and myself. I had horned in on general principles, and nobody kicked. I suppose they thought my general entanglement with this extraordinary series of events entitled me to more than was coming to me as ordinary cow hand. For a long time we proceeded in silence. Then, as we neared the hills, Buck began to lay out his plan.

"When we come up on Cockeye," he was explaining, "I want you to take a half dozen men or so and throw around the other side on the Cochise trail——"

His speech was cut short by the sound of a rifle shot. The country was still flat, unsuited for concealment or defence. We were riding carelessly. A shivering shock ran through my frame and my horse plunged wildly. For an instant I thought I must be hit, then I saw that the bullet had cut off cleanly the horn of my saddle—within two inches of my stomach!

Surprise paralyzed us for the fraction of a second. Then we charged the rock pile from which the shot had come.

We found there Old Man Hooper seated in a pool of his own blood. He had been shot through the body and was dead. His rifle lay across a rock, trained carefully on the trail. How long he had sat there nursing the vindictive spark of his vitality nobody will ever know—certainly for some hours. And the shot delivered had taken from him the last flicker of life.

"By God, he was sure game!" Buck Johnson pronounced his epitaph.

CHAPTER XVII

We cleaned up at the ranch and herded our prisoners together and rode back to Box Springs. The seven men who had been segregated from the rest by Buck Johnson were not among them. I never found out what had become of them nor who had executed whatever decrees had been pronounced against them. There at the home ranch we found Miss Emory very anxious, excited, and interested. Buck and the others in authority left me to inform her of what had taken place.

I told you some time back that this is no love story; but I may as well let you in on the whole sequel to it, and get it off my chest. Windy's scheme brought immediate results. The partnership agreement was recorded, and after the usual legal red-tape Miss Emory came into the property. She had to have a foreman for the ranch, and hanged if she didn't pick on me! Think of that; me an ordinary, forty-dollar cow puncher! I tried to tell her that it was all plumb foolishness, that running a big cattle ranch was a man-sized job and took experience, but she wouldn't listen. Women are like that. She'd seen me blunder in and out of a series of adventures and she thought that settled it, that I was a great man. After arguing with her quite some time about it, I had to give in; so I spit on my hands and sailed in to do my little darndest. I expected the men who realized fully how little I knew about it all would call me a brash damn fool or anyway give me the horse laugh; but I fooled myself. They were mightily decent. Jed Parker or Sam Wooden or Windy Bill were always just happening by and roosting on the corral rails. Then if I listened to them—and I always did—I learned a heap about what I ought to do. Why, even Buck Johnson himself came and stayed at the ranch with me for more than a week at the time of the fall round-up: and he never went near the riding, but just projected around here and there looking over my works and ways. And in the evenings he would smoke and utter grave words of executive wisdom which I treasured and profited by.

If a man gives his whole mind to it, he learns practical things fast. Even a dumb-head Wop gets his English rapidly when he's where he has to talk that or nothing. Inside of three years I had that ranch paying, and paying big. It was due to my friends whom I had been afraid of, and I'm not ashamed to say so. There's Herefords on our range now instead of that lot of heady long-horns Old Man Hooper used to run; and we're growing alfalfa and hay in quantity for fattening when they come in off the ranges. Got considerable hogs, too, and hogs are high—nothing but pure blood Poland. I figure I've added fully fifty per cent., if not more, to the value of the ranch as it came to me. No, I'm not bragging; I'm explaining how came it I married my wife and figured to keep my self-respect. I'd have married her anyhow. We've been together now fifteen years, and I'm here to say that she's a humdinger of a girl, game as a badger, better looking every day, knows cattle and alfalfa and sunsets and sonatas and Poland hogs—but I said this was no love story, and it isn't!

The day following the taking of the ranch and the death of Old Man Hooper we put our prisoners on horses and started along with them toward the Mexican border. Just outside of Soda Springs whom should we meet up with but big Tom Thorne, the sheriff.

"Evenin', Buck," said he.

"Evenin'," replied the señor.

"What you got here?"

"This is a little band of religious devotees fleein' persecution," said Buck.

"And what are you up to with them?" asked Thorne.

"We're protecting them out of Christian charity from the dangers of the road until they reach the Promised Land."

"I see," said Thorne, reflectively. "Whereabouts lays this Promised Land?"

"About sixty mile due south."

"You sure to get them all there safe and sound—I suppose you'd be willing to guarantee that nothing's going to happen to them, Buck?"

"I give my word on that, Tom."

"All right," said Thorne, evidently relieved. He threw his leg over the horn of his saddle. "How about that little dispossession matter, deputy? You ain't reported on that."

"It's all done and finished."

"Have any trouble?"

"Nary trouble," said Señor Buck Johnson, blandly, "all went off quiet and serene."

REVOLUTION

A SELECTION FROM
"PERSONAL HISTORY"
By Vincent Sheean

VI

Revolution

Baku surveyed the Caspian Sea with an air of brash, complacent wealth. There was so much oil that it stood ankle-deep in the fields, and the whole landscape outside the city looked like a marsh across which an army of Don Quixote's giants waded impassively as far as the eye could reach. The aëroplane (a Junker, with two German pilots) came down efficiently at the appointed place, where a customs inspector, a political inspector, and a representative of Junkers were waiting for it. I had no more luggage on leaving Persia than on arriving, and the customs inspector wasted little time on me. The political officer, a solemn young man, was more careful. When he found a pad of that excellent toilet paper upon which the health and greatness of the British Empire depend, he examined it sheet by sheet, holding the first few sheets to the light to see if they had been written on. Even this admirably conscientious examination did not take long, and within ten minutes of landing I was released to the immensities of Russia.

Those immensities were less striking to me than they are said to be to European travellers. Baku, in spite of its great Mosque and its visible mixture of Oriental peoples, seemed violently Western and almost familiar after the sleepy dignity of Persia. The only thing difficult to understand was the direction taken by the wealth you could smell in the air. In the American West there were just such bustling oily encampments as this, but for a different purpose: to enrich everybody who could get rich, particularly the shrewd or lucky entrepreneur upon whose land the gush of wealth had chanced to come. It took an effort to realize how different was the canalization of wealth here, where busy men supposedly bestirred themselves all day long for the benefit of the Soviet state. The analogy with America—in spite of such differences of purpose—grew stronger after the train moved out of Baku. On the next morning we were running through plains that might have been those of Nebraska or Kansas. The train was European, with wagon-lit and wagon-restaurant, but the landscape seemed to me American. Hot, flat fields of wheat, vast spaces, few people, and a general barbaric sharpness of sun and air, cast my mind back to one of my earliest journeys, at the age of five or six, from Illinois to Colorado. Only when we came into Great Russia, in the neighbourhood of Moscow itself, did the country become definitely European, with villages and copses that might have been almost anywhere in northern France or southern England.

Moscow excited me, at first view, more than any city I had seen. Its original savage splendour, slightly down-at-heel, set off by a variety of contrasting styles of architecture, was enhanced by the vitality of its inhabitants. Perhaps that vitality was more noticeable by contrast with the passive indolence I had seen in Persia, but in any case it could not have failed to impress a newcomer. The city had retained a few of its Muscovite glories—the Kremlin, the Cathedral of St. Basil, the Kitai Gorod—and a short distance away, at the convent of the Trinity (Troitzkaya Lavra) were the carefully preserved treasures of Russian ecclesiastical art and architecture, but for the most part it was a city of the nineteenth and twentieth centuries, no older than (say) Brooklyn. Much of its nineteenth-century architecture was ugly. It abounded in museums of every description, for the Bolsheviks had an exalted idea of the value of historical study; and in the museums of painting, particularly in the great collection called the State Museum of Modern Western Art, it afforded delights almost wholly new to me.

My acquaintance with painting, by the time I got to Moscow, was an oddity of the oddest sort: I knew a good deal about Venetian art, was aware of almost every picture in Venice, and had seen no others at all, save on hasty visits to the Vatican and the Louvre. The magnificent collections of modern painting in Moscow therefore made their impression upon a mind unprepared for them. Renoir, Cézanne, Van Gogh, Gauguin, Signac, Seurat, Bonnard

Vuillard, Matisse, Picasso—all were new to me. It is extraordinary that anybody could have lived in Europe during the closing years of such an era of painting without having taken the trouble to notice it. I knew the names of these artists, of course (what names does not a journalist know?), and had even occasionally read a book in which they figured, but as for the works in which they cast their brilliant and revolutionary view of the world, I had missed them all. The fine collections in Chicago and New York, the Camondo at the Louvre, the current shows at galleries—I had seen none of them.

The misfortune was more than compensated for in Russia. Indeed, the Shchukin and Morosov collections in Moscow, with some additions from other sources, formed, in their united impression as a 'museum of modern Western art,' the most dramatic introduction the world at large could offer to the vigorous genius of late nineteenth- and twentieth-century painting. Anybody must be accounted lucky who makes his first acquaintance with the sombre green slope of the Mont Ste Victoire, or the amiable figure of Madame Cézanne, from the examples of these subjects in Moscow. Jungle pictures by the Douanier Rousseau, lush and dank with imagination; the cool green lawns of Pierre Bonnard, the golden Café de Nuit of Van Gogh; Matisse's lovely Moroccan pictures and his celebrated *ronde des danseurs* on the staircase of the Shchukin house; and a huge collection of pictures of all periods and styles by the restless Picasso, combined with scores, even hundreds, of pictures only a little less brilliant, to give a sudden, wonderful view of the genius of modern art in all its range. It was the discovery of a new world.

Moscow itself fascinated me from the beginning by its bizarre and violent contrasts. I had not then read Trotzky, and had never heard of the 'law of combined development,' according to which extremely backward countries are said to be able to skip whole centuries of economic development, their backwardness producing a higher degree of revolutionary readiness than can be found in more advanced countries. But although the phrase was unknown to me, Moscow appeared even then, as I can see by the notes I kept, as a concrete example of 'combined development.' Inside the ancient Kitai Gorod, one of the Oriental roots of the semi-Oriental city, I saw a detailed public exhibition of plaster casts and anatomical models to demonstrate every variety and stage of venereal disease. The chapel of Catherine II in St Basil's Cathedral, one day when I was there, was the scene of a Communist lecture to visiting peasants, who made no secret of their feelings. The red flag draped the arch where once all Russia had revered the shrine of the Iberian Virgin; and the new tomb of Lenin stood foursquare against the glowering Kremlin wall. The whole spectacle suggested a compression of time, a hasty, vaulting vigour, too concentrated to be understood at first by a visitor from the more timid world outside. My eyes and mind registered these phenomena and many more (I even recorded them carefully in the daybook), but I was not yet prepared to examine the fundamental ideas of which they were the direct or indirect results. Indeed, I shied off political implications on that first visit to Moscow with the nervousness of a suspicious colt. Aside from a general disillusionment with Europe, a dislike of Imperialism, and a half-conscious emotional sympathy for the Bolshevik effort (as distinguished from its methods or results), I had no preparation to receive political theory of any kind, and no hospitality to it. I believed, as the valuable daybook shows, that I could keep on my way as a perpetual spectator, so far as the historic movements of mankind were concerned, without any pronounced inclination towards any of them, and without personal interest in their consequences. In this state of suspended development, lasting through the year and a half between my departure from the Rif and my arrival in China, I appear to have believed that books and music, to which I was becoming more and more addicted, and works of art, which I had discovered in Persia and Russia, combined with the satisfaction of physical needs, would have to be (for me) the whole material of life. The desire to find some relationship between this one life and the millions of others into which it was cast—that search for sense, vividly pursued and sharply disappointed during my first adult years—could fall off and cease to be; it could come, in time, to seem as foolish as a desire to tell the future by tea leaves. Accepting the fact that there was no sense in things, that it was a solipsist's world, books, music, friends and the changes of seasons could then take up the whole of it, and life pass as pleasantly as a good play. I might be able to say, in the end, as Lady Mary Wortley Montagu is supposed to have said on her deathbed, 'It has all been very interesting.' This was the frame of mind of the dilettante, into which the first disappointments of a more vigorous attitude had partly precipitated me. In that frame of mind I was naturally not susceptible to any but the spectacular aspect of Russia, and denied, as much as I could, any other interest. It was also a frame of mind in which the State Museum of Modern Western Painting would inevitably exert more fascination, leave a more permanent impression, than anything else in Moscow.

We take what we are ready for. I might have seen hundreds of modern paintings in Chicago or Paris without discovering any intimate response to their vision. It so happened in Moscow that a phenomenal collection of those pictures was open to me at the moment when my belated awareness of the power of art had put me into a state of capacity to see them. Some of the keenest pleasures of the next few years were due to the discovery thus made, and although it may appear on the surface to be purely accidental that these pictures were seen in Bolshevik Moscow, I am persuaded that a relationship exists between the revolt of the artists— their expression, the most perfect in its results, of the general revolt against middle-class ideas—and the conflicts that accompanied that rebellion on the plane of exterior events. Instead of being, as one Bolshevik told me, 'bourgeois and decadent,' the works in the State Museum of Modern Western Painting were as revolutionary as the Communist Manifesto. When Picasso threw the left side of his grey-pink dancing boy out of drawing to give it lightness and animation, in the beautiful early picture in the Morosov collection, he was beginning a career as disruptive to the received prejudices in painting as Lenin's became to academic politics and economics. The artist's revolution was the only one that engaged my sympathies then, but it was not without significance that I had encountered it in Moscow.

2

I returned to Paris by way of Riga and Berlin. My immediate problem was to get the journalistic results of the Persian journey down on paper as quickly as possible, in fulfilment of various engagements; and to do so without undue interruption I found a village on the Normandy coast, Les Petites Dalles, where, for a minute monthly payment, a family of fisher people gave me their house. I remained there through the late summer and autumn; but once the information gathered in Persia had been duly set down, sent off, and (happily) paid for, I left Normandy for Paris and London. I was already hankering after China, where the armies of the Kuomintang were making their belated advance towards the north. This time, I determined, there would be no book-writing about it. Journalism of the most immediate variety (temporary information) had no place within book covers, as the Persian experience had shown. Not only was it presumptuous to write anything about a country on such scant acquaintance, but the skin-deep phenomena, those I still felt qualified to observe, changed so rapidly that the only place for them was the convenient, perishable newspaper. True, I already knew a great deal more about China than I ever had known about Persia. I had been reading books about China all my life, and if much (even most) of what I knew was wrong, out of date, inadequate or distorted by the prejudices of various worthy authors, it still constituted some kind of familiarity with the subject, enough to keep me from being at the mercy of the first talkative person I might meet after getting off the boat at Shanghai. In fact I thought, reading the contradictory and sketchy reports in the London and Paris papers, that the Chinese Revolution in its present stage was an event—a whole school of events—that I could hardly bear to miss. Certain kinds of events to which newspapers gave their attention had this effect on me for years, and had to be explained (when I thought of it) by the antique fancy that newspaper men, like fire horses, could never outgrow their instinct for the 'game.' It seems to me now that this was no explanation, for the events that aroused my fire-horse instinct were not, actually, the ones the newspapers found most interesting. I cared nothing about such events as earthquakes, murders, political elections in the United States, divorces, or transatlantic flights (except Lindbergh's, which captured every imagination). The events that aroused in me the desire to attend, to witness, were invariably those in which large

numbers of men were engaged in some difficult enterprise involving a fundamental idea—an idea of race, class or even of nation.
In what looked like the impending triumph of the Chinese Revolution there was an event of the kind that excited my imagination to the utmost. Without regard to what kind of job I might do
in China, I wanted above all to get there.

I wrote from Paris to my friends on the North American Newspaper Alliance in New York. They hesitated. By this time I had a
set of ready-made characteristics in my profession and was not
regarded as fit for any kind of newspaper work that did not involve crawling through barbed wire or galloping across deserts
in Arab disguise. The injustice of this legend was obvious, for a
newspaper man who could only work in Arab clothes and on a
horse would soon starve to death. But my last bits of newspaper
work had been the two journeys to the Rif, of which the second
had been (from the employers' point of view) eminently successful; consequently I was expected to repeat that experience or
do nothing. China was regarded as too large, too complicated,
too political, and in a general way too unexciting to justify the
employment of a young man whose only gift, it seemed, was for
running through blockades.

I wrote again, waited, and wrote again. In the meanwhile the
wolf had long since passed the door, and to support him adequately I worked for two months on the Paris *Times*, where a
number of my old friends from the Chicago *Tribune* had migrated.[1] Thus the winter passed, and in February the armies of the
Kuomingtang captured Shanghai. This event instantly endowed
China with all the attributes of suitability and excitement that had
been lacking before, and a cable from the N. A. N. A. summoned
me to New York. I could have reached China much more quickly
by way of Russia, but it was believed that instructions delivered
viva voce were more efficacious than instructions by letter, and
to New York I went.

I spent several days in New York receiving instructions and
collecting (whether I wanted them or not) letters to people in
China. Most of these letters were never presented, but one among

---

[1]The Paris *Times*, an amiable curiosity among newspapers, belongs to the next
chapter, where, if the print holds out, it will be found.

them was to prove a document almost as valuable as my passport. It was an open letter ('To Whom It May Concern') written by the senior Senator from Idaho. Mr Borah's fame throughout the world was at its height during the reactionary era of Harding and Coolidge, and his reputation for liberalism and anti-imperialism was nowhere greater than in China; his letter was to constitute my best introduction to the leaders of the national revolution.

From New York to Shanghai by way of Seattle, Yokohama and Kobe seemed to me an unnecessarily lengthy journey, but at last, on the fourteenth of April, my ship pushed through the swarming Whangpu River to the dock at Shanghai.

The International Settlement and the French Concession, the two foreign enclaves that constituted the original city of Shanghai, around which a colossal Chinese city has grown up, gave an instant impression of pompous and rather purse-proud arrogance. The confrontation of European power and the swarming, fluid, antlike life of the poverty-stricken Chinese was more obvious here than anywhere else in China, as I was to learn; the great banks towered above streets where the Chinese appeared chiefly in the guise of coolies, beasts of burden: a physical contrast as vivid as that between the foreign cruisers and gunboats in the river and the innumerable Chinese junks and sampans that clustered noisy and impotent about them. The arrogance of the European city was, just now, tempered by a certain amount of apprehension, for the Cantonese armies had occupied the surrounding Chinese city a month before and were held to be 'threatening' the existence of the foreign settlement. The frontiers of the Anglo-American-French city were guarded by sailors and bluejackets, and one of my earliest impressions in China was that of the glint of bayonets above barricades of sacks filled with dirt. It was strange and not very pleasant to see slovenly Spanish sailors, representatives of a nation that had never had any real interest in China, searching Chinese men and women as they attempted to pass the boundary. I took myself and my belongings off to the Majestic Hotel, a luxurious establishment in the midst of a parklike garden some distance out the Bubbling Well Road. This splendid empty château was then the only alternative to the celebrated Astor House, which was filled with newspaper correspondents and 'old China hands' expounding their philosophy of *Gott strafe China* all day long. At the Majestic I was slightly irritated by too much grandeur, too many servants, too much obsequiousness, but at least the place was quiet, insulated from the two kinds of noise that made Shanghai difficult—the actual physical noise of the streets and the no less positive uproar of hatred and recrimination in which the Shanghai foreigners habitually lived.

If I had to find an example of a place and time in which calm reflection was apparently prohibited by the conditions of life, I think I should name Shanghai in 1927. Even Jerusalem, that home of hatred and despair, during the worst moments of 1929, was not without forms of refuge. It had its architecture and its religions. Shanghai had nothing—nothing but its money and its ghastly fear of losing it. Cowering angrily behind its barricades, it exhibited human nature without dignity or generosity, denying any fact that might sooner or later threaten its hold over wealth and the sources of wealth. As a portal of China, it was at least characteristic of the conflicts within.

3

I arrived in China at the most fateful moment of the national revolution, that in which the victors surveyed the field and took stock of themselves. It was not a good moment for a journalist: from the professional point of view, I was too late. The capture of Shanghai and the sack of Nanking had been the high points of interest for the newspapers in America, and by the time I got to Shanghai the 'story,' as we say in the language of the trade, was already fading into obscurity. After a few more weeks it vanished altogether, for Colonel Lindbergh's flight to Paris drove all other news out of the American newspapers and the American mind for most of the summer. If China had been swallowed up by an earthquake and tidal wave it could scarcely have excited much attention in the United States just then. Moreover, the particular kind of personal exploit that my employers wanted of me—what they called, in their cabled instructions, 'personal adventures'—proved impossible in a country where, so far as I could discover, all the inhabitants when treated with courtesy were invariably courteous and kind. I made various attempts to encounter these 'personal adventures' in parts of China from which all foreigners had fled, and never got so much as a harsh word out of any Chinese. Consequently the whole result of my experience in China was, so far as my newspapers were concerned, flat failure.

But from another point of view, the one adopted in this history, the experience was richer in consequences than any other I have to record. Here, for the first time, I began to approach the fundamental meaning of those vast disturbances that had fascinated me (in part unconsciously) for years—began to be able to discern the general under the particular, to take what Borodin called 'the long view.' In my first direct meeting with the Bolshevik philosophy in action (even in rather circumscribed action), I was disturbed by the precision with which it answered the questions I had begun to think unanswerable—the questions of a sensible relationship between one life and the many. Whether the Bolshevik solutions were the correct ones was another matter, which might take a long time to determine, but they were at least solutions, and represented the effort of human thought to bring order into the chaos that on every side oppressed and appalled the imagination.

I do not mean to say, of course, that I had known nothing about the Communist view of life before I went to China. I had as much acquaintance with it as most people have—perhaps more—and had even read a certain amount of its literature, including huge indigestible lumps of Karl Marx. But the difference between an academic acquaintance with Communism and an actual perception of its spirit is very great. The step required to pass from the first state to the second is so easy that it may be accomplished in a moment, and so difficult that it may involve the effort of a lifetime. It may be compared, I think, to the step by which, at an equally momentous frontier in literature, we pass into the world created by the *Divina Commedia*. Every schoolboy knows about the *Divina Commedia:* how Dante, having lost his way in a dark wood, was found by Virgil and conducted into the depths of hell, rising from there to Purgatory and to the circles of Paradise through which he was led by the blessed Beatrice. But this knowledge of the vast, perfect poem is no knowledge at all; it is like being told in the schoolroom that Paris is the capital of France, a bald statement that can only become a living fact when we have smelled the acacias and eaten the food and investigated the literature that make it true. With Dante the difficulty of the language supplies another barrier (even for Italians); but when the step has at last been taken, the barrier passed, we enter a world in which all parts of the structure of existence are so related and harmonized, so subjugated to a sovereign system, that its ordered beauty and majesty give us the sensation of a new form of life, as if we had actually moved off into space and taken up our abode, for a time, on another star. Such miraculous translations are rare and difficult; it took me thirty-four years to set foot inside the world of Dante. The world of Lenin (which is, after all, all around us) can be entered in a moment, but only if the disposition of circumstances, persons, influences, can conquer the laziness of a bourgeois mind. The required combinations occurred for me at Hankow, and were given force and form, particularly, by Michael Borodin and Rayna Prohme.

But before I went up the river to Hankow I had to make the acquaintance of the parts of the Chinese revolutionary movement that had already begun to be corrupted by power—the counterrevolutionary group of Shanghai and Nanking. Its position was interesting and typical; some such position is always assumed by middle-class revolutionaries at the moment of triumph, and Chiang Kai-shek, the shrewd young man, was even then engaged in the Kerensky-like manœuvres that were to make him President (so to speak) of China. It might be useful to recall, just here, what the course of the Chinese national revolution had been up to 1927. It was a long, slow, cumulative movement, the awakening of a giant; it had been going on for thirty-odd years. Its original organization was the work of the great revolutionary Sun Yat-sen, whose power to move and convince throngs of people had made him the natural leader of the whole south, and, for a time, of all China. In 1911, with the overthrow of the Manchu dynasty, Sun Yat-sen had been proclaimed President of China at Nanking, but, robbed of the actual power by the clever reactionary, Yuan Shih-kai, had retired to Canton to establish there the central point, the focus, for all revolutionary activity. Even in Canton Sun Yat-sen's career was checkered; he was always being driven out and returning in triumph. In 1923, pursuing their announced policy of friendliness to all Asiatic national movements, the Bolsheviks (through Joffe, their ambassador at Peking) made an agreement with Sun Yat-sen by which they were to supply him with military and political advisers, money and munitions. From this point onward the development of the Cantonese revolutionary movement was rapid and overwhelmingly successful. The Bolsheviks had given Sun Yat-sen what he needed: an army. They also moulded, to some extent, the ideas of the movement, although Sun Yat-sen himself never became a Communist, and always, apparently, believed that it would be possible for China to assume the forms of an organized industrial society without going through any kind of class warfare. Sun Yat-sen himself died in 1924, but the movement, becoming increasingly social and economic, with an intensive labour propaganda, became harder to resist after his death than it had been before. The various war lords who governed China on the feudal system dreaded it, and with reason, for it was by its nature inimical to them, even when it made use of their services.

Finally, in 1927, the armies of Canton had swept all the way up to the Yangtze-kiang, had taken Hankow, Shanghai and Nanking, and with them the revenues of the richest part of China. The capture of Nanking, about two weeks before I arrived in Shanghai, had been marked by a collapse of discipline; certain of the Cantonese troops had run wild in the city, looting, raping and killing. These incidents—'the Nanking outrages'—had been promptly avenged by an Anglo-American bombardment of the city, in which numerous noncombatants were killed. Anti-foreign feeling, always strong among the Chinese revolutionaries, was at a high pitch, and all foreigners had been ordered by their own government to leave the interior of China and concentrate at Shanghai and Tientsin. The Cantonese movement had, practically speaking, won its victory, for it was only a question of time until the remaining war lords (the chief of whom was old Chang Tso-lin, supported by the Japanese) would be swept out of the way by the better trained and equipped soldiers, and by persuasive propaganda, from the south.

This moment of triumph was inevitably the one in which the two elements among the Cantonese victors would separate. Genuine revolutionaries—those who wished to change the conditions of life in China, and not simply the forms or names of government—found themselves obliged to cling to the Left Wing of the Kuomintang, in which Russian influence was paramount. The others—those who took part in the revolution for their own advantage, or were prevented by the tenacity of middle-class ideas from wishing to disturb the established arrangement of wealth—collected around the treasuries of Shanghai and Nanking, under the patronage of the Chinese bankers of those cities and their new ally, Chiang Kai-shek. The Left Wing had its capital at Hankow, and the Right Wing at Nanking. The division was not yet open and public, and the Kuomintang (People's party—Sun Yat-sen's old organization) kept up a pretence of unity for some time, but the opposition of the two tendencies was too glaring to be denied in private talk, and constituted, in fact, the chief immediate problem of the revolution.

I went, first, to see Mr T. V. Soong. He was a young man of about my own age, trained at Harvard, intelligent, competent and honest, and had been Minister of Finance for the Cantonese government. The same post had been assigned to him at Hankow and also at Nanking, but at the precise moment of my arrival he had resigned it. He continued resigning it for years, only to take it up again, until he was to become a kind of permanent Minister of Finance in all the Kuomintang governments. His usefulness came not only from the confidence inspired by his known capacity and honesty, but from his relationship to the semi-divine figure of Sun Yat-sen; he was a brother of the great man's widow. When I arrived in Shanghai he was living in Sun Yat-sen's house in the French Concession, the house given the old hero by the city for a permanent refuge in his turbulent career.

Mr Soong—'T. V.,' as he was always called—received me well, thanks to the Borah letter. He spent some time explaining to me the difficulties of his own position, a problem that always worried him a good deal. As I came to know T.V. rather better in the following months, I grew to regard him as the most typical Liberal I had ever known—honest, worried, puzzled, unable to make up his mind between the horrors of capitalist imperialism and the horrors of Communist revolution. If China had only been America his happiness would have been complete, for he could have pretended not to know about the horrors. But in China it was impossible to step out of doors without seeing evidence, on every hand, of the brutal and inhuman exploitation of human labour by both Chinese and foreigners. T. V. was too sensitive not to be moved by such spectacles. And yet he had an equally nervous dread of any genuine revolution; crowds frightened him, labour agitation and strikes made him ill, and the idea that the rich might ever be despoiled filled him with alarm. During a demonstration in Hankow one day his motorcar was engulfed by a mob and one of its windows was broken. He was, of course, promptly rescued by his guards and removed to safety, but the experience had a permanent effect on him—gave him the nervous dislike for mass action that controlled most of his political career and threw him at last, in spite of the sincerity of his idealism, into the camp of the reactionaries. He was an amiable, cultivated and charming young man, but he had no fitness for an important rôle in a great revolution. On the whole, I believe he realized it perfectly, and was made more miserable by that fact than by any other.

T. V. gave me a note to Chiang Kai-shek, who was then at Nanking, and another to Mme Sun Yat-sen in Hankow. He intimated that I might find some difference of opinion between these two dignitaries, but at the time he was still trying hard to pretend that no split between the elements of the Kuomintang had taken place. As I knew later on, the pretence was hollow, for actually the split had taken place in the exact middle—the very place where T. V. wished to stand—and had probably been more painful to him than to anybody else. So far as I was able to determine, he was the only real Liberal among the revolutionary leaders, and as the others moved freely, almost happily, towards their natural positions to Left or Right, he went through all the agonies of mind and spirit to which, on a larger scale, world liberalism had been subjected since 1918.

The idea of going to Nanking was regarded as foolhardy by the foreigners in Shanghai, and particularly by my colleagues; nevertheless, I went. It was an illuminating little journey. The foreigners had withdrawn from the railroad and from the Chinese city of Shanghai as well as from Nanking and the whole interior. The train, therefore, was about two hours late in starting and four hours late in arriving. It was crowded with Cantonese soldiers, but instead of tossing me about on their bayonets, as my Shanghai friends wished me to believe was their habit, they made way for me and actually gave me a seat in one of the best compartments. I was accompanied by an interpreter obtained through one of the missionary groups. This young man had studied in the United States and talked the 'Oh, boy!' and 'Geez! You said it!' kind of English. His ideas were as shallow and chaotic as his language. He had a great enthusiasm for the Revolution and the Kuomin-tang, but knew remarkably little about either. I spent an hour or so explaining to him what the party organization was (its rôle in the 'era of tutelage' as outlined by Sun Yat-sen), as I wanted to be sure that my questions to Chiang Kai-shek would be correctly understood in transit. As we carried on this conversation, packed tight into a corner of the carriage with soldiers all over us, I noticed that a long-gowned Chinese (i.e., a member of the middle or educated class) was listening. Presently he joined in the talk, but in the accents of Oxford, with such a command of literary English that my interpreter was abashed. The long-gowned Chinese was one of the secretaries to Quo Tai-chi in the Ministry of Foreign Affairs, and had just the kind of fluid, voluble intelligence that the Shanghai foreigners most disliked. He spent an hour or so airing the grievances of the Shanghai Chinese, their constant humili-ations in the foreign city, the insults their pride suffered in not being allowed to go into parks or clubs, etc., etc. It was not a sympathetic character or a sympathetic complaint, but I listened with interest. When I ventured to say that there seemed to me to be more valid subjects of grievance in Shanghai, and men-tioned, as an example, the dreadful conditions I had glimpsed only the day before in certain textile mills where men, women and children worked twelve hours a day for a wage barely sufficient to buy rice, my long-gowned friend shut up like a clam. The Revolu-tion, for him, apparently meant that educated Chinese ought to be admitted to social equality with the half-educated foreign mer-chants in their clubs and parks and houses—a strange ambition, but one I was to meet with fairly often among the heirs of the Mandarinate.

In Nanking I repaired to a Chinese inn with my interpreter and sent a note to headquarters with T. V. Soong's line of introduction. An hour or so later I was summoned to see the general, Chiang Kai-shek.

This remarkable young man, who was then about thirty and looked less, had been born a poor Cantonese and was, to begin with, a common soldier. He was without education even in Chinese, and spoke only the dialect of his native city. (His name, too, was always pronounced in Cantonese—Chiang Kai-shek, whereas in Chinese it would have been Ch'ang Kai-shih.) He had been singled out for advancement by Sun Yat-sen, and showed enough ability to be pushed ahead through all ranks until he became, in 1927, commander-in-chief of the armies and, so far as the public was concerned, the military hero of the Revolution. Having arrived at his present eminence in great part by the aid of the Russians, he had now decided—under the persuasion of the Shanghai bankers and the immense revenues of the maritime provinces—to break with them and establish himself as a war lord, modern style, with all the slogans and propaganda of the Kuomintang to cover his personal aggrandizement and give it a patriotico-revolutionary colour.

Chiang seemed (rather to my surprise) sensitive and alert. He was at pains to explain that he intended to carry out the whole programme of Sun Yat-sen, the Three People's Principles (*San Min Chu I*) and all the rest of it, but without falling into 'excesses.' I was unable to bring him to any clear statement of his disagreement with the Russians or the Left Wing, and his thin brown face worked anxiously as he talked round the subject, avoiding its pitfalls. I cursed the necessity for an interpreter—particularly one whose command of both languages was obviously so limited— and wished, not for the first time, that the Esperantists had been more successful in their efforts. But even through the clouds of misapprehension set up by my friend the returned student from the United States I could discern the eager, ambitious nature of Chiang Kai-shek's mind, his anxiety to be thought well of, his desire to give his personal ambitions the protective coloration of a revolutionary doctrine and vocabulary. The phrases adopted by all members of the Kuomintang, from Right to Left, were used by him over and over again: 'wicked gentry' (i. e., reactionary land-lords), 'foreign imperialism' and 'unequal treaties,' the traditional enemies of the Cantonese movement. But upon the methods he intended to use to combat his enemies he was vague. It was impossible to avoid the conclusion that with this young man, in spite of his remarkable opportunities, the phrases of the movement had not sunk beyond the top layer of consciousness. He remained a shrewd, ambitious, energetic Cantonese with his way to make in the world, and I fully believed that he would make it. I thought I detected, about his mouth and eyes, one of the rarest of human expressions, the look of cruelty. It may, indeed, have been only the characteristic look of a nervous, short-tempered man, but in later weeks, when his counter-revolution reached its height and the Communists were being tortured and butchered at his command, I was to remember the flickering mouth and anxious eyes of Chiang Kai-shek.

The remarkable thing about my visit to Nanking—where I remained three days—was that everybody in the streets, in the inn, at headquarters and wherever I went, treated me with courtesy. I was a citizen of a country whose ships, only a few days before, had bombarded the city, killing scores of people and setting fire to many houses. I was, I believe, the only foreigner in the area; I was neither armed nor guarded; the guns of the American and British ships were still trained on the city from the middle of the Yangtze River, and an informal state of war was felt to exist between the Chinese of the river towns and the hostile foreign navies that frowned upon them. From Hankow to Shanghai there was no communication between the foreign warships and the shore: for another five or six weeks the tension remained acute. And yet nothing whatever happened to me—not a shout, not a stone, not a gesture—to indicate that my presence was a reminder of the miseries and humiliations of China. Perhaps the inhabitants of Nanking were ashamed of the disorders of a fortnight before, and perhaps they were afraid of the gray ships in the river. But, on the whole, I took the experience as another confirmation of a principle in which I had always firmly believed: that human beings of whatever complexion or nation were 'safe' enough if one clearly wished them no harm. The excited troops had disproved this principle, you might say, in Nanking itself only a short time before; but had they? In the frenzy of victory, drunk with success and mob anger, they had attacked the houses and persons of the 'foreign imperialists'—those foreigners who lived in conspicuous luxury among them by means of the exploitation of their labour and their markets, supported visibly at all times by foreign warships in the Chinese river. The Nanking outrages, however deplorable, were easy to understand; they were an inevitable consequence of the conditions under which the foreign colonies were imposed upon China. Such things might happen anywhere when an oppressed population gets out of hand. They have, indeed, happened in most countries at one time or another. But it seemed to me that the lone foreigner, unarmed and friendly, with no wealth to excite envy and no power to excite fear, would certainly be safe enough among any people, and particularly among the courteous Chinese, if the pretences of superiority could be abandoned.

I returned to Shanghai, the atmosphere of which had already begun to seem fantastically artificial. Its inhabitants considered that they had built Shanghai out of nothing, and, in the most obvious sense, they had; the site of the city had been a worthless mudbank, given to the British, Americans and French because the Chinese did not want it. The British, Americans and French had reclaimed the land, built upon it with increasing pompousness, and now regarded it as an exhibition of their own superiority to the despised natives of China. It never seemed to cross their minds that every penny spent upon Shanghai had been wrung from the Chinese in one way or another, either by the exorbitant profits of foreign trade—the exploitation of what is called an 'undeveloped market,' which is to say a market made up of people who do not know when they are being cheated—or by the direct exploitation of Chinese labour. The second source of wealth was more recent, and its profits had been enormous. The British, Americans and Japanese were able to employ Chinese people of all ages in their factories for any number of hours a day, for wages so small that they barely supported a half-starved and ever-threatened life.

The coolie population, which never had enough to eat and often no place to sleep, was easy prey for manufacturers who wished to make the modest profit of a thousand per cent. Against any mention of these unpleasant facts the Shanghai foreigner, sipping his cocktail reflectively in the cool recesses of one of his clubs, would reply with a number of statements that seemed to him irrefutable. He would say that many Chinese of the middle class, compradores,[1] had grown rich with the foreigners; that conditions in the British and American factories were not so bad as in the Japanese, and conditions in the Japanese factories not so bad as in the occasional Chinese establishments; that the prosperity of Shanghai benefited all China; and that, in any case, the Chinese were an inferior race, had never been used to anything but starvation and overwork, misery and oppression, and consequently 'don't feel anything—not, at least, as we do.' I never met anybody in Shanghai who revealed the slightest feeling of shame, the slightest consciousness of degradation, in thus taking advantage of human misery in its most appalling forms. On the contrary, the Shanghai foreigners felt virtuous because they gave their coolies a slightly better chance of survival than did the worst of the Chinese employers. Shanghai saw itself as the benefactor of all China, and was horrified at the rising Chinese demand for better conditions of life and a recognized share in the spoils.

A different attitude was, perforce, adopted by the missionaries, whose religion compelled them to concede in theory the fraternity of all creatures. They were, on the whole, better educated and temperamentally more civilized than the other foreigners, those who had come to China simply to make all the money they could out of the country. But the missionaries had as their supreme objective the conversion of the Chinese to Christianity. Such an objective, so contrary to common sense, good manners, and the genius of Chinese civilization, was pursued by the best of the missionaries for the best of reasons—that they firmly believed in a future life eternal, to which only those who adhered to their particular sect could be admitted. To bring the Chinese into the fold

---

[1]Compradores were interpreting middlemen, always Chinese, who worked on a kind of double-commission basis with foreigners from the earliest days of foreign trade in China.

was thus an act of Christian charity. Their effort brought about a considerable incidental benefit in the form of education and good works—for which they were detested by the other foreigners—but the supreme objective was still religious conversion, and the American missionaries, in particular, tended to count their harvest of souls in much the same way as the merchants counted their profits, with a similar convenient disregard of motives and methods. This organized attempt to impose a foreign god and an alien system of supernatural beliefs on the rationalistic character of the Chinese was not likely to be successful no matter how many hundreds of years it was continued; it was essentially an incongruous and presumptuous enterprise, which the Chinese could scarcely take seriously even when they made use of it; but it created a large class of especially privileged foreigners in the country, enjoying the protection of foreign armies and navies, presenting a strange religion of mystery and dogma in a mixture of free rice, machine guns, schools, gunboats, and unintelligibility. The finest of the missionaries—and there were admirable, even noble, characters among them, however unsympathetic their purposes—often bewailed the conditions under which Christianity had to be presented to the Chinese, when a sermon about brotherly love might be interrupted by a murderous bombardment from the loving Christian navies.

Like the merchants of the treaty ports, the missionaries had grown to think of themselves as an integral part of China; not at all as visitors to be tolerated so long as they behaved themselves, but as benefactors without whom the country could scarcely continue to exist. The difference between the merchants and the missionaries, then, it seemed to me in Shanghai and afterwards, was that the first group frankly asserted themselves a superior race, designed by nature to make money out of the Chinese, while the second group, denying racial superiority but acting upon the assumption that it existed, felt themselves appointed by the same mysterious nature to bring light, charity and faith to the heathen. It was the old, jerky rhythm of capitalism and philanthropy: the system of profit was accustomed to take all it could get, and then throw off a little of the unneeded surplus on its victims. There should be no surprise if such a muddled relationship appeared, at times, wholly incomprehensible to the rationalistic Chinese. One had to belong to the great, dominant, all-wonderful races of western Europe and the United States to appreciate how greed and sanctimoniousness could inhabit the same house, speak the same language, fight with the same weapons.

4

Hankow, Wuchang, Hanchang, the three great cities called, together, Wuhan, blackened the flat shores of the river early on our fifth day from Shanghai. Of the three cities, Hankow was the most important, although not the largest. It was the one in which the foreigners had built their own city, in concessions taken from the Chinese in the nineteenth century. The Germans, Russians and Americans having been counted out for assorted reasons, the foreign city consisted, in 1927, of the British, French and Japanese Concessions—or, practically, of the first two, since the Japanese Concession was almost indistinguishable from the surrounding Chinese town. Foreign women and children had left Hankow when the Cantonese captured the city the preceding winter; many of the men had followed them; the city was consequently regarded as 'evacuated,' although a handful of Americans, British and French remained in charge of their various properties. The British Concession had been (by the Chen-O'Malley Agreement a few months before) entrusted to the Chinese to administer under a régime of transition—a conciliatory move that infuriated most of the British in China. But the French still guarded their streets with small Annamite soldiers, and the British and American navies, represented in great strength at Hankow, filled the town from morning to night with sailors on leave and the naval police sent out to guard them. In spite of this excessive protection, the foreigners persisted in regarding Hankow as dangerous. Mr Lockhart, the American Consul, offered me a bed. He already had a number of fortuitous guests, and it was his duty to warn all Americans, I believe, that they could be protected only if they lived in the consulate under guard. But the large, comfortable Hôtel des Wagons-Lits in the French Concession was almost empty, and as I could see no immediate likelihood of its being stormed by an angry Chinese mob, I installed myself there. Its only 'protection' was a stolid little brown Annamite who stood wearily with rifle and bayonet under the arc light on the corner, and even his presence was, so far as I ever saw, quite unnecessary. For in Hankow, as in Nanking, I saw no real disorder. I remained there two months or more, and the nearest thing to an international incident that came under my observation was the effort of a drunken American sailor to pick flowers in Mr Eugene Chen's garden. This occurrence had no dire results, and on the whole Hankow, in spite of its hysterical atmosphere and its baleful reputation, was an abode of peace.

My first interviews were with Borodin and Chen, whose names were best known in the world at large as representatives of the point of view of Hankow, of the Left Kuomintang. Borodin had never sought public attention and disliked giving interviews, but by this time it was no longer possible for him to avoid them. Eugene Chen loved public attention as a cat loves milk, and was at his best in an interview, rolling forth his grand, oratorical sentences with long pauses so that they might be written down in detail. Both Borodin and Chen used English, not only with representatives of the press, but in their communications with each other and with most of the other members of the Hankow government; for neither had a good command of Chinese. Chen was Foreign Minister, the spokesman for all his colleagues, and so could freely exercise his gifts as a proclamation-monger; Borodin, chief of the Russian advisers, tried to avoid speaking for the Hankow government, and restricted himself as much as he could, with interviewers whom he did not know, to discussions of principle.

My first impressions of both Borodin and Chen were overlaid by a mass of later impressions, by a whole tangle of experience in China and Russia in which they figured, and yet that first view of them in Hankow still seems to me clear and substantially correct. Borodin, a large, calm man with the natural dignity of a lion or a panther, had the special quality of being in, but above, the battle, to which I have already referred in speaking of Abd el-Krim—the particular quality that seems to me to deserve, in itself and without regard to the judgment of the world, the name of greatness. His slow, resolute way of talking, his refusal to be hurried or to get excited, his insistence upon the fundamental lines of action that determined detailed events, gave a spacious, deliberate character to his conversation, lifting it far above the shallowness of journalism and the hysteria of politics. He seemed to take 'the long view' by nature, by an almost physical superiority of vision. As I knew him better I perceived—or, rather, he showed me—how his political philosophy made breadth and elevation inevitable in the mind that understood it. He was an Old Bolshevik; that is, he had been a member of the Leninist school since its underground days before the war. His exile had been spent in the United States, where he acquired a better first-hand knowledge of the industrial system than was common among Bolshevik intellectuals. He had returned to Russia in 1917, to 'party work,' and had been entrusted with the Chinese mission in 1924. His whole adult life had been lived by a system of thought in which the immediate event was regarded as meaningless unless related to other events on both sides in time; in which the individual was valued by his relationship to his fellow beings; in which the most important of processes was held to be the comprehension, however disagreeable, of cause and effect. Disregarding the economic structure (Marxian economics) with which the Bolshevik mind was preoccupied, it could be seen that the method of thought in itself was 'good'—produced, as in the case of Borodin, a clear, calm view of life. Borodin himself would have attributed the quality I have called greatness (the quality of being in, but above, the battle) to the political philosophy and to nothing else. He would have said that the philosophy gave 'historical perspective,' and that historical perspective, once thoroughly understood, enabled the mind to inhabit a clearer air. But as, during the succeeding months, I came to know a number of other Communists more or less well, I was obliged to conclude that this was not so. However adequately they may have learned their political philosophy, it did not always lift them above the mud in which we flounder, and a Communist could be just as stupid, petty, and egotistical as any bourgeois. Borodin would have said that such a Communist was not a good Communist—which, although probably true, demolished the idea that an acquired political philosophy was alone enough to raise human beings to the highest power of which they were capable in the sense of life. The political philosophy had to be thoroughly understood, articulated and applied, made into a constant medium in which the good Communist could live as the saints lived in God, as the fish live in the sea. Something like this must have happened before 'the long view' and the reasoned plan of existence came to be Borodin's native element, from which he could look calmly upon the chaos of immediate events; but since it worked for him and not for others, there must also have been in his nature, from the beginning, an aptitude for reflection, a capacity for detached thought, superior to the aptitudes and capacities of other men who professed the same beliefs without thereby coming a shade nearer the stars.

Eugene Chen was, in some ways, a relief after Borodin. Borodin's large calm, his preternatural certainty, although they made an instant impression upon me, did, at first, leave me puzzled and a little humiliated—made me feel, as I used to tell Rayna Prohme, insignificant. Borodin was too big to be absorbed all at once. Mr. Chen, a small but concentrated dose, could be absorbed thoroughly in fifteen minutes, and although subsequent events did reveal fact upon fact in his complex character, no single fact about him ever surprised me after our first meeting. He was all of a piece, a small, clever, venomous, faintly reptilian man, adroit and slippery in the movements of his mind, combative in temper, with a kind of lethal elegance in appearance, voice and gesture. His talent for grand, bad phrases had made him famous throughout the world. He was English secretary to Dr Sun Yat-sen, and some of the documents to which the great revolutionary's name was attached in his declining years, in particular the Farewell to Soviet Russia, bear the unmistakable marks of Chen's style, florid, grandiloquent and theatrical. After Sun Yat-sen's death the clever secretary became Foreign Minister, a post in which he remained until the collapse of the revolutionary government at Hankow. In 1927 he was probably the best known of all Chinese political leaders to the world outside, and one of the least known among the Chinese.

I went from Borodin's great barracks straight across the road to the elegant Foreign Office where Chen dwelt and gave audience. In less than half an hour I had been stuffed with sharp, crackling phrases until neither my notebook nor my head could contain any more. The Foreign Minister was a remarkable man; but although remarkable, the type was not new to me. Wherever partisan political life offered a congenial career to clever and ambitious men with an axe to grind, there would naturally be Eugene Chens. Physically and in some of his ways of speech Mr Chen reminded me of the French politician Malvy; his complacency was like that of Austen Chamberlain; his delight in his own language, and the care he took to see that it was written down in all its baroque magnificence, suggested Mussolini. He was as theatrical as Briand, without any of the old fox's charm; he was as ingratiating as Stresemann, as bitter as Poincaré. In short, Mr Chen was a politician. Within a few minutes after my arrival in his spacious office —to which I had come with my head still a trifle confused from the unexpected nobility of the Bolshevik across the road—I knew exactly where I was: I was a journalist interviewing a clever politician, engaged in the old game of trying to pick out the truth from the lies, the sense from the welter of phrases.

When he began on his favourite subject, the inconceivable selfishness and brutality of the white foreigners in China, particularly of the British, I attended not so much to the immoderate language of the man as to the accents in which it was delivered, the quickened pulse and rhythm of the sentences, the added sharpness of eye and voice. For in spite of my youth—which probably encouraged Mr Chen to believe that I was a suitable subject for his eloquence—I was, by this time, experienced to the point of satiety in the art of interviewing gentlemen who had an axe to grind. The interesting thing in that process, which remained interesting after all the other tricks and devices of the art had palled, was to locate the axe.

In the case of Mr Chen I hesitated for a long time to believe that his axe was where my instinct and experience told me it was. The influence of Borodin's unquestionable selflessness, the spectacle of so many single-minded and devoted Chinese in the service of the Kuomintang at Hankow, and the general atmosphere of the place, suggestive of the gallantry of a lost cause, inclined me to think that Chen, too, must be sincere. If he had wanted personal aggrandizement only, he could have found it better on the other side, the side of Nanking. And yet I never met him without realizing that here was an intense egoist, for whose revolutionary impulses there must be intensely personal reasons. His every phrase and act displayed the character of the careerist politician. Months passed before I was willing to recognize what my instinct had told me at our first interview: that Mr Chen was indeed a careerist politician, but that his particular motive power—the axe he had to grind—was a hatred. As a pure careerist politician he would normally have gone over to the side of the money and the big battalions. He was prevented from doing so by the hatred that was the original spring of all his action—a hatred of the pretentious white race, particularly of the British. His hatred made and kept him a revolutionary.

Mr Chen had been born a British subject, at Trinidad in the West Indies. His name as a British subject was not Chen. He was of mixed race, part Chinese, part Negro; he received the education of an Englishman, studied at London University, and elected to become Chinese after the Revolution of 1911 had made a career there possible for him. These were the bare facts; but behind them it was easy to discern a tale of thwarted ambition, offended sensibilities, and dreams that turned to nightmare. Without unduly romancing about a character and situation common among us, we may suppose Mr Chen to have suffered greatly from the injustices to which persons of the coloured races are subjected in the Anglo-Saxon world. His hatred of that world was too intense and personal not to have been produced by intense and personal injuries. He had chosen his wife from the Negro race, and in his four charming children the Chinese strain seemed almost to have vanished. In him it was very strong—strong enough to bring him back to China from the other side of the world, and to engage his considerable talent, his hate-driven energy, his huge vituperative vocabulary, in the service of the Chinese Revolution.

Three years before, in a series of conversations with Blasco Ibáñez, I had obtained my first view of the romantico-literary and poseur revolutionist. Mr Chen provided me with a view of a more interesting pseudo-revolutionary type, that of the careerist with powerful personal motives. He was on the right side (if I may be allowed to call it that) for the wrong reasons.

The door at the end of the darkened reception room on the second floor of the Ministry of Finance opened, and in came a small, shy Chinese lady in a black silk dress. In one of her delicate, nervous hands she held a lace handkerchief, in the other my note of introduction from T. V. Soong. When she spoke her voice almost made me jump: it was so soft, so gentle, so unexpectedly sweet. The shutters had been closed to keep out the heat, and I could not see her until she had come quite near me. Then, looking down in bewilderment, I wondered who on earth she could be. Did Mme Sun Yat-sen have a daughter of whom I had never heard? It did not occur to me that this exquisite apparition, so fragile and timorous, could be the lady herself, the most celebrated woman revolutionary in the world.

'You saw my brother in Shanghai,' she said hesitantly. 'Tell me, how is he?'

It was Mme Sun.

For a good ten minutes we were at sea. I had heard an enormous number of things about her, most of them lies. The American newspapers had surpassed themselves on the subject. According to them, Mme Sun was 'China's Joan of Arc'; she was the leader of a Chinese 'woman's battalion'; she was this, that and the other thing, depending on the fantasies of the headline writers. The notion that she had actually led troops in battle was so widespread that even in China some of the foreigners believed it. In Shanghai this grotesque legend was complicated by more offensive lies, in which her personal character and motives were attacked—a favourite method of political argument in the treaty ports. Although I had sense enough not to believe most of the stories about her, they must have made, collectively, an impression; for I had certainly expected to meet something formidable. And instead, here I was face to face with a childlike figure of the most enchanting delicacy, only too plainly trembling with terror at the sight of me. Never had I felt so big and clumsy, so hopelessly barbarian.

But Mme Sun was aided by a number of characteristics that always enabled her, with an effort, to conquer her own timorousness —not only with me, that is, but in the general conduct of life. She had a dignity so natural and certain that it deserved the name of stateliness. The same quality can occasionally be observed in royal princes or princesses of Europe, especially in the older ones; but with them it is a clear result of lifelong training. Mme Sun's stateliness was of a different, a more intrinsic quality; it came from the inside out, instead of being put on like a harness. She also possessed moral courage to a rare degree, which could keep her steadfast in grave peril. Her loyalty to the name of Sun Yat-sen, to the duty she felt she owed it, was able to withstand trials without end. These qualities—dignity, loyalty, moral courage—gave her character an underlying strength that could, at times, overcome the impressions of fragility and shyness created by her physical appearance and endow her figure with the sternest aspect of heroism. I shall have occasion, in the course of this narrative, to show that death could not intimidate her; that poverty and exile, the fury of her own family and the calumnies of the world were unable to bend her will towards courses she felt to be wrong. She was, in a truer sense than the merely physical one intended by the headline writers, 'China's Joan of Arc,' but you had to know her for a good while before you realized the power of the spirit beneath that exquisite, tremulous envelope.

Mme Sun was born Rosalind Soong (Soong Ching-ling), of a family of rich Shanghai merchants. The Soongs belonged to the very compradore class attacked by the Chinese Revolution— the class that had grown rich in traffic with the foreigners, and had strong economic interests in the maintenance of the old régime. Soong Ching-ling was educated in the United States (in the Wesleyan college for women at Macon, in Georgia) and returned to China when she was nineteen. It was then that the Tsung Li met, fell in love with and married her. He was a great deal older than she was, but he had all the magic of a name that had already assumed symbolic significance in China; and whatever his other qualities may have been, Sun Yat-sen must have possessed a rare and wonderful power of personal influence. Few men in history have had his gift of commanding devotion. In his long, adventurous life, which reads like the invention of a romantic writer, he was constantly being saved from disaster by the fidelity of his friends. The last of his faithful followers was his second wife, his present widow, who was to carry her loyalty to his person and his ideals (quixotically, perhaps) far beyond the grave.

Mme Sun's friends used sometimes to discuss a question suggested by the contrast between her natural shyness, her love of privacy, and the public rôle she was obliged to play. It was this: what might have been the development of her life if she had never met Sun Yat-sen? A theory advanced was that, left to herself, she would have married 'well' and spent her time in all the private dignity and family self-sufficiency of a rich Chinese lady in Shanghai. It is possible. But no character can be studied in this way after the events that shaped it have taken their place in the ordered memory of the past. A fusion has occurred; single strands of character no longer mean anything; the nexus alone can be made to yield some of the secrets of a human personality. The nexus in this case was the marriage, which subjected Soong Ching-ling in her first youth to the most powerful influence of revolutionary idealism China has ever known. She travelled with Sun Yat-sen, acted as his secretary, participated with him in mass meetings and party councils, public triumphs and secret flights. She learned to share his passion against injustice of every kind, his determination to organize and prolong the revolt of the masses until the whole country had been brought under a national party dictatorship for the three objectives of his revolution—the San Min Chu I: Democracy, Nationalism, Social Welfare. When Sun Yat-sen died she took her place in the Central Executive Committee and the other governing bodies of the Kuomintang, and in spite of her dislike for debate, public speaking or public appearances, she performed her duties to the party without complaint. At the time of my arrival in China, in the open schism in the party, she had already resolutely taken her place with the faction of the Left Kuomintang and its Communist minority.

That was Mme Sun when I first saw her. The events of the following months, the massacre of the Communists, the crushing of the labour movement in blood, were to arouse her indignation to such a pitch that she seemed, before one's eyes, to take on stature. Without physical or intellectual power, by sheer force of character, purity of motive, sovereign honesty, she became heroic. In the wreck of the Chinese Revolution this phenomenon was one of the most extraordinary: generals and orators fell to pieces, yielded, fled, or were silent, but the one revolutionary who could not be crushed and would not be still was the fragile little widow of Sun Yat-sen. A 'doll,' they used to call her sometimes in the treaty ports. The world would be a less painful object of contemplation if it contained a few more such 'dolls.'

6

I was not, to begin with, a 'sympathizer' in Hankow. It was part of the middle-class dilettante view of life that I had half adopted, to accept experience of this kind much as the translated experiences of art (a play or a poem) are accepted, and to value them, what is more, as separate parts of a continuous process of education. To the dilettante the Chinese Revolution might have been of interest as an exciting spectacle, like a new ballet of Diaghilev's, and of value as a contribution to his own education, like the acquirement of a new language. By 1927, after constant exposure to the atmosphere of London and Paris, such ways of receiving experience, although not natural to me, had ceased to be altogether alien, and it was in some such frame of mind as that of your plain seeker-after-curiosity that I first went to Hankow.

To Hankow, then, I brought the mind and character of an American bourgeois, twenty-seven years old, who had divided his adult years between the subjects to which this book has been chiefly devoted—the living history of the time—and the preoccupations of personal taste. In these preoccupations, which had assumed greater importance in the last two years, influences of a powerful order had deflected what must originally have been a nature of considerable vigour and simplicity into channels where it was not wholly at ease. The character of the American bourgeois —let us call him Mr X—had been tinged with the colour of his surroundings, had taken on some of the flavour of Paris and London, and disengaged, no doubt, a light aroma of decay. The American character is not made to withstand, over long periods of time, the influence of older cultures in their most self-conscious forms. Our Mr X was almost—and could in time have become—a dilettante. That is, he already possessed by nature, and had fertilized by experience, those tastes by which a man could live through sensation alone. Books, pictures, music and the satisfaction of physical appetites constituted this world of sensation, and although it had always existed in some degree for our Mr X —as it exists for everybody—it had only recently shown signs of taking over the whole of his life.

He was preserved, then and afterwards, from this fate. Aside from any possible reasons that might be sought in deeper regions of the personality, he was preserved by two rather obvious circumstances. The first was that he had no money at all except what he could earn. The second was that, independently of the first, he wanted (why, God knows) to 'write'—that is, to put into words whatever he could learn about the mysterious transaction of living. His attitude towards work was neither consistent nor serious; he was capable of writing the most undisguised piffle to make money when he needed it; but he did possess, at the core, a determination to do some little work of which he need not be ashamed before he was finished. These two circumstances fought against the world of sensation at every point. A man who has to earn his living cannot spend his whole time, or even much of it, in pursuit of the experiences in art and life that might yield sensation; and a man who wants to do good work at some time or other can only learn how to do it by working.

The second circumstance was the really powerful combatant. Money, in the world in which Mr X lived, could be come by in various ways. For instance, it was not wholly impossible (however unlikely) that somebody might die and leave him a million dollars. But even with a million dollars in pocket and all the pleasures of the world at hand for the taking, he would still have been harassed by the thought that his time, the most precious and the most precarious of his possessions, evaporated with terrifying speed; that he had done nothing with it, was doing nothing with it; and that he must learn how to light the light before darkness descended.

Mr X was thus, through no effort of his own, and indeed almost automatically, protected against the worst results of his own laziness and self-indulgence. But he was lazy and self-indulgent, just the same. He preferred the line of least resistance, avoided conclusions that might be troublesome to himself, and was tending, more and more, to treat the whole of the visible universe as a catering firm employed in his service. The mind he directed upon people and things in China, and upon the whole drama of revolution, had been originally a good one, acquisitive, perceptive, and retentive, but it was softened and discoloured beneath later influences, which constantly suggested that fundamental questions were not worth bothering about. The shock of general reality was what he needed, and he was about to receive it —a seismic disturbance of greater intensity and duration than he would have believed possible a few months before.

So much for Mr X.

7

Misselwitz of the New York *Times* was staying at the American Consulate.

'One thing you ought to do right away,' he said, 'is to go and see Mrs Prohme.'

'Who's that?'

'You know—you must have heard something about her. Red-headed gal, spitfire, mad as a hatter, complete Bolshevik. Works for Borodin.'

'Oh, yes, I remember. Somebody told me about her. American.'

'Yeah—American. But I don't know if she still has a passport. There was some talk about her giving up her nationality. You can't pay any attention to what she says—she's the wildest Bolshevik in town—but she's a nice girl, anyway, and you'll enjoy talking to her. I kid her along all the time, but she doesn't seem to mind. She can laugh, anyway, and that's more than most of these people can do.'

'O.K., let's go see her now.'

This conversation must have taken place early in May, soon after my arrival in Hankow; but it was so casual, and led to an event of such seeming inconsequence, that it was not even mentioned in my daybook. I remember it, however, far better than I do many of the circumstances that seemed worthy of careful recording. Misselwitz—Missi—led the way down a shaded side street in the Concession to a low building that served as the editorial office of the *People's Tribune*, the propaganda newspaper of the Hankow government. It appeared in two daily editions, one in Chinese and one in English, and I had already had the pleasure of reading some copies of it.

'Bill Prohme, her husband,' Missi went on, 'is another wild one—gets excited and shouts at you. He's in Shanghai now, I think. Fine Bolshevik pair. You ought to hear the way the navy people talk about 'em!'

'Are they Communists, do you mean?'

'Oh, sure—must be. Of course, they say they're not, but you can tell. Everybody that's got anything to do with this government is a Red, whether they admit it or not.'

We reached the office just as Mrs Prohme was coming out, and she stopped to talk to us on the step.

'Hello, Missi,' she said, laughing at him, 'what's the matter now? More outrages to report?'

'Oh, no,' he said. 'We just came round to get a little dose of propaganda. Any news?'

He introduced me, and we walked down the street with her. She was on her way home to dinner, and it was neither the time nor the place for any kind of serious conversation. She was slight, not very tall, with short red-gold hair and a frivolous turned-up nose. Her eyes were of the kind the anthropologists call 'mixed,' and could actually change colour with the changes of light, or even with changes of mood. Her voice, fresh, cool and very American, sounded as if it had secret rivulets of laughter running underneath it all the time, ready to come to the surface without warning. All in all, she was most unlike my idea of a 'wild Bolshevik,' and I told her so. She laughed. I had never heard anybody laugh as she did—it was the gayest, most unselfconscious sound in the world. You might have thought that it did not come from a person at all, but from some impulse of gaiety in the air.

'You've been listening to Missi,' she said. 'Don't believe anything Missi says about us. He thinks everybody in Hankow eats bourgeois babies for breakfast. As a matter of fact, I'm not sure what people mean when they say Bolshevik in this place. It seems to me a Bolshevik is anybody that doesn't want to make coolies out of the Chinese.'

'That's true enough,' said I. 'In Shanghai they all thought I was a Bolshevik because I talked to some Chinese and went to Nanking.'

She inspected me for the first time with sudden gravity—the kind of gravity in which there lurks a suggestion of suppressed laughter. I was shaved within an inch of my life, and was dressed in the white uniform of the foreigner in China.

'No,' she said soberly, 'you flatter yourself. I don't believe anybody could possibly think that you were a Bolshevik.'

'You ought to be glad I'm not,' said I. 'If I were I couldn't get anything printed in an American paper about your Revolution, and as it is, I do.'

'I know,' she said reflectively. 'You're what they call "fair to both sides." You sit on the fence and say, "On the other hand." How's the weather up there? Is it a nice fence?'

'It's comfortable,' I said, 'and I get a good view. How do you like it down there where you are? You don't see much, do you?'

'Oh, I'm all right,' she said. 'I can see over the fence if I try hard. But it's more interesting down here where the stuff is growing. I don't care about the view, anyway; I've seen it.'

This kind of sparring was not uncharacteristic of our talk even when I knew her much better. In the beginning of our acquaintance it was inevitable, for she could see at a glance all that I have been at such pains to explain in the preceding section—the character of Mr X, the American bourgeois as modified by Paris and London, with a goodish but lazy mind. She could see it at once, not only because it was to some degree apparent to anybody, but because her acquaintance with the original material of the character was so exact and complete that its discolorations and the subsequent shapes to which it had conformed became immediately obvious. She could easily, perhaps too easily, consign me to the pigeonhole where many of her own friends and relations belonged. She was from Chicago, had been educated at the University of Illinois, and must have known hundreds of our contemporaries of the same general social, economic and intellectual stamp as myself. Her instinctive attack or defence took the form of a quizzical flippancy, as it might with a contemporary (a brother or friend) known years ago in Illinois, who had, since the days of remembered acquaintance, gone off in an opposing direction and acquired a set of ideas that she could not regard as idiosyncratic.

Exactly the same thing was true, of course, on my side of the argument. She was the kind of girl I had known all my life, but she had, by the direction she had taken, acquired a purpose and point of view that did not seem to me to belong to her. From the first I was conscious of a great puzzle, the puzzle of why she was doing this particular thing at this particular point of the world's compass. The easiest suggestion for a solution was that she was a romantic idealist, to whom a 'cause' was a necessity—any 'cause.' Nobody, after one glance at her, could have supposed her to be animated by ordinary selfish reasons. Her sincerity floated over her like a banner. The hunger for a 'cause'—that was it: the kind of thing that made so many nice American girls go out and get themselves cracked over the head by policemen during the suffragist campaigns. Some of these same nice girls, now that they had the vote, were busy with other 'causes,' getting prohibition either repealed or enforced, getting prisons reformed, or organizing the local ball for charity in their own home town. It must have taken a peculiarly insatiable cause-hunger to bring a girl like this into the exact middle of the Chinese Revolution, but except for the difference in degree, it was the same motive as that which caused ladies to spend a day or two in the suffrage jail in Washington and then come out and write books with titles like *Jailed for Freedom*. Perhaps Mrs Prohme, too, would write a book about her work in China—an excited volume in large print, with pictures, called *Up from Canton* or *China in Travail*.

These assumptions, however frivolous—and nobody knows better than I how grotesquely frivolous they were—controlled my mind in the earlier stages of our acquaintance and had their complement in similar assumptions on her part. She had, in a sort of way, 'known me all her life'; not only that, but I was an American newspaper man from Paris (i.e., the worst kind), and she could not take me seriously. She was obliged to assume, from what experience had taught her, that it was useless to expect a rational and unshrinking examination of any subject from such a person as myself. Neither of us was willing, therefore, to risk an attempt at discussion of the central reality towards which we were both un-escapably magnetized—she because she already knew, or thought she knew, where it was, and did not believe me capable of the drastic enterprise of reaching it; I because I was profoundly un-certain and did not realize that the obscure necessity was felt in the same way by anybody else. There was a basis of perfect misunderstanding, with a superstructure of familiarity (sameness of culture, social and economic identity, Illinois, Illinois!); and as a result we could only throw our whole relationship into a key of sustained flippancy. Sometimes the flippancy wore thin, but it seldom broke down altogether. The most important conversation in my life—in the true sense, the only conversation I have ever had—began, and for months continued, as a kind of joke.

8

For a few months in 1927, a little more than half of the year, Hankow concentrated, symbolized and upheld the hope for a revolution of the world. Delegations came there from all over Europe, Asia and America to see for themselves what constituted Hankow's success, the surprise and delight of a generation of thwarted Communists. The great expectations of 1917 had come to nothing. Social revolution had failed in Europe, partly (as in Germany) because of the repressive power of the upper classes, partly (as in Austria) by the treachery of socialist leaders, and partly (as in Hungary) through isolation in the midst of reaction-ary forces. Revolutions in Asia, towards which some elements of organized Communism had directed their highest hope after Lenin's great speech in 1921, had either failed to materialize or had turned (as in Turkey) into purely nationalist-republican movements. Even in Russia it was no longer possible to conceal the life-and-death struggle of opposing elements in the Com-munist party: one that wished to fight for the world revolution and one that wished to advance it by concentration on the existing Soviet State. Communists everywhere regarded Hankow as not only the most conspicuous success of revolutionary technique since 1917, but as the test case: if its success could be extended and made permanent, the victory of the international (Trotzkyist) tendency was assured; but if Hankow failed, the militant world-revolutionists failed as well, and even in Russia the future became obscure.

You could not be in Hankow a week without being aware of all this. French Communists, German Communists, Hindoo Communists, British I. L. P. people, and numerous agitators responsible to the Komintern[1] gave the place a fine mixed flavour of international revolt. The fact that many of these revolutionists preferred not to appear in public, and liked to conceal their comings and goings as much as possible, made the phenomenon more significant. The beautiful carved-oak head of Manabendra Nath Roy, head of the Far Eastern section of the Komintern, could be seen across a restaurant table in effective contrast to the dishevelled pate of Jacques Doriot (the Doriot who had once caused a rumpus by trying to read a piece of my prose into the minutes of the Chamber of Deputies). Russians with ill-defined functions appeared and disappeared. One of them, who said he had been employed by the Komintern but was probably employed by a very different organization, aroused the treaty ports at about this time by publishing some 'revelations' and 'confessions' that represented the life of the agitators in China to be as full of adventures as a story by the Baroness Orczy. When I saw agitators they were not adventuring but talking—talking, talking, talking, as only theoretical Communists can talk when they see under their eyes the materials for a manipulation of history. The impression given by much of their conversation was like that of a modern composer's —too much theory and not enough music. For the music, the thing itself, I always had to go either to the Chinese or to Borodin.

Nobody could be blamed for assuming, after one glance round Hankow, that the government there and the movement that supported it were Red. The numerous foreign revolutionists were only the froth of the brew, but they caught the eye. Other immediately visible phenomena: frequent strikes, mass meetings and demonstrations; the workmen's place (the New World, it was called, a centre in the Russian and Italian style), and the conduct of

[1]The Third or Communist International, abbreviated to Komintern in the revolutionary vocabulary, will have to be mentioned rather frequently, and for the sake of brevity I shall call it by the name ordinarily used among its adherents.

students or trades unionists, gave the illusion of a highly organized social-revolutionary movement that might, at any moment, seize the machinery of production and proclaim the dictatorship of the proletariat.

But it didn't happen. Month after month passed and it didn't happen. Far away in Moscow Trotzky and Radek and others, consumed with impatience, were writing and speaking as if the Chinese Soviets already existed and had only been prevented from asserting themselves by the fatal short-sightedness of Borodin and the Kuomintang. In England, France, and the United States the opposite fallacy was held, and a Chinese Communist government was supposed to have been created by Borodin and the Kuomintang with Russian support. The European press referred to 'the Communist government at Hankow' as soberly as if the thing had been recognized by all parties and powers. Even now, seven years afterwards, it is not unusual to run across a reference to the 'Communist experiment at Hankow,' although the supreme characteristic of the Hankow experiment was that it was not Communist at all.

It is impossible to imagine a Communist state, or even a Communist experiment, in which private capital would be at liberty to maintain and fortify the domination of the employing classes over the workers. And yet this is exactly what happened at Hankow throughout the time of the so-called 'Communist' experiment. Private capital was at liberty to move where it liked, to lock out strikers, to emigrate, to shift and to re-invest. Neat little fortunes could be made in those days by buying depreciated property, and the entrepreneur who was tired of labour troubles had only to lock up his establishment and try his money on the New York stock market. The operations of exchange, credit and transfer were at all times free in Hankow—had to be, as will be shown hereafter. The processes of production were hampered, it is true, by strikes, and the labour committees did make some demands that foreshadowed a possible share in the control of industry, but it was all the kind of thing that could happen in a capitalistic country. What made it ominous to the entrepreneur and raised the terrified cry of 'Communism!' round the world, was the fact that it took place at the instigation of known Communists, supported by the Left Kuomintang and the Chinese Communist party, to the accompaniment of all the shouting and hallooing of revolutionary propaganda.

If the capitalist press of Europe thought Hankow 'a Communist experiment,' the Communists themselves did not. They hoped it might become a Communist experiment, sputtered with rage because it did not, exerted themselves in every way to push it in the desired direction, and, finally, when nothing seemed to be of any use, looked about them for somebody to blame. It was only natural that they, like the press of Europe and America, should have blamed the most conspicuous figure for everything that happened; and Borodin quietly slipped into the rôle of universal scapegoat for the Chinese Revolution. The Europeans held him responsible for its success, the Russians for its failure, the Chinese for its division into two parts. By the beginning of June he was not only the most famous, but the most execrated person in China, and the official representatives of the Komintern had no more love for him than had the official representatives of the Standard Oil Company.

'There is only one thing to do,' the Komintern people would say, 'and it should have been done in April. That is: Proclaim the Soviet!'

The fact that there were no Soviets in China made no difference to a full-fledged Komintern delegate from Moscow.

'There's just one thing to do,' the Standard Oil representative would say, 'and that's to call off all these strikes and patch it up with Chiang Kai-shek. It should have been done long ago.'

The fact that 'to call off all these strikes and patch it up with Chiang Kai-shek' would have meant abandonment of the Revolution was not the sort of fact a Standard Oil man could regard as relevant.

Between the unrealistic demands of the theoretical Communists and the reactionary demands of foreign capital Borodin was bound to become the scapegoat, not because he attempted to keep a middle course or believed in compromises, but because the situation did not permit a daring experiment in Communism. At first I, like most of my journalistic colleagues, assumed that Hankow was Red; then, seeing that the endless strikes led nowhere, that capital was as firmly entrenched as ever, and that the proclamation of proletarian dictatorship was apparently never going to be made, I assumed that Hankow was not Red—that its character was that of a Left national revolution with no subversive aims. It took a considerable acquaintance with the mood and temper of the revolutionaries, as well as with their current literature and specific manifestations (speeches, mass meetings, party and union decisions) to reveal the truth: that Hankow represented the *desire* to create a Red China, frustrated at all important points by the coalition of the great Western powers, which (in fact if not in theory) occupied China with their armies and navies and protected all capital in the foreign banks. Hankow was as Red as possible, but the limits of the possible were reached much too soon to satisfy any thorough-going Communist. To put it into other terms, the movement was subjectively but not objectively Leninist.[1]

The Red desire and the Red machinery were there. I could support these statements by details that no longer have much interest, but they need no such proof, for the facts are not contested. In four years Borodin had transformed the whole Left (i.e., active) part of the Kuomintang into a social-revolutionary movement, with Chinese and Russian agitators indefatigably at work among the workers and peasants. Why, then, did he hesitate to take the final step in April or May and proclaim the Communist formula of

---

[1]A question of nomenclature arises in writing of these subjects. It should be explained that I call revolutionary quantities by the names they bear in revolutionary literature. Many such names come from the Russian, but they may as well be adopted into English when our language has no exact equivalents. Red, for instance, is the colour symbol used by partisans of the social revolution of the world, whether they are party Communists or not. In Russian the word Red (*krassny*) has overtones that it does not possess in English, and for this reason it has always been popularly extended far beyond the mere meaning of colour. The Red Square in Moscow was so named centuries before the birth of Lenin. A bright, charming or attractive girl can be called 'red' in Russian no matter what her complexion. The word is almost an equivalent of 'bright' and suggests the general mood of hope as well as the particular hope for a proletarian revolution. I use it not only because it is a commonly accepted word in revolutionary literature, but because it includes ideas and shades of meaning that are excluded from the rigid word Communist. The word Communist, as I use it, refers only to members of the international Communist party and their system of thought and action. Having served warning, I shall proceed on this principle without further explanation.

'All Power to the Soviets'? Why, having gone so far and threatened so much, did he not take his revolutionary machine (the Chinese Communists and the Left Kuomintang of which they were minority members) and with it defy the world? The question was being asked by exasperated Communists everywhere, most of all in Moscow, and, as it turned out, the fate of the Communist party in every country hung upon the answer. It was a question that was asked even in the most bitterly anti-revolutionary circles, and I well remember a pause in a poker game one night in Hankow, when a local magnate (American) turned to me and said: 'When is Borodin going to go the whole hog? I wish he'd hurry up and get it over.'

All these people, Communist or reactionary, in every shade of thought from Trotzky to Rockefeller and back again, seemed to think that Borodin could make exactly what he pleased out of the Chinese Revolution, or at least with the more advanced wing represented by the Hankow government. And Borodin himself?

He had no such illusions. Calm, slow and thoughtful, without a trace of personal ambition or egotism, he examined his problem as if it had been one in his favourite game, chess. He could do certain things, and certain results would ensue; he could do certain other things, and certain other results would ensue; but there remained a large class of things that he could not do at all. Two things that he unquestionably could not do—that Trotzky himself could not have done—were: first, abolish the navies of America, England, Japan and France; and, second, make flexible and resolute revolutionary instruments overnight out of the mass of half-awakened Chinese workers and peasants (the '*Lumpumproletariat*'). He knew better than anybody else exactly how far the process of political education had gone even in the most advanced labour unions, and just how much sacrifice it was possible to ask of people who had only begun to understand the principles of revolutionary action. And as for the navies—! He had only to look out of his window to see the river choked with them, their guns trained on the shore, their officers and men openly, boastfully anxious for a chance to 'clean up the mess,' as they put it, with machine gun, rifle and bayonet.

These were the realities with which Borodin lived every day

of his life in China—with which he had lived for three years. Trotzky, the most brilliant technician of the Russian Revolution, its hero and its historian, was a long way from China; and although he undoubtedly knew everything there was to know about the subject on paper (as did Radek, Bukharin and the rest), he was betrayed into absurdities by the fact that he had no practical acquaintance with the material. Borodin should have proclaimed a Soviet Republic at Hankow in April, should he? Well, exactly, how?

Let us develop the hypothesis. A proclamation of power to the Soviets is made, the bourgeoisie disenfranchised, the machinery of production, credit and commerce taken over. What happens then is that Chinese capital flies to the foreign banks—such Chinese capital as is not already there—and half the productive property raises foreign flags. (This is not guesswork, for the thing has happened, is constantly happening whenever political events make Chinese capital slightly nervous.) Then, to give effect to your proletarian dictatorship, you *must* confiscate properties belonging in whole or in part to foreigners. Not to do so would be to make Communism impossible. But the moment you confiscate or seriously interfere with any property belonging to foreigners you are desperately, irretrievably in the soup; the foreign navies fill the river, the foreign governments are irate, the foreign marines are in your streets, and within twenty-four hours your Communist government, your dictatorship of the proletariat, has been drowned in blood.

Men who have not actually seen the Chinese river cities can scarcely believe how easy it is for the British, Japanese, French and American navies to overawe them. All these cities are built along the river, depend upon the river, exist for and through the river. And the river is no more Chinese than I am. Its waters are navigable even for large cruisers up to Hankow, and for gunboats up to Chungking and Ichang. The parts of China bordering the Yangtze-kiang, therefore, cannot be considered independent except in theory, and if maps were made according to realities instead of according to political fiction, the map of China would show a country impaled upon its terrible foreign river.

Borodin saw the facts as clearly as if they had been diagrammed on a blackboard. He knew that riparian China was at the mercy of the foreign ships, and that genuine independence for China could only be hoped for when the navies of Europe could be kept out of the Yangtze-kiang. He had intended to pass over Hankow and reach Peking: that was his plan in the autumn of 1926, and if Chiang Kai-shek had carried out the decisions of the Central Executive Committee (decisions made upon Borodin's advice) no attack would have been made on Nanking and Shanghai until the whole of China had been conquered and united. But Chiang Kai-shek, to whom Nanking and Shanghai had long been a tempting plum, disobeyed his instructions, took the ripe plum when he could get it, and satisfied himself, afterwards, by declaring his independence of the central organization and Borodin. The Yangtze-kiang, which has always defeated every popular revolutionary movement in China, triumphed again in 1927, and in April and May—the very months when, according to the Trotzky school of thought, Borodin should have forced or persuaded his Chinese clients to proclaim a proletarian dictatorship —the Chinese Revolution already lay in ruins.

I saw Borodin frequently. As I knew him better, and overcame the feelings of insignificance and frivolity that had originally oppressed me in his presence, I was able to discuss anything with him. Later on, when he was sick in bed with a serious attack of malaria, I used to go to see him every day; and although the conversation during these visits ranged over a wide field, involving many subjects that had nothing to do with the Chinese Revolution, the intellectual resources he displayed were at all times those of a trained Bolshevik—his cast of mind was Leninist. Whether he was discussing a new book (*Elmer Gantry* was one that aroused his interest just then) or an old political theory, reminiscing or analyzing, telling a story or advancing a hypothesis, he took 'the long view.' I had never before examined such a mind at close quarters, and there is no doubt that I was profoundly impressed by its clarity and consistency. But I do not believe that the influence of Borodin shaped any of my opinions; I was too old and too independent to accept other people's ideas about phenomena that I could easily observe for myself. What did happen was something a little more complicated. In Borodin I found an older, better disciplined, better trained and more experienced intelligence than my own: it had already traversed regions that still lay before me. Sometimes Borodin was able to disentangle a principle from the confusion of external events and show it to me; sometimes he was able to point out a historical direction or a prevailing tendency. He never made the slightest attempt to impose his opinions— often, indeed, he talked as if I were not in the room. He was concerned with the truth, and his object in conversation was to extract and demonstrate it. If, therefore, I found every conversation with him illuminating, and approached, in the end, more nearly to his view of the Chinese Revolution than to any other, it was not because of any personal influence he exercised, but because the truth, for me, lay on his side.

There were plenty of other influences in Hankow, and I was subjected at one time or another to most of them, but they missed their target in me. Eugene Chen used to address me in long, hifalutin sentences, even when we were quite alone and I knew him a good deal better: they left me cold. The American and British business men, the naval officers, the foreigners in general, harangued me on the subject of their grievances, and many Chinese revolutionists did likewise. But among the foreigners the personal motives were so obvious that it was impossible to treat their statements with respect. No one of them could see beyond the end of his own nose. I enjoyed playing poker with the business men and hearing their opinions leak out as they dealt the cards, or drinking whisky with the navy people and sampling the ferocity of their desire to murder the Chinese population; but such diversions were, after all, only diversions.

The Chinese revolutionists impressed me often by their self-abnegation, their willingness to endure and to persevere, their loyalty to ideas that meant life to China even though they might mean death to the individual. But no single Chinese revolutionist ever set my mind on new paths, as I believe Borodin did. One reason was that I never met the intellectual leaders of the Chinese Revolution. Sun Yat-sen died three years before I went to China, and his written works seemed to me to lack logic—to lack, above all, a genuinely long view. The other great revolutionist of modern China, Li Ta-chao, founder and head of the Chinese

Communist party, was strangled to death by the reactionaries in Peking before I had been in China a month. The leaders I did know all professed to follow the teachings either of Sun Yat-sen or of Li Ta-chao, with, occasionally, a Confucian or Christian coloration. Some of them were admirable in character, like Mme Sun Yat-sen; others were striking or picturesque, like Wang Ching-wei, the type of the fiery, romantic revolutionary; still others engaged my personal liking and respect, like T. V. Soong; but it happened that I never met a Chinese intellectual who could put his view of history into terms of absolute truth as Borodin did.

Even so, it was not Borodin alone, but the Chinese Revolution with Borodin as its interpreter, that gave me my first perception of the spirit of revolution in general. Borodin alone, talking in a vacuum, would have been merely a Communist intellectual. It was in his relation to the whole mass movement in China, the immense and complicated disturbance of which he was temporarily both the directing genius and the interpreter, that he acquired grandeur. His calm may have been a native characteristic, but it seemed singularly noble in the midst of confusion and danger; his political theory may have been as simple as geometry (they taught it, after all, at the Lenin Institute in Moscow) but it seemed profound and irrefragable when it was seen to support the weight of otherwise meaningless events. He exemplified in his own person, and pointed out in the phenomena around him, the peculiar qualities of intellectual consistency, social philosophy, selflessness and determination that combine to form something I have called (for lack of a more exact term) the revolutionary spirit.

That spirit was abroad in Hankow from the time the Cantonese armies entered the city until the collapse of the revolutionary government on July 5th. It was to be seen in Chinese and Russians, Left Kuomintang organizers and Communists, workmen, students and agitators—not in all of them, of course, but in a large enough number to confirm the existence of something new in the confusion of China. There were Communist students, sometimes of rich families, who became coolies so as to be able to organize the coolies for revolution. There were educated Chinese girls who risked death in the effort to tell the workers and peasants who their real enemies were. One of these girls—we all knew her in Hankow—was disembowelled by Chiang Kai-shek's soldiers on June 21st in Hangchow for saying that the Nanking war lord did not represent the party or principles of Sun Yat-sen. Her intestines were taken out and wrapped around her body while she was still alive. Girls and boys were beheaded for saying what they believed; men were hung up in wooden cages to die of hunger and thirst or were broken on the rack. Little Phyllis Li, the seventeen-year-old daughter of the hero Li Ta-chao, was tortured by Chang Tso-lin's men for three days and three nights before they mercifully strangled her, and in the whole time she told them nothing. The horrors of the counter-revolution were not unexpected: these young Chinese knew what awaited them and went ahead just the same. The impulse that made them offer their lives for the cause was not a suicidal, neurotic yearning for Nirvana, as it might have been in similar crises in India or Japan. Such varieties of mystic ardour were, so far as I ever saw or heard, unknown to China. The Chinese operated on a colder and purer conviction, the belief that courageous sacrifice in the service of an idea was the best means of propagating that idea. The individual was, as so often in China, sacrificed to the race, and the young men and girls died for generations unborn.

The Chinese surpassed all others in such extreme forms of heroic devotion, and for every case of treachery and cowardice in the dark days of their Revolution there was at least one case of loyal courage. But the other agitators, in particular the Russians, could produce evidences of the same spirit in their own way. It was a less obviously heroic way, as the Russians believed it to be a revolutionist's duty to save his life for the cause if he could. A Russian agitator was supposed to live for the Revolution, not to die for it. Consequently he had to change his name and appearance, his passport and his ostensible business, and evade danger even on occasions when he might have preferred to stay and face it. There were Russian agitators in China whose lives had been as adventurous as those described in the 'revelations' printed in the British-Chinese press, although not quite in the same penny-dreadful style.

Borodin showed iron control of the personal motive during the weeks in which his wife, Fanny Borodin, was imprisoned by the northern reactionaries. Mme Borodin was on her way to Vladivostok to join him when she was arrested by soldiers of Chang Chung-chang, the Shantung war lord. Chang kept her in prison for some weeks and then turned her over to his feudal superior, the Manchurian bandit Chang Tso-lin, who governed at Peking with Japanese support. Chang Tso-lin was as bloodthirsty a tyrant as any modern China has seen, and his first decision was to strangle Mme Borodin without ceremony. He was dissuaded from this course by some of the foreigners in Peking, who suggested that it would make a better impression on the outside world if the lady had a trial.[1] I shall come to the end of Fanny Borodin's story later on, but the part that here concerns us is the effect of these events on Borodin in Hankow during April and May. He betrayed no anger and no excitement, in spite of the personal nature of the attack. He pointed out simply that Mme Borodin had never been engaged in Communist party work in China, that she took no part in politics, and that Chang Tso-lin's vengeance was vicarious—the old *hung-hutze*[2] was unable to get at the real object of his ire, and took it out on an innocent hostage; that she was in prison and in danger of death for one reason only: that her name was Borodin.

The ardent but impersonal devotion to which I have applied the name 'revolutionary spirit' was apparent in many characters and incidents in Hankow, and I have named only a few of them. There was one other, more important to me, as it turned out, than all the rest, a more significant and memorable example of that spirit than any in my experience. I mean Rayna Prohme. The flippancy in which our acquaintance had begun continued for weeks, but before long I began to have an uneasy feeling that my judgment of her character had been ludicrously inaccurate. I made a number of small discoveries that shook my first ideas. She had no enthusiasm for 'causes' in general, had never been the kind of romantical busybody I had at first assumed her to be. She

[1] The American Senator Bingham, from Connecticut, was one of those who were said to have influenced the old marshal in favour of a form of trial.

[2] A *hung-hutze* ('red beard') is a robber chief on the Manchurian plains. Chang Tso-lin had been a *hung-hutze* before the Japanese discovered his usefulness.

had had a sound education in economics and sociology; her interest in social revolution had been aroused at an age when I was still learning new steps in the fox trot. She had already acquired a remarkable revolutionary past in the service of the Kuomintang, and she enjoyed, in the spring of 1927, the confidence of many Chinese Left leaders. She not only edited the official newspaper, but had a general consultative usefulness to the Hankow régime in matters of propaganda designed to appeal to foreigners. Borodin, Mme Sun Yat-sen, Eugene Chen and Sun Fo treated her opinions with respect. I still could not take her seriously as a revolutionist—it was like expecting me to believe my cousin Cecilia, with whom I grew up, had suddenly turned into a Red—but I had to concede that this revolutionary phase, however temporary it might be, was an interesting and unexpected development in the character of a charming American girl. I fell into the habit of going to see her every day, and as I knew her better I came to depend heavily on that daily visit for many things—not only, that is, for the pleasure of conversation with somebody who so thoroughly spoke my own language, and not only for the delight of her high spirits, the refreshment of her laughter, but also for the daily necessities of my job as a journalist, to learn the news and to learn, so far as possible, what the news meant. For a peculiarity of Rayna Prohme's, I found out, was her ingrained dislike of lying. She was a very bad liar indeed, and although it was often a part of her duty to make things appear under a somewhat artificial light, her candour was such that she did not succeed in doing so, at least with me. I could always tell when she was saying something she did not herself believe: her looks gave her away. She took her instructions from Borodin and Chen; and although Borodin had a high respect for the truth and avoided deviations from it as scrupulously as anybody I have ever known in public life, the same could not have been said of Mr Chen. Consequently, for propaganda purposes, Rayna Prohme was often obliged to write and say things her own candour resented. The official newspaper contained these statements, but she could never make them convincingly enough in conversation. After a bit she gave up attempting to give me official versions of anything, and either told the plain truth or else confessed, with a wry smile, that she could not speak. It was no small thing, in a place like Hankow and a profession like mine, to know somebody in whom I could believe without reserve.

Bill Prohme, her husband, returned to Hankow after I had been there a week or so, but we did not hit it off as well as might have been expected. His violent revolutionary enthusiasm resented my bourgeois lethargy, my innumerable changes of white silk clothes, my Scotch whisky and Egyptian cigarettes. In turn I disliked his excitability, his refusal to argue a subject through in a calm and logical manner; I suspected that his revolutionary convictions were not sufficiently grounded in economic and social science—that he was an emotional Red, if a Red at all; and that his presence in China in his present rôle was due to the accident of his marriage to Rayna Prohme. Partly for these reasons, and partly because his absences and illnesses made our meetings infrequent, I never knew him well in Hankow. It was only long after I had left China and Russia that I learned to respect his intelligence and value his friendship. During the period with which this chapter deals, he was a rather shadowy figure to me, and his name does not appear in the notes I put into my useful daybook.

Rayna's assistant was an American woman journalist who regarded every moment I spent in the office of the *People's Tribune* as a calamity. Under these circumstances a more sensitive subject might have stayed away, but I didn't. The daily conversations with Rayna Prohme had become such a necessity that when a day passed without my seeing her at all (as happened twice when she was ill) it left an extraordinary feeling of blankness and malaise. This being so, it is strange to remember, and stranger still to record, that I never understood her importance to me until months later. I was as stupid as M. Jourdain with his prose; I had already passed under the most powerful and significant personal influence to which I have ever been subjected, but I did not know it.

Hankow, then—to sum up—was a marvellous revolutionary spectacle, in which the courage and devotion of the Chinese agitators, the skill of the Russians, the high hope and frenzied determination of the workers, and the individual splendour of characters like those of Mme Sun Yat-sen, Borodin and Rayna Prohme, combined to give me a glimpse into a new world. In its spirit, at least, if not in its accomplishment, it was the world of Lenin. That the dead bones of economics and sociology could be animated with such irresistible life was something I would never have believed six months before in Paris, when the principal event of the century had seemed to be the anniversary performances of *Pelléas et Mélisande* at the Opéra Comique. But although this glimpse into the world of Lenin did supply an electrical thrill, and the characters of the spectacle aroused my sincerest admiration, I still did not surrender to the logic of their being. It seemed to me that the whole revolutionary system of thought reposed upon a number of assumptions that defied proof. This became apparent when the fundamental question of revolution was put into the form of a simple syllogism, like this:

> A controlled egalitarian economy is desirable;
> Revolution is the only way to obtain a controlled egalitarian economy;
> Therefore Revolution is desirable.

The only part of such a syllogism that needed no defence was the major term *desirable*. The major premise, although probable enough, could not possibly be proved because models for a controlled egalitarian economy did not exist, even in Russia. The minor premise was equally shaky; it might be true or not, but it was not susceptible of proof. The conclusion, therefore, had to be taken on faith, or (at best) as the result of two probabilities.

The logic of revolution can be put into other and more persuasive syllogisms than this; indeed, at a later time, Rayna Prohme and I used to spend hours trying to get the fundamental question into its barest and simplest terms; but during the Hankow period the syllogism I have given seemed to me the correct one, and no matter how much my sympathy and admiration were engaged on the side of the revolutionaries, I could not share their conviction. As I have said, the one indisputable thing was that something was desirable in a world of misrule; something that could bring order out of chaos had to be found if the human race was to justify its pretence of intelligence. But whether or no the desirable something was revolution did not seem to me susceptible of proof, and the revolutionary spectacles that moved me most deeply were still only that and nothing more.

9

I went down to Shanghai in June. The purpose of the trip was, of course, to see what was going on, and from that point of view it was uninteresting; not only did I see little, but whatever I had seen would have been of no value to my newspapers, engrossed, as they were, with the affairs of Colonel Lindbergh. But there were incidental results of the Shanghai journey, and two incidents of the week amuse me still when I think of them.

One was a luncheon given by the proprietor of the *North China Daily News*. The guest of honour was the colonel of the Grenadier Guards, Lord Gort, a pleasant and modest soldier with a brilliant war record. (He had won the V. C., the rarest of military distinctions, seldom given to persons of his rank.) To meet the distinguished guest came the cream of the Shanghai merchants, a prosperous and important company.

I had scarcely been inside that hospitable house for ten minutes before I realized a number of things. One was that I had changed a good deal since my last visit to Shanghai; another was that I could never again take the Shanghai *taipans*—big merchants—seriously. Their strange remoteness from the country on whose edge they perched had never struck me so forcibly; when they talked about China (as, of course, they constantly did) they revealed a point of view that now seemed to me fantastic. Many of them had been born in Shanghai, and they all knew the Chinese very well in the rôle of servants; but as for any other knowledge or sympathy, they might as well have been people from a distant planet. I had never been sympathetic to the Shanghai point of view, but at least it had been arguable before. Now it was only funny.

In the middle of lunch Lord Gort started to ask me questions about Hankow, and particularly about Borodin, who was always the centre of curiosity for foreigners. I answered that I knew Borodin rather well and both liked and admired him. If I had taken off all my clothes and jumped on the table I could not have shocked the company more. (Not Gort, of course—he was a soldier, fresh from England, and had none of the Shanghai prejudices.) One of the *taipans*, looking rather as if he thought he had not heard correctly, asked: 'But what sort of fellow *is* Borodin, then?'

I answered this at some length, and then returned to my food with a feeling that the subject had been disposed of. But the *taipan* was still puzzled. I had spoken of Borodin's mind, which was not at all the sort of thing the *taipan* wanted to hear.

'But that's not what I mean,' he said, leaning forward from the other side of the table, 'I mean, what sort of fellow *is* he? I mean, is he a *gentleman?*'

I was afraid to laugh for fear that I might not be able to stop.

The other incident of my Shanghai visit—not so much comic as tragi-comic—was my effort to bring T. V. Soong back to Hankow with me.

Hankow needed T. V. badly. The ability of that young man to inspire confidence, to make the books balance, to coax money out of hiding places, was an ability nobody at Hankow possessed. Nanking needed him for exactly the same reasons. In Hankow the financial situation was beginning to be desperate. The bank notes of the Central Bank of China (to which T. V. nostalgically referred as 'my bank notes') had been falling in value so rapidly that the point of worthlessness would certainly be reached before long. When I was ready to go to Shanghai I asked Rayna Prohme if I could do anything for her there.

'You can bring T. V. back,' she said.

'All right,' said I confidently, 'I will.'

Borodin did not ask me to do this, but as I was taking my leave of him he remarked that it would be an excellent thing if T. V. returned. And T. V.'s lovely sister, Mme Sun Yat-sen, gave me a note to give to him; she too remarked that she wished he would return to his post in Hankow.

I thought the enterprise would be easy—all I had to do was to bring T. V. along with me under some kind of assumed name, as my interpreter. Travelling in my cabin on a British boat he would have been safe enough, for the boldest of Chiang Kai-shek's soldiers would never have dared break in. But in taking the idea so lightly I reckoned without T. V.

When I went to see him in Shanghai he seemed ready to fall in with the plan. He was living in Sun Yat-sen's house in the Rue Molière, and after his years of work for the Kuomintang he was miserable in idleness. He could see—or said he could see—that the true inheritor of the Kuomintang ideal was the Hankow government, and not Chiang Kai-shek's military dictatorship. He had steadily refused to join Chiang Kai-shek's government in spite of persuasion and threats. The house was constantly watched by spies (it is one of the houses that are under observation at every hour of the day and night, as it has always been since it was built); and T. V. was very nervous. He did not dare go outside the French Concession and the International Settlement, for Chiang Kai-shek's soldiers were everywhere in the Chinese city, and they would have seized upon him in a moment. His alternatives, if Chiang Kai-shek ever caught him, were simple: the Ministry of Finance or the gaol. I do not believe he would have been put to death, but he was not at all sure of it. He was, in fact, in a rare state of funk, and the suggestion I brought from Hankow seemed to offer him a way out of all his troubles. He agreed almost at once, asked me to take a ticket for him in my cabin in the name of Mr Wong of Canton, and displayed a lively curiosity about the course of events at Hankow.

On the next day he had changed his mind. In the interim he had talked to his mother, his sisters, his brother-in-law, and they were a fundamentally reactionary family.

'There's no point in my going to Hankow,' he said, worried and nervous. 'You see the truth is that I'm not a social revolution-ary. I don't like revolution, and I don't believe in it. How can I balance a budget or keep a currency going if the labour policy frightens every merchant or factory owner into shutting up shop? I can't make the Central Executive Committee understand. . . . Look at what they've done with my bank notes, my beautiful bank notes! . . . They've been inflated out of existence. . . .'

'Your sister said——'

'Oh, my sister . . . ! My sister doesn't understand. Nobody un-derstands how difficult it is. How do I know I won't be dragged out of the Ministry of Finance and torn to pieces by the mob the day after I get to Hankow? How do I know I can stop the currency from falling? Nothing can be done if they keep on encouraging strikes and mass meetings. They get the people into a state of excitement in which they expect everything, and they're bound to be disappointed. . . . And I'm not popular, mind you. I've never been popular. The mob doesn't like me. They would have killed me last winter if the soldiers hadn't come in time. . . . They all know I don't like strikes and mass meetings. . . . What could *I* do at Hankow?'

On that day he was definitely anti-revolutionary. But on the next he had switched again—took a more hopeful view of the possibility of persuading the Central Executive Committee to modify the labour policy; yearned over his beautiful bank notes; agreed that the Nanking régime was only a disguised form of personal dictatorship, and that Hankow still represented, in spite of the Communists, the pure party tradition of the Kuomintang.

These fluctuations of sentiment ruled his mind throughout the week. It was the most vivid illustration of the typical Liberal hesitancy I had ever seen, or have seen since. T. V. wanted to work for China; he proved it afterwards in illogical fashion by entering the government of Chiang Kai-shek, of which he could not have approved. But at this time he was unable to reach a decision that remained stable for as much as an hour. I had always liked him, and liked him even more as I watched his painful struggle to make up his mind, but I could hardly regard him as a statesmanlike figure. Nothing but accident—the accident that made him a brother of Mme Sun Yat-sen—could explain his connection with a militant revolutionary movement. He was one of those politicians who might have been happy and useful in private life, but could only, in the uncongenial surroundings of a 'career,' be forever harassed and afraid.

When the day on which I was to sail for Hankow came round, T. V. happened to be in one of his pro-Hankow states of mind. We made all our arrangements with great care. I was to leave the Majestic Hotel at midnight in a Rolls-Royce car as big as a house, which I sometimes rented in Shanghai. I was to draw all the blinds on leaving the hotel. (I assured T. V. that I was not under observation, but he saw spies everywhere.) The car was to take me to the Rue Molière, drop me at the corner some distance from the

Sun Yat-sen house, and then, after circling about in the French Concession for a few minutes, was to creep quietly into the Sun Yat-sen garden, as if to call for me. When I got into it again I was to be accompanied by Mr Wong of Canton, my interpreter, but in the darkness the spies would presumably not see him.

The first part of the programme went off well enough. I saw no watchers in the Rue Molière, but no doubt they were on duty. The rest of the events of that night must have given the spies a queer puzzle and a good deal of leg work; for T. V. had changed his mind again.

'I can't go,' he said the moment he came down the stairs. 'I can't do it. I'm sorry I've caused you all this trouble, but I simply cannot do it.'

He was excited and very jumpy. I sat down on a stair step in the hall and gaped with surprise. That very afternoon his mind had been conclusively made up, and now——!

'What am I to say to your sister?' I asked.

We must have talked for an hour round and about the subject while T. V. paced the floor and I sat wearily on the stairs. Suddenly he reached for his hat.

'Let's go talk to my family,' he said.

We clambered into the Rolls-Royce and made a round of visits at about one o'clock in the morning. I took no part in the conversations with the Soong family, and can only imagine how they all urged T. V. not to cross the Rubicon. One of the persons to whom he spoke was his hyper-Americanized sister Mei-ling, who afterwards incomprehensibly married Chiang Kai-shek. Another was Dr H. H. Kung, his brother-in-law. After some hours of argument T. V. came out of the recesses of the Kung house and spoke —dejectedly, gloomily.

'It's all settled,' he said. 'I'm not going. Tell my sister I shall write to her. I'm sorry you were troubled for nothing.'

I drove him home in the immense, hearse-like car, and neither of us said a word. I was exhausted from the sheer indecision of the proceedings, and he was very gloomy. I have never seen him since, and the events of that night were to give my final impression of Soong Tse-vung both as an individual and as a type, the honest Liberal at sea between opposing shores.

Perhaps T. V. will think it inexcusable of me to have told this story. I have never told it before, and only tell it now because it belongs in the record of these events as a significant detail that was not without its influence on history. The line of journalistic license rightly excluded such a private happening as this from the light of print; but history is a different matter, and this book is, or sets out to be, a history. And besides, if T. V. dislikes the story enough he has only to deny it. There are still a great many people who believe official denials.

10

The idea of smuggling T. V. Soong through Chiang Kai-shek's blockade and restoring him to his place in Hankow may seem a strangely partisan one for an American newspaper correspondent to entertain, but at the time I was, or believed I was, animated by the desire to 'get a good story.' Yet when I returned to Hankow without T. V., and reported the circumstances to Borodin, Mme Sun Yat-sen and Rayna Prohme, I perceived, rather abruptly, that my feelings in the matter had been partisan all along. There was no harm in this, so long as nothing but my individual feelings were concerned, but I began to be conscience-stricken about my New York office. There was a danger that I might get so interested in the fate of Hankow that the purposes for which I had been sent to China at considerable expense would be forgotten. I cast about for some definite enterprise that might yield material of interest for my newspapers, and decided that I ought to go to Changsha and see the first Chinese Soviet in operation.

The Chinese Communists were in control in Changsha and had proclaimed the dictatorship of the proletariat some weeks before. The movement was premature and badly organized; reports from Hunan were confused, but the embryo Soviet was clearly not doing very well; the Hankow government was unable to support or patronize too openly a movement with which it was actually in sympathy. All this made the position of Hunan obscure, and I had wanted some weeks before to go and investigate it for myself. I have ever since regretted that I did not do so while there was still time, for that Changsha Soviet was the beginning of a Chinese Communist state that was to endure, against innumerable difficulties and with many territorial changes, for years.

But I had not been back in Hankow long before the approaching catastrophe became evident; and with the fall of the government in sight—the end of the Kuomintang-Communist alliance, the end of the worldwide hope for an immediate social revolution in China—it would have been foolish to go away. My superiors in New York had repeatedly asked me to ignore the news and write my personal impressions, but it seemed to me that the collapse of the Hankow government, with all it represented to the world at large, was an event too significant to miss. And I knew it was coming long before it happened—so long before that I did not dare put it into my cables to America. A piece of news that is one month early is as worthless as a piece of news one month late.

My daybook records, on June 21st: 'Situation very serious. Borodin ill, Feng Yü-hsiang cutting capers. The end is in sight.'

And on July 2d: 'The Government here is doomed. It will fall very soon, any day. God knows what will happen to Rayna.'

This is, by the way, the first time Rayna Prohme's name appears in my notes.

The fall of Hankow was to determine the conduct of the Communist International for years afterwards; it was to turn the mind of the Russian Soviet government away from the militant internationalism of Trotzky to the national socialism of Stalin; it was to drive the genuinely subversive or revolutionary forces in China underground for a desperate struggle that has not yet fully come to the surface; it was to chasten the impatience of Communists all over the world more than any single event since 1917. In view of these proved results, most of which I could obscurely foresee (with the help of Borodin) before the event had taken place, I was determined to cling to Hankow to the last possible moment, to see the drama played out, to be in at the death. In doing so I got myself into an awkward position vis à vis my New York office, for I was unable to explain such complicated affairs in cablegrams at a dollar a word, especially as nothing had yet happened. In the end, as shall be told, I was peremptorily ordered off to find 'personal adventures' and missed the actual catastrophe at Hankow by ten days.

The Hankow government lasted approximately three months after the rebellion of Chiang Kai-shek. It had retained the loyalty of twenty-one out of the thirty-three members of the Central Executive Committee of the Kuomintang. It was supported by the greater part of the civilian Kuomintang and clearly represented the later tradition of Sun Yat-sen; but in military force it was weak. Its generals were not trustworthy, and the best of them could not compare in ability or popularity to Chiang Kai-shek. A series of rebellions against the civilian authority of Hankow took place in April and May. General Li Chi-sen revolted at Canton, the home of the Kuomintang, and proclaimed a government of his own; Hunan, half Communist and half reactionary, was almost detached from Hankow's control; the armies of Szechuan began to move down from the west.

A god from the machine was badly needed, and the Russians undertook to provide one in the person of Feng Yü-hsiang. Feng, the 'Christian General' (save the mark!), had been driven out of Peking in March, 1926, by Chang Tso-lin, and had gone to Moscow for a year. Now he suddenly appeared in Mongolia with an army, marched across Shansi without encountering resistance, and entered Honan as the saviour of the Kuomintang. Everything he possessed, from his army to the shirt on his back, he owed to the Russians, and it never seems to have occurred to them that he would forget it. The news of his progress across Honan was received with rejoicing in Hankow. The *People's Tribune* called his forces the 'new revolutionary army,' and the labour unions and Communists celebrated his every 'victory' with a mass meeting.

As a matter of fact he had no victories. He marched across Honan without difficulty; the elegant Fengtien troops of Chang Tso-lin, of which so much had been written in the foreign press, retired before him. His Mohammedan cavalry entered Chengchow, the capital of the province, just as the last of the northerners vanished up the railway towards Peking. He was now in control of the central province of China, and from Chengchow, on the Peking–Hankow railway, he could strike either at his friends in Hankow or his enemies in Peking.

He did neither. To the consternation of the Russians and even some of the Chinese (who should have known their 'Christian General' by this time), he went into a conference with Chiang Kai-shek and declared himself opposed to the whole policy of the Left Kuomintang. His game was, as it always had been, to carve out a principality for himself and exploit it. He really supported neither Hankow nor Nanking, but his performance removed the last hope for an assertion of Hankow's authority and the survival of the revolutionary government.

The 'Christian General' started to bombard Hankow at about this time (early June) with an extraordinary series of telegrams in which the utmost cynicism was combined with the formulas of old-fashioned Chinese 'face-saving' and political politeness. He suggested, for example, that 'Mr Borodin, who has already resigned, should return to his own country.' Borodin had never resigned, but these forms of speech are usual when one war lord drives out another, and Feng Yü-hsiang was a war lord through and through. He pointed out, with exquisite courtesy, that 'those members of the Wuhan government who may wish to go abroad for their health should be allowed to do so.'

The episode of Feng Yü-hsiang seemed to me a piece of mediæval buffoonery that might have discouraged the most ardent believer in the Chinese Revolution. What was to be done in a civilization harmonized to such extremes that an illiterate coolie with an army at his back could dominate the relationships of capital and labour, of men and government, of parties and programmes?

Borodin retained his calm. Sick in bed and stuffed with quinine as he was, he kept his emotionless objectivity and his faith in the cause he served.

'I shall remain until the last possible minute,' he told me one day. 'When I am forced to go, I shall go. But do not suppose that the Chinese Revolution is ending, or that it has failed in any but the most temporary sense. It will go back underground. It will become an illegal movement, suppressed by counter-revolution and beaten down by reaction and imperialism; but it has learned how to organize, how to struggle. Sooner or later, a year, two years, five years from now, it will rise to the surface again. It may be defeated a dozen times, but in the end it must conquer. The revolutionary impulse is profound in China, and the country is filled with wonderful revolutionary instruments. For every one of those instruments destroyed by the war lords two or three new ones will arise. What has happened here will not be forgotten.'

He seldom discussed specific dangers until they were past, but on that particular day it was known that the city was almost defenceless. An army from the west (a Szechuan force to which Ho Chien and a Kuomintang army had 'gone over') was very near, and it was currently believed that Hankow would be captured that night. I told Borodin what I had heard and asked him what he was going to do. He smiled, looked out the window, and replied without any evidence of feeling.

'We have asked all or part of the "Iron army" to return to defend the city,' he said, 'but if it does not come, the city will be captured. After that, who knows?'

He turned back to me.

'A few heads will come off,' he said mildly.

That one of the first heads to come off would be his own was understood, but he appeared to face the possibility without excitement.

On that same day (it was July 1st) an extraordinary conversation took place in Rayna Prohme's office. I had gone in there to talk to her and had found Mme Sun Yat-sen. We sat in the back office and drank tea. Mme Sun had resisted persuasion and pressure for the last three months from her own family. It was no light thing for any Chinese woman to defy the influence of mother, brothers, sisters; it had been particularly difficult for Mme Sun, so sensitive and so modest; it had been an ordeal from which she emerged ready for any contingency. The conversation on that day was restricted to the immediate situation, which was canvassed in all its aspects. I had already urged Rayna Prohme to take refuge in the American Consulate, and asked Mme Sun if she did not think this wise. Rayna said—half laughing, as usual—that she was not at all sure the American Consulate would take her in or that she wanted such protection even if it were available. Mme Sun, speaking with sudden gravity, said that she agreed with me:

that the capture of Hankow would be a terrible event, in which only those under the protection of the foreign guns would be safe; and that Mrs Prohme had already done enough for the Chinese Revolution without dying for it.

Then, suddenly, the conversation took a gruesome turn. It would have been gruesome under any conditions, but on that particular day, in the presence of two women who stood in such awful peril, it made my blood run cold. Mme Sun began it by speaking of the tortures to which the twenty Communists (including little Phyllis Li, the daughter of Li Ta-chao) had been subjected in Peking. She explained the difference between garrotting and plain strangling, named a number of the more agonizing torments in use among the Chinese reactionaries, and discussed the relative merits of the various forms of execution from the point of view of the person to be executed. Although she seemed a little nervous, and was conscious that the dangers she discussed were only a few hours away, I do not believe she was primarily thinking of herself; she was indirectly attempting to persuade Rayna Prohme to go to the American Consulate for the night.

When Mme Sun went home and Rayna returned to her work I went to see Lockhart, the American Consul. He was as slow and impassive as Borodin, reluctant to express himself clearly on any political matter, but his inner satisfaction at the approaching defeat of the Reds shone unmistakably in his face. I asked him flatly if the consulate would protect the three Americans who worked for the Hankow government, the Prohmes and Mrs Mitchell.

Lockhart answered with immense deliberation. I felt sure that he was enjoying the moment, for the Prohmes had been something of a thorn in his flesh for many months.

'You tell Mrs Prohme for me,' he said, 'that I will protect every American citizen who takes refuge in this consulate. I can do nothing for anybody outside it.'

I was a little annoyed at his assumption that Mrs Prohme had sent me to see him.

'I don't know that the Prohmes want to be protected,' I said. 'I was only asking on my own hook, because I think they are in serious danger. If Mrs Prohme is tortured to death in the streets of

Hankow while half the American navy looks on, it won't make a very pleasant impression at home.'

This was a stupid and flighty remark, but Lockhart did not take it up.

'I cannot protect Americans in Borodin's office,' he said, still smiling. 'I can protect this consulate, and shall do so. If the Prohmes and Mrs Mitchell come here they will be protected. That is all I can say.'

He was quite right, of course. I record the incident merely to show what contradictions can arise in a mind under stress. I disliked the whole principle of extraterritoriality, and regarded the presence of American warships in the Yangtsze-kiang as an unwarrantable invasion of China; and yet here I was asking Lockhart to extend his consular protection to absurd lengths. The only thing that can be said to justify such a request is that American business men and missionaries had often been protected at equally absurd lengths, and (in the case of the missionaries) even against their own will.

But Rayna Prohme dismissed the whole subject with a plain no. Her husband was at home, seriously ill; she had no desire to make a contrite pilgrimage to the consulate; she very nearly agreed with the navy people, who used to say that people who worked for the Chinese Revolution had no right to expect American protection. She thanked me for speaking to Lockhart, but was sorry I had done so. And that was that.

I made up my mind to a course of action that would force her to be rescued if the city fell. These were the counsels of alarm, of course, and as it happened they were useless; but sometimes what might have happened has a curiously revealing light to shed on what did happen. I was going to wait until the army from the west had taken the city. Then, at the first shot—all the western army had to do was fire a few rounds, as the city was without defenders —I was going to ask the Prohmes to go to the consulate. If they refused, I intended to demand of Lockhart a naval detachment to remove them to the consulate—to 'evacuate' them, as the strange diplomatic language puts it. Lockhart then would have been obliged to march them to the consulate under escort, or to take the responsibility before American opinion and his own superiors for whatever happened to them. It may be seen that in my excitement I was ungenerous to Lockhart, who would have been put in an awkward position in either case. It is even possible that the navy would have refused him the detachment necessary to rescue three people from a house some distance from the Bund; for the naval officers were unanimous in their dislike of the 'American Reds,' and would have loathed the necessity for helping them. But in the high temperature to which I had been brought by Mme Sun's description of the tortures and death that might be expected that night, I was ready to go to any extremity.

The necessity did not arise, and in a few days I was ashamed of my truculence. Fortunately neither Lockhart nor Rayna knew just how extreme had been my intentions, and all I had to my discredit was a hot-headed remark or so. But the might-have-been of this incident not only reveals the strength of sympathy that already attached me to the red-haired revolutionist from Illinois, but does, also, involve a principle. I was too excited to state the principle clearly at the time, but I felt it, however obscurely. It was this: that extraterritoriality either should be abolished altogether or enforced altogether. The tendency of the American authorities to protect such Americans as they thought worthy of protection and to let the others take their chance had been shown clearly enough in the Mitchell-Burton incident in Peking. On that occasion two Americans working for a partisan Chinese newspaper had been jailed by Chang Tso-lin and treated with considerable indignity. Until American public opinion had been aroused by the press, and the State Department had sent formal instructions, the American Legation in Peking had done nothing for these two. The general idea in the consular and diplomatic services, and above all in the navy, was that Americans who sympathized openly with the Chinese Revolution or associated themselves with it were not entitled to American protection. On the surface this was a reasonable contention, but it did not survive the second look. Any stray missionary, engaged in the futile and unnecessary effort to convert the Chinese to an alien religion, was considered worthy of having his life saved no matter how many other people might be killed in the process. Still more, any employee of the Standard Oil Company, engaged for the most part in the effort to sell low-grade petroleum for the best possible price to a population that didn't know the difference, was to be protected by navy and marines against every accident of the Chinese civil war. But persons who (like Rayna Prohme) were in China neither to squeeze money out of the Chinese nor to mystify them with religion, but to work for and with them, belonged to a small, special category, excluded from the benefits of the pernicious treaties. Lockhart would have protected her only if she had come to the consulate; but he would have sent the whole navy, if necessary, to rescue the vaguest missionary or the most insignificant little trader. This was the potential situation that aroused me to such a fury on the night of July 1st, and that it remained potential does not diminish its significance as a landmark in this story.

In the morning the immediate danger had passed. The western army (troops of Yang Sen and Ho Chien) had unaccountably failed to press onward in time, and during the night a large part of the 'Iron army' of Canton, which had been camped along the railway in Honan, poured into Hankow in crowded trains. The 'Iron army' was the one army out of the Cantonese hosts that remained faithful to the civilian Kuomintang and obeyed the orders of the committees. It was commanded by Chang Fa-kwei, who was credited with being a Communist. But however dependable this one army might be, it was alone, encompassed on every side by superior enemy forces. The tradition of Chinese warfare was overwhelmingly against fighting under such conditions. Battles took place in China only when the contending forces were of equal or nearly equal strength; when one side obviously outnumbered the other, it was customary for the smaller force to surrender or to join the larger. These customs, which the cheap humour of foreign newspapers found very comic, were in fact a proof of the profoundly civilized nature of the Chinese even in such barbaric enterprises as warfare; and without some such convention the loss of human life in the constant but meaningless civil wars of 1911–26 would have been frightful. By 1927 civil warfare had come to be genuinely significant, it is true, and there were plenty of Chinese who had the courage to die for their convictions; but the professional soldiery—however much affected by revolutionary propaganda—could not shake off the whole tradition of war as China had known it for thousands of years. This being true, it was obvious that the Hankow government, having lost its provinces and all but one of its armies, could not survive for many more days.

I knew that Borodin intended to make his escape, when the collapse came, by way of Mongolia. It was my intention to go with him if possible, and he was quite willing. The flight from Hankow, the journey across the interior to the desert and across the desert to Siberia, would make the kind of story my newspapers wanted, I thought—an 'exclusive' story, a 'personal' story, of exactly the genre stipulated in my contract. But I was not allowed to wait for the fall of Hankow. At this precise moment, when the climax was at hand, my New York office cabled me the last and most peremptory of a strange series of instructions.

The idea behind all my instructions had been, in brief, this: that I had not been sent to China to write about politics or the Chinese Revolution, but to engage in some kind of personal enterprise, capers or high jinks, that would carry on the tradition of romantic adventure (the 'Richard Harding Davis tradition,' it was called) to which my various employers insisted on assigning me. I have already explained that this legend corresponded to no reality whatever. My two Rif journeys had been adventurous, it is true, but only incidentally: I had not gone to the Rif in pursuit of adventure, but to learn what I could about the Riffians and their country. Adventure for the sake of adventure seemed to me dull and silly, of no value to the adventurer or to anybody else. I disliked the assumption that I was incapable of doing anything except gallop about foreign fields on a horse; and although I made attempts in China to satisfy this strange requirement of an unfortunate reputation, all my real interests were in the revolutionary movement itself, its meaning, progress and failure. The misunderstanding between my employers and myself was therefore complete.

The last of my instructions came on July 2d. It was a longish cablegram, and I cannot quote it exactly, but the gist was this: You are sending us entirely too much about politics; this kind of news is adequately provided by all the established news agencies; what we expect of you is something quite different, and we want you now to 'have personal adventures.'

Even in the desperate anxiety and tension of Hankow that lovely phrase 'have personal adventures' made an instant success. Borodin laughed out loud when I told him about it, and Rayna Prohme—even though she realized what a predicament it put me in—thought the wonderful cablegram should be framed and kept as a monument to American journalism.

But there it was, just the same, and no amount of laughing would get rid of the necessity: I had to find a Rosinante and go off in some direction to tilt at windmills. The Changsha trip was now out of the question, and would in any case have been far too political in interest to satisfy the requirements. I consulted Borodin, hoping that his escape to Mongolia might be near enough to justify me in waiting for it; but he could fix no date. He was, as always, determined to hang on until the last possible moment in the hope that the accidents of Chinese politics might turn in his favour. He believed the end might come 'any day, any night,' but he was not going to anticipate it.

I waited two or three days more, and then, when an opportunity came to visit Feng Yü-hsiang at his camp in Honan, I took it. The journey across China from Hankow to Peking at this particular time represented at least the possibility of 'personal adventure,' as the whole interior was beset by the confusion of rival armies and robber bands, peasant volunteers and individual outlaws. All foreigners had left the interior three months before, and, by and large, the proposed trip looked dangerous enough to satisfy even the most captious employer.

'If you get your throat cut,' Rayna said helpfully, 'just telegraph us and we'll send off the story. You might write it in advance, and then there won't be anything lost if you're killed.'

I said good-bye to my Hankow friends and their remnant of a revolutionary government on July 5th. Ten days later Tang Seng-chi, one of their generals, proclaimed the expected counter-revolution; Borodin, Mme Sun Yat-sen, Chen, the Prohmes and the rest scattered in flight, escaping in various disguises and under various names from the vengeance of the war lords. I did not see them again for many weeks, and not the least of my troubles was the constant speculation as to what had become of them. The last entry made in my notebook in Hankow was a line of Shakespeare: 'So foul a sky clears not without a storm.' I no longer remember why it was written in the book on that particular day, but it is not a bad description of the point of view of those who had, in the tremendous effort of 1926 and 1927, attempted to raise the storm.

22

The journey from Hankow to Peking took three weeks. It was an interesting journey, but no more perilous than an ordinary trip from London to Paris. It was uncanny how the Chinese forestalled my every effort to 'have personal adventures.' They got up and gave me their seats in trains or inns; they treated me with the utmost consideration; they made me presents of fans; sometimes they even refused to let me pay for my board and lodging. I was surrounded by courtesy from the time I left Hankow until I arrived in Peking; and although the journey involved incidental hardships, they were invariably lessened as much as possible by the anxious politeness of the inhabitants of the country. I am at a loss to explain this, except by luck. The fact is that the country was very disturbed, and my friend Basil Lang, correspondent of the London *Times*, who followed me to Honan ten days later, was certainly murdered; he vanished in the middle of Chengchow and has never been heard of since. But the day I spent in Chengchow was—except for the heat—no more dangerous than a day in any provincial town. I wandered about the streets and shops, accompanied only by my interpreter, and never a rude word or gesture disturbed the general impression of smiling calm. On the next morning we went on across Honan to Loyang at the other end of the province, where Feng Yü-hsiang had his headquarters.

My visit to the Christian war lord was pretty much what I had expected. He turned out to be a big, slow brute with a highly developed sense of his own power. He was ignorant, violent, and authoritative, but probably sincere; his staff and his armies in general had the most salutary fear of him. In his speeches, his public prayers, and the little booklet printed to distribute to his armies, he exhibited a system of thought based partly upon

Christianity and partly upon Confucianism—an ethical system, not a religious one. Except in the matter of prayer, he did not pay much attention to the supernatural element in religion, but his prayers were wonderful. He used to issue his requests to the Almighty regularly, and they ranged all the way from a demand for rain to a modest petition that his enemies be exterminated. Most of the ethical notions put forward in his book of the Kuominchun (People's army—the name he called his own bands) could be found in the Confucian Analects, but they were simplified to skeleton form by Feng's primitive mind, and lost all the lofty philosophical quality of the ancient Chinese. Such qualities as Modesty, Magnanimity, Meekness, Liberality, Love, Humility and Purity were as highly prized by Feng as by Confucius, but whereas they came naturally from the meditative nature of the old philosopher, they struck me as being inappropriate to the character of the treacherous coolie war lord.

The train from Hankow went back on July 9th, and I left its relative luxury and safety for a Chinese inn at Loyang. There (July 10th) my interpreter and I climbed aboard a troop train bound for Hwei-hsin-chen, the last point on the Lung-hai railway in the western end of Honan. The train was slow, filthy, crammed with soldiers, indescribably hot, and yet the innumerable belching, spitting, stinking passengers were most polite to the stray foreigner. I sat in a corner of a box car stuffed to overflowing with coolies in uniform, and the heat and smells were the worst I can remember; but in the midst of the journey, to my astonishment, one of the soldiers took off his jacket, rolled it up and gave it to me for a cushion.

My daybook has only this to say of Hwei-hsin-chen: 'Arrived at night and stayed in Chinese inn (bugs).'

On the next morning we crossed the Yellow River in the ferry to Mao-chin-tu in Shansi, the territory of the 'model war lord' Yen Hsi-shan. From Maochintu to Taiyuanfu, the capital of the province, was a long, uneventful journey in mule carts, on foot, and at times in a ricksha. Sometimes I slept in the abandoned houses of the missionaries who had fled the country three months before, but oftener the only refuge was a roadside inn. The inns were invariably verminous, and sometimes the heat and vermin made it impossible to sleep inside at all; on such occasions I moved out into the courtyard and slept on the ground with the coolies. My interpreter, Peng Ta-mu, was a jewel. At night, when the vermin retarded sleep, Peng Ta-mu told me old Chinese stories or answered, with admirable tolerance and restraint, my questions about life in his native province. He wanted to be a doctor, but the revolution had played ducks and drakes with his family, his money and his plans. Peng had almost no interest in politics, but he was fascinated by rocks or plants, geological specimens or the leaves of a tree. It gave me no small satisfaction to think that I might be able, through the Rockefeller Foundation or in some other way, to start Peng off in his medical career and leave a good doctor in China as a trace of my passing.

We reached Taiyuanfu nine days after the start of our journey. The old city seemed restful and charming after the rigours of the road, and the railway hotel (French) could not have delighted me more if it had been run by César Ritz himself. Yen Hsi-shan, the 'model governor' of the province, received me with the gentle, old-fashioned courtesy of an educated Chinese. He had governed Shansi in uninterrupted peace and prosperity ever since the night in 1911 when he, as the head of the Kuomintang faction in the garrison, had expelled the imperial authorities and raised the flag of the Republic. Yen's record was unique in China. His province, although large and rich, was remote enough to guarantee him immunity from the hazards of the civil wars that agitated the rest of the country. It was not directly in contact with any of the great powers and had no fatal river to open it up to foreign gunboats. Yen himself, intelligent and benevolent, had known how to take advantage of his geographical advantages; he had welcomed French and German technical advisers, who were always less dangerous than Japanese, Russian or British; with their help he had built roads, sunk artesian wells, widened and lighted his streets, encouraged commerce and maintained public order. But in the past two years the Kuomintang and Communist oganizers had been at work, and Shansi was no longer the sleepy, prosperous backwater Yen had tried to make it. He professed to be a follower of Sun Yat-sen, but of the Sun Yat-sen of 1911—not of the Socialist Sun Yat-sen of 1924. The idea that coolies might be organized to demand better wages and better conditions of life shocked him, and he was even then engaged in the effort to suppress the labour and peasants' unions.

The philosopher king gave me a motorcar to go to Kalgan in, and there, at the point where Shansi, Mongolia and the China of Chang Tso-lin came together, Peng and I took a troop train for Peking. My contract with the North American Newspaper Alliance had expired, and for the rest of my stay in China I was released from the necessity of finding something to put into cablegrams. My employers had had no reason to be satisfied with me, but to my surprise they did not complain. They had done well enough with my Rif articles to counterbalance the failure of the Chinese journey, and philosophers, it seemed, could exist as well in a New York office as in a Chinese garden.

12

Peking in the summer of 1927 was a nervous capital. Old Chang Tso-lin still governed there with the help of the Japanese, and my Hankow friends were regarded with horror by most of the foreigners and the Peking Chinese. Foreign women had been ordered to leave the city three months before, and many had obeyed. I spent a week in Peking and felt that I knew it well. It was not hard to know the Peking of the foreigners: it consisted of the legations and hotels, a few shops, a club, some dance halls and a great deal of whisky. I enjoyed these amenities as well as anybody could, but to get a little reading and writing done I moved up into the Imperial Hunting Park in the Western Hills, and thereafter went in to Peking only when I felt the need of conversation or a drink.

I could learn nothing about the fate of Hankow except that the government there had collapsed. The most contradictory reports were printed in the English and American newspapers about Borodin, Mme Sun Yat-sen, the Prohmes and Eugene Chen. It was clear that nobody really knew where they were; they had all vanished. One report about Rayna, published in a Shanghai reactionary newspaper, made me curse with rage. It said that she and Borodin had gone to Kuling, where they had given gay parties every night, using up most of the hotel's supplies of champagne. I had never seen Borodin drink anything but water, and Rayna's limit was a glass of beer; the story in the newspaper was ridiculous, but the sheer malice of it infuriated me. The same kind of invention was exercised at the expense of Mme Sun Yat-sen, and worse: China was filled with rumours about her, one of the principal ones being that she had married or was about to marry Eugene Chen. The poor lady herself was the last to hear this absurd story, and when she did hear it, months later in Moscow, it gave her a nervous breakdown.

Randall Gould, the correspondent of the United Press, introduced me to the Soviet Embassy, where there was some likelihood of getting news of the Hankow people; but even the Bolsheviks were without information.

I found friends among the Bolsheviks, and two of them, Grinievich and Kantorovich, were ready to argue with me on any subject for any number of consecutive hours. Perhaps for this reason, perhaps because I had grown to dislike the bourgeois point of view in China too intensely to enjoy the company of my own people, I spent more time with the Bolsheviks than with any other foreigners. Roy Chapman Andrews gave me a dinner or two in his beautiful old Chinese house; the American Minister fed me at lunch one day; the club was always hospitable and my colleagues of the press friendly; but I actually felt more at ease with the Bolsheviks than with anybody in Peking. Their way of searching for the sense of events had been made familiar to me by Borodin, and although Borodin's luminous intelligence was not a common quality even among Bolsheviks, I could at least *talk* to Kantorovich, Yurishkevich, Grinievich and the rest. Communication with Americans and British was more difficult, oddly enough, for the fact that we used the same language only made more obvious the fundamental opposition of ideas. Except for Randall Gould and his wife, there was not an American of my acquaintance in Peking who had any tolerance for the spirit of Hankow. One American lady gave me an excellent dinner in her fine Chinese house and said to me afterwards:

'Will you tell me what's the good of organizing coolies into labour unions? What good have labour unions ever done to anybody? They've ruined America, so that you can't get a decent servant in the whole country. Why can't Mme Sun and all those people leave the coolies alone? They're quite happy as they are.'

I had reached the point where conversation with anybody like this good lady was impossible. I might have said that her feelings would be different if she were a coolie, but this would have seemed to her irrelevant and rude. She represented the Peking point of view, and while it was being expounded I could only smile politely and try not to be bored.

The Peking point of view showed remarkably little acquaintance with the laws of historic development, but it was at least more civilized than the point of view of Shanghai and the treaty ports. The characteristic of the Peking foreigners was, in a word, civility. In Peking there had always been an equal association of foreigners and upper-class Chinese in society, and every foreigner there had a few Chinese friends. Some had many. Peking foreigners were kind to their servants, interested in Chinese art and literature, fond of jade, embroideries, the theatre of Mei Lan-fang and the inventions of Chinese cookery. They really did establish some kind of relationship to the country they lived in; they were interested in China in a dilettante way; they liked, admired and sometimes even understood the culture of the Chinese, and the simple savagery of the treaty-port foreigners seemed as bad to them as it did to me. But it seemed bad to them for social reasons —because it was bad taste, or vulgar, or characteristic of uneducated persons. They were all very cultivated, polite and upper-class in Peking, and their lovely Chinese houses, filled with soft silken embroideries and beautiful carvings, were among the most charming I have ever seen. What made their point of view alien to me was their perfect contentment with the state of things around them. The world seemed a good world to them; the coolies of China, human creatures ground into equality with the beasts, seemed to them 'perfectly happy as they are'; and anybody who wished to change this state, particularly any active revolutionary, was a weird monster. If one lived long enough in Peking drawing rooms almost any kind of activity involving exposure to the heat, dust, smells and rude behaviour of the poor might come to seem ridiculous.

The Bolsheviks, I strongly suspect, knew little about jade and embroideries. Certainly the Soviet Embassy would have caused shudders to course up and down the back of any interior decorator. But the remnants of the Embassy staff kept up a lively interest in everything that went on in China, and my friend A. I. Kantorovich, in particular, had a passion for thought and discussion. You could throw any idea at him, and he would pursue it until he had run it to ground and thoroughly examined or rejected it. On one occasion, when he came to lunch with me at the Imperial Hunting Park, I remarked (I forget why) that Queen Victoria seemed to me to have left her impress all over the age in which she lived—that the age would have been different if the Queen's character had been different. Kantorovich pounced upon this notion and proceeded to destroy it. The Queen had not made the Victorian Age; the Victorian Age had made the Queen. He knew a great deal about the subject, and the argument grew vigorous. Napoleon had not remade Europe; Europe had called for, had in truth created, the necessary Napoleon. The stumbling block in his ultra-Bolshevik argument seemed to be, for a long time, Alexander Makedonsky, who was the one example of a pure personal accident with immense historical results. I was puzzled about this gentleman until the turn of the conversation revealed that he was only, after all, our old friend Alexander the Great in Russian guise. The argument continued for many hours; and Kantorovich, who had come to lunch, did not return to Peking until midnight.

I lived in a temple in the Hunting Park—a temple that had turned into a hotel. My part of the temple was a separate little house in the silver birch trees, isolated from the sights and sounds of the main buildings. There it was possible to spend days without seeing anybody but the silent Chinese who brought my food, and without hearing a sound but the slither of a scorpion across the terrace, or the chatter of a bird in the silver trees.

From the Hunting Park I went down to Peking once a week and saw either the gay world or the Bolsheviks or both. The Peking expeditions were liquorous affairs, for the only diversion offered a rather bored and worried visitor on the hot summer nights was whisky—unless, indeed, it was champagne or beer. There was a dinner or banquet given to a departing journalist by the Anglo-

American press one evening, and somebody rashly invited me to it. Whoever my host was, he probably saw his error before the evening was over. I consumed so much beer that I was puffed with eloquence, made a speech to the assembled Fourth Estate, quarrelled with an American marine captain, and ended up by sleeping on the Tatar Wall to prove that I could evade the vigilance of the marine sentries.

When you feel as foolish as I did the next day it is small consolation to have won a silly bet. I made up my mind to leave Peking at once, drove out to the Hunting Park before lunch, packed, and was ready to go. I had no destination in particular, but as a general principle I intended to end up in Moscow; for there, sooner or later, Rayna Prohme and the rest of my Hankow friends would be sure to come if they were still alive. The last thing Rayna had said to me, as the train started to move out of Hankow, had been: 'We'll probably meet in Moscow.' This 'probably' was the nearest thing to information on the subject that I had been able to obtain from anybody.

But a delay occurred at this point—a very special delay. I had recently acquired a new relative, whom I had never seen, and I could not leave Peking until I was sure whether or not she would be able to accompany me.

There can be no harm, at this late date, in telling the true story of Fanny Borodin. Chang Tso-lin is dead; the whole state of affairs in China and Russia has changed; the circumstances of the Borodin case are unlikely to be repeated in our time. What was a secret of state in 1927 is only an amusing anecdote in 1935. It differs from many amusing anecdotes in that it really happened.

It will be remembered that Borodin's wife was captured by the Shantung war lord in May and turned over by him to his feudal superior, Chang Tso-lin. The old bandit was dissuaded from strangling her, and after a great many delays and legal quarrels she was brought to trial in July. The person in charge of her defence was my friend A. I. Kantorovich, whose work in the Soviet Foreign Office was supposed to be that of an economic jurist (or juridical economist). Actually he had been obliged to spend most of his time for three months attempting to defend the fifteen or sixteen Soviet citizens who had been imprisoned by Chang Tso-lin, and the chief of these, at least in the judgment of public opinion, was Mme Borodin. To save her from torture and death was Kantorovich's job, and in view of the importance of the case and the innocence of the prisoner his methods need not be questioned too closely; they were the methods of Peking in 1927.

As a matter of fact, I never knew exactly what the method was, but the results were as follows: the judge before whom the case was to be tried suddenly called it one morning before Chang Tso-lin was up. Mme Borodin was heard and immediately acquitted. When Chang Tso-lin got out of bed Mme Borodin had vanished, and so had the judge. He was next heard of in Japan, a pleasant country to which his peaceful habit of mind had urgently invited him as soon as the hearing in the Borodin case was over.

Chang Tso-lin flew into a terrible rage. He had counted on being able to strangle Mme Borodin, but to have lost the principal victim and also the judge in one morning was too much for any war lord. Peking was turned upside down, the trains were watched, suspected houses were raided. The Soviet Embassy suavely invited Chang's men to search the premises, in which Mme Borodin was not to be found. Chang Tso-lin believed—and rightly—that it would be difficult for a Russian woman with Mme Borodin's known appearance to travel far in China. Photographs of the lady were circulated, and the ships at Tientsin were watched. Chang announced in the newspapers that he was determined to catch her at whatever cost; the foreign press displayed the liveliest interest; and all in all there was a fine to-do about it.

Then, some ten days after the acquittal and disappearance, a dispatch from Vladivostok reached the Chinese and foreign press. It had been sent out by the Rengo News Agency (Japanese), which exchanges news dispatches with other agencies. It described the arrival of Mme Borodin from China and Japan on a Soviet steamer and quoted in detail the things she had to say about her imprisonment and trial in Peking. Eight days later Mme Borodin arrived in Moscow on the Trans-Siberian Express and was interviewed again, this time by the Tass (Soviet) news agency. There was no doubt about it, for it had been printed in every newspaper in the world: Fanny Borodin had escaped from Chang Tso-lin and was now safe in Moscow. Chang Tso-lin, suspicious and bitter, had to confess himself beaten and call off the search.

Mme Borodin's odyssey had taken place at about the time of my arrival in Peking, and by the end of August it was no longer a burning subject. Lunching with Kantorovich one day at the Grand Hôtel de Pékin, I was struck by the unwonted earnestness of his manner when he spoke of this faded episode. After a good deal of preamble he asked me if I would do something for him and for Borodin—something required by the iniquities of the Peking régime, something to save a human life. I agreed to do so if I could. And only then did I learn that Fanny Borodin had never left Peking at all—that she had been under Chang Tso-lin's nose the whole time that his cutthroats were ransacking the town for her; that she was still in hiding, in only slightly diminished peril, in the house of a Chinese friend.

The proposal was that I might take Mme Borodin with me to Japan as a relative (sister, cousin, aunt) and there, at Shimonoseki, get her aboard a Soviet steamer that would be warned of our coming. The dangerous part of the trip would be that from Peking to Tientsin, on trains watched by Chang Tso-lin's soldiers, with officials and fellow passengers who had all seen photographs of Mme Borodin at some time or other. The hope was that if my sister, cousin or aunt pretended to be ill, and only my extremely un-Bolshevik appearance was presented to the view of ticket takers and soldiers, no questions would be asked.

I agreed to this proposal at once; it delighted me. Nothing could have pleased me more than to smuggle a victim away from the irate war lord, and the mere notion of that trip from Peking to Tientsin made me feel cheerful. That the victim was Borodin's wife and Kantorovich's client added to the rosy aspect of the whole enterprise. I made only one stipulation: that my American passport must not be touched or in any way involved in the business. I had a healthy respect for my passport, and life would have been nearly insupportable without it. Kantorovich laughed at this.

'What do you think we are?' he asked. 'We can't do anything about American passports. Our only hope is to borrow one.'

So for some days I had a new relative. But in the end the American lady who had at first intended to supply the all-important passport changed her mind; I could not very well travel with a sick female relative who had no papers; the most blatantly un-Bolshevik appearance would not have guaranteed safety under such conditions, and the whole plan fell through. I was disappointed. I should have enjoyed that trip.

On the day when Kantorovich's plan was given up for lack of a passport, the newspapers carried a dispatch from Vladivostok that aroused my impatience to be off. Mme Sun Yat-sen, the Chens 'and their party' had arrived in Vladivostok on a Soviet steamer from Shanghai and were taking a special train to Moscow. Mme Sun had said only a few words, but Eugene Chen had talked at length, and I recognized the characteristic turns of his phrases. I might have had my suspicions of the Vladivostok dispatch, so strangely like the one announcing Mme Borodin's arrival a month before; but no Vladivostok correspondent was likely to be able to parody Mr Chen's style as well as he parodied it himself. I took my leave of 'that Mongolian encampment known as Peking,' went down to Tientsin to collect my belongings from various parts of China, and crossed to the other side of the Great Wall early in September.

Manchuria unfolded like a dusty carpet, one half of it infested by Japanese, and the other half crowded with Russians. I had never known quite how obvious the Japanese control of their zone was until I reached Mukden and found the Japanese currency, stamps, police and language everywhere. Harbin was even stranger—an almost purely Russian city, with street after street in which the Chinese were outnumbered by foreigners. The architecture and complexion of Harbin were the most foreign I had seen anywhere in China, and here even the lowliest kinds of labour—those reserved in other cities for Chinese coolies alone —were performed by white men. I never heard a word of Chinese spoken in my hotel or in the restaurants I frequented during my three days there. These were fleeting and trivial impressions, to which no undue importance should be attached, but I did certainly feel when I reached Harbin that I had left China behind. I recorded the feeling in my journal with a sweeping comment:

'Five months in China and everything I thought worth a damn has gone to pot: depressing experience.'

The Trans-Siberian journey is at best monotonous and exhausting. It takes the traveller over a country so flat, limitless and dreary that one day seems exactly like another, and by the time we reached Moscow I felt that I had been on the train most of my life. There had been floods on part of the line, and the train could not keep up to its schedule; we arrived in Moscow twenty-four hours late. The journey from Harbin had taken nine full days.

AN ANTHOLOGY
OF MODERN AMERICAN POETRY

ESPECIALLY SELECTED FOR
"AN AMERICAN OMNIBUS"

BY MARK VAN DOREN

Edwin Arlington Robinson
MR. FLOOD'S PARTY

OLD Eben Flood, climbing alone one night
Over the hill between the town below
And the forsaken upland hermitage
That held as much as he should ever know
On earth again of home, paused warily.
The road was his with not a native near;
And Eben, having leisure, said aloud,
For no man else in Tilbury Town to hear:

"Well, Mr. Flood, we have the harvest moon
Again, and we may not have many more;
The bird is on the wing, the poet says,
And you and I have said it here before.
Drink to the bird." He raised up to the light
The jug that he had gone so far to fill,
And answered huskily: "Well, Mr. Flood,
Since you propose it, I believe I will."

Alone, as if enduring to the end
A valiant armor of scarred hopes outworn,
He stood there in the middle of the road
Like Roland's ghost winding a silent horn.
Below him, in the town among the trees,
Where friends of other days had honored him,
A phantom salutation of the dead
Rang thinly till old Eben's eyes were dim.

1

Then, as a mother lays her sleeping child
Down tenderly, fearing it may awake,
He set the jug down slowly at his feet
With trembling care, knowing that most things break;
And only when assured that on firm earth
It stood, as the uncertain lives of men
Assuredly did not, he paced away,
And with his hand extended paused again:

"Well, Mr. Flood, we have not met like this
In a long time; and many a change has come
To both of us, I fear, since last it was
We had a drop together. Welcome home!"
Convivially returning with himself,
Again he raised the jug up to the light;
And with an acquiescent quaver said:
"Well, Mr. Flood, if you insist, I might.

"Only a very little, Mr. Flood—
For auld lang syne, no more, sir; that will do."
So, for the time, apparently it did,
And Eben evidently thought so too;
For soon amid the silver loneliness
Of night he lifted up his voice and sang,
Secure, with only two moons listening,
Until the whole harmonious landscape rang—

"For auld lang syne." The weary throat gave out,
The last word wavered, and the song was done.
He raised again the jug regretfully
And shook his head, and was again alone.
There was not much that was ahead of him,
And there was nothing in the town below—
Where strangers would have shut the many doors
That many friends had opened long ago.

SELECTION FROM "TRISTRAM"

By the same parapet that overlooked
The same sea, lying like sound now that was dead,
Mark sat alone, watching an unknown ship
That without motion moved from hour to hour,
Farther away. There was no other thing
Anywhere that was not as fixed and still
As two that were now safe within the walls
Below him, and like two that were asleep.
"There was no more for them," he said again,
To himself, or to the ship, "and this is peace.
I should have never praise or thanks of them
If power were mine and I should waken them;
And what might once have been if I had known
Before—I do not know. So men will say
In darkness, after daylight that was darkness,
Till the world ends and there are no more kings
And men to say it. If I were the world's maker,
I should say fate was mightier than I was,
Who made these two that are so silent now,
And for an end like this. Nothing in this
Is love that I have found, nor is it in love
That shall find me. I shall know day from night
Until I die, but there are darknesses
That I am never to know, by day or night;
All which is one more weary thing to learn,
Always too late. There are some ills and evils
Awaiting us that God could not invent;
There are mistakes too monstrous for remorse
To fondle or to dally with, and failures
That only fate's worst fumbling in the dark
Could have arranged so well. And here once more
The scroll of my authority presents

Deficiency and dearth. I do not know
Whether these two that have torn life from time,
Like a death-laden flower out of the earth,
Have failed or won. Many have paid with more
Than death for no such flower. I do not know
How much there was of Morgan in this last
Unhappy work of Andred's, or if now
It matters—when such a sick misshapen grief
May with a motion of one feeble arm
Bring this to pass. There is too much in this
That intimates a more than random issue;
And this is peace—whatever it is for me.
Now it is done, it may be well for them,
And well for me when I have followed them.
I do not know."
                        Alone he stood there, watching
The sea and its one ship, until the sea
Became a lonely darkness and the ship
Was gone, as a friend goes. The silent water
Was like another sky where silent stars
Might sleep for ever, and everywhere was peace.
It was a peace too heavy to be endured
Longer by one for whom no peace less heavy
Was coming on earth again. So Mark at last
Went somberly within, where Gouvernail
And silence wearied him. Move as he might,
Silence was all he found—silence within,
Silence without, dark silence everywhere—
And peace.

Robert Frost

THE RUNAWAY

ONCE when the snow of the year was beginning to fall,
We stopped by a mountain pasture to say "Whose
   colt?"
A little Morgan had one forefoot on the wall,
The other curled at his breast. He dipped his head
And snorted at us. And then he had to bolt.
We heard the miniature thunder where he fled,
And we saw him, or thought we saw him, dim and grey,
Like a shadow against the curtain of falling flakes.
"I think the little fellow's afraid of the snow.
He isn't winter-broken. It isn't play
With the little fellow at all. He's running away.
I doubt if even his mother could tell him, 'Sakes,
It's only weather.' He'd think she didn't know!
Where is his mother? He can't be out alone."
And now he comes again with a clatter of stone
And mounts the wall again with whited eyes
And all his tail that isn't hair up straight.
He shudders his coat as if to throw off flies.
"Whoever it is that leaves him out so late,
When other creatures have gone to stall and bin,
Ought to be told to come and take him in."

STOPPING BY WOODS ON A
SNOWY EVENING

WHOSE woods these are I think I know.
His house is in the village though;
He will not see me stopping here
To watch his woods fill up with snow.

My little horse must think it queer
To stop without a farmhouse near
Between the woods and frozen lake
The darkest evening of the year.

He gives his harness bells a shake
To ask if there is some mistake.
The only other sound's the sweep
Of easy wind and downy flake.

The woods are lovely, dark and deep.
But I have promises to keep,
And miles to go before I sleep,
And miles to go before I sleep.

Carl Sandburg

WHIFFS OF THE OHIO RIVER
AT CINCINNATI

I

A YOUNG thing in spring green slippers, stockings, silk
vivid as lilac-time grass,
And a red line of a flaunt of fresh silk again up under
her chin—
She slipped along the street at half-past six in the evening, came out of the stairway where her street
address is, where she has a telephone number—
Just a couple of blocks from the street next to the
Ohio river, where men sit in chairs tipped back,
watching the evening lights on the water of the
Ohio river—

She started out for the evening, dark brown calf eyes,
    roaming and hunted eyes,
And her young wild ways were not so young any more
    nor so wild.

Another evening primrose stood in a stairway, with a
    white knit sweater fitting her shoulders and ribs
    close.
She asked a young ballplayer passing for a few kind
    words and a pleasant look—and he slouched up
    to her like an umpire calling a runner out at the
    home plate—he gave her a few words and passed
    on.
She had bells on, she was jingling, and yet—her young
    wild ways were not so young any more, nor so wild.

II

When I asked for fish in the restaurant facing the Ohio
    river, with fish signs and fish pictures all over the
    wooden, crooked frame of the fish shack, the young
    man said, "Come around next Friday—the fish
    is all gone today."

So, I took eggs, fried, straight up, one side, and he
    murmured, humming, looking out at the shining
    breast of the Ohio river, "And the next is some-
    thing else; and the next is something else."

The customer next was a hoarse roustabout, handling
    nail kegs on a steamboat all day, asking for three
    eggs, sunny side up, three, nothing less, shake us
    a mean pan of eggs.

And while we sat eating eggs, looking at the shining
    breast of the Ohio river in the evening lights, he

had his thoughts and I had mine thinking how
the French who found the Ohio river named it
La Belle Riviere meaning a woman easy to look at.

Sara Teasdale

THE LONG HILL

I MUST have passed the crest a while ago
   And now I am going down—
Strange to have crossed the crest and not to know,
   But the brambles were always catching the hem of
     my gown.

All the morning I thought how proud I should be
   To stand there straight as a queen,
Wrapped in the wind and the sun with the world under
     me—
   But the air was dull; there was little I could have
     seen.

It was nearly level along the beaten track
   And the brambles caught in my gown—
But it's no use now to think of turning back,
   The rest of the way will be only going down.

ARCTURUS IN AUTUMN

WHEN, in the gold October dusk, I saw you near to
   setting,
   Arcturus, bringer of spring,
Lord of the summer nights, leaving us now in autumn,
   Having no pity on our withering;

Oh then I knew at last that my own autumn was upon
　　me,
　　I felt it in my blood,
Restless as dwindling streams that still remember
　　The music of their flood.

There in the thickening dark a wind-bent tree above me
　　Loosed its last leaves in flight—
I saw you sink and vanish, pitiless Arcturus,
　　You will not stay to share our lengthening night.

John Gould Fletcher

SONG OF THE MODERNS

WE MORE than others have the perfect right
To see the cities like flambeaux flare along the night.

We more than others have the right to cast away
Thought like a withered leaf, since it has served its
　　day;

Since for this transient joy which not for long can
　　burn
Within our hearts, we gave up in return

Ten thousand years of holy magic power
Drawn from the darkness to transcend death's hour.

For every witch that died an electric lamp shall flare,
For every wizard drowned, the clear blue air

Shall roar with jazz-bands into listening ears;
For every alchemist who spent in vain his years

Seeking the stone of truth, a motor-horn
Shall scare the sheep that wander among the corn.

And there shall be no more the spirits of the deep,
Nor holy satyrs slumbering upon the steep,

Nor angels at a manger or a cross.
Life shall go on; to ugly gain or loss;

Yet vaster and more tragic, till at last
This present too shall make part of the past:—

Till all the joy and tragedy that man knows
To-day, become stiff gravestones in long rows:

Till none dare look on the mountains ranked afar,
And think "These are the cast-off leavings of some
    star."

BRAHMA

BRAHMA sleeps.
On his broad palm, the world
Rose against blue,
A lotus-leaf
Silently shed, is curled.

Brahma dreams,
In the thick dull blur
Of his mind, unfathomed—
Fathomless ever—
Dreams stir and blur
Worshipped and worshipper.

Brahma wakens,
Bids Shiva play;
Shiva dances,
Springs and dances;
The universe, time,
Man and his madness,
Sun, wheeling planets,
Sirius, Orion,
Worlds gleaming, perfect,
Woman's white shoulders,
Dust, worms and ruin—
All things to nothing
Are swept away.

H. D.

LEDA

WHERE the slow river
meets the tide,
a red swan lifts red wings
and darker beak,
and underneath the purple down
of his soft breast
uncurls his coral feet.

Through the deep purple
of the dying heat
of sun and mist,
the level ray of sun-beam
has caressed
the lily with dark breast,
and flecked with richer gold
its golden crest.

Where the slow lifting
of the tide,
floats into the river
and slowly drifts
among the reeds,
and lifts the yellow flags,
he floats
where tide and river meet.

Ah kingly kiss—
no more regret
nor old deep memories
to mar the bliss;
where the low sedge is thick,
the gold day-lily
outspreads and rests
beneath soft fluttering
of red swan wings
and warm quivering
of the red swan's breast.

William Rose Benét

THE FAWN IN THE SNOW

The brown-dappled fawn
Bereft of the doe
Shivers in blue shadow
Of the glaring snow,

His whole world bright
As a jewel, and hard,
Diamond white,
Turquoise barred.

The trees are black,
Their needles gold,
Their boughs crack
In the keen cold.

The brown-dappled fawn
Bereft of the doe
Trembles and shudders
At the bright snow.

The air whets
The warm throat,
The frost frets
At the smooth coat.

Brown agate eyes
Opened round
Agonize
At the cold ground,

At the cold heaven
Enameled pale,
At the earth shriven
By the snowy gale,

At magic glitter
Burning to blind,
At beauty bitter
As an almond rind.

Fawn, fawn,
Seek for your south,
For kind dawn
With her cool mouth,

For green sod
With gold and blue
Dappled, as God
Has dappled you,

For slumbrous ease,
Firm turf to run
Through fruited trees
Into full sun!

The shivering fawn
Paws at the snow.
South and dawn
Lie below;

Richness and mirth,
Dearth forgiven,
A happy earth,
A warm heaven.

The sleet streams;
The snow flies;
The fawn dreams
With wide brown eyes.

THE WOODCUTTER'S WIFE

TIMES she'll sit quiet by the hearth, and times
She'll ripple with a fit of twinkling rhymes
And rise and pirouette and flirt her hand,
Strut jackdaw-like, or stamp a curt command
Or, from behind my chair, suddenly blind me;
Then, when I turn, be vanished from behind me.

Times she'll be docile as the gentlest thing
That ever blinked in fur or folded wing,
And then, like lightning in the dead of night,
Fill with wild, crackling, intermitting light
My mind and soul and senses,—and next be
Aloof, askance as a dryad in a tree.

Then she'll be gone for days; when next I turn,
There, coaxing yellow butter from the churn,
Rubbing to silver every pan of tin,
Or conjuring color from the rooms within
Through innocent flowers, she'll hum about the house
Bright-eyed and secret as a velvet mouse.

'Tis not your will They do,—no, nor the Will
That hushes Anslem's chapel overhill.
Something that drifts in clouds, that sings in rain,
That laughs in sunlight, shudders in the pain
Of desolate seas, or broods in basking earth
Governs Their melancholy and Their mirth.

Elusive still! Elusive as my reason
For trudging woodward in or out of season
To swing the ringing ax, as year by year
The inexplicable end draws slowly near,
And, in between, to think and think about it,—
Life's puzzling dream,—deride, believe, and doubt it.

But if I leave her seriously alone
She comes quite near, preëmpts some woodland stone,
Spreads out her kirtle like a shimmering dress
And fills my mind's remorseful emptiness
With marvelous jewels made of words and wit
Till all my being sings because of it.

Sings of the way her bronze hair waves about
And her amber-lighted eyes peer out;
Sings of her sudden laughter floating wild,
Of all her antics of a fairy child,
Of her uplifted head and swift, demure
Silence and awe, than purity more pure.

So I must scratch my head and drop my ax,
While in her hands my will is twisted wax;
So when she goes, deaf, dumb and blind I sit
Watching her empty arm-chair opposite,
Witched by evasive brightness in the brain
That grows full glory when she comes again.

Robinson Jeffers

CONTINENT'S END

At the equinox when the earth was veiled in a late
    rain, wreathed with wet poppies, waiting spring,
The ocean swelled for a far storm and beat its bound-
    ary, the ground-swell shook the beds of granite.

I gazing at the boundaries of granite and spray, the
    established sea-marks, felt behind me
Mountain and plain, the immense breadth of the con-
    tinent, before me the mass and doubled stretch
    of water.

I said: You yoke the Aleutian seal-rocks with the lava
    and coral sowings that flower the south,
Over your flood the life that sought the sunrise faces
    ours that has followed the evening star.

The long migrations meet across you and it is nothing
    to you, you have forgotten us, mother.
You were much younger when we crawled out of the
    womb and lay in the sun's eye on the tideline.

It was long and long ago; we have grown proud since
    then and you have grown bitter; life retains
Your mobile soft unquiet strength; and envies hard-
    ness, the insolent quietness of stone.

The tides are in our veins, we still mirror the stars, life
    is your child, but there is in me
Older and harder than life and more impartial, the eye
    that watched before there was an ocean.

That watched you fill your beds out of the condensa-
    tion of thin vapor and watched you change them,
That saw you soft and violent wear your boundaries
    down, eat rock, shift places with the continents.

Mother, though my song's measure is like your surf-
    beat's ancient rhythm I never learned it of you.
Before there was any water there were tides of fire,
    both our tones flow from the older fountain.

BIXBY'S LANDING

They burned lime on the hill and dropped it down here
    in an iron car
On a long cable; here the ships warped in
And took their loads from the engine, the water is deep
    to the cliff. The car
Hangs half way over in the gape of the gorge,

Stationed like a north star above the peaks of the red-
    woods, iron perch
For the little red hawks when they cease from hovering
When they've struck prey; the spider's fling of a cable
    rust-glued to the pulleys.
The laborers are gone, but what a good multitude
Is here in return: the rich-lichened rock, the rose-
    tipped stonecrop, the constant
Ocean's voices, the cloud-lighted space.
The kilns are cold on the hill but here in the rust of
    the broken boiler
Quick lizards lighten, and a rattlesnake flows
Down the cracked masonry, over the crumbled fire-
    brick. In the rotting timbers
And roofless platforms all the free companies
Of windy grasses have root and make seed; wild buck-
    wheat blooms in the fat
Weather-slacked lime from the bursted barrels.
Two duckhawks darting in the sky of their cliff-hung
    nest are the voice of the headland.
Wine-hearted solitude, our mother the wilderness,
Men's failures are often as beautiful as men's triumphs,
    but your returnings
Are even more precious than your first presence.

Elinor Wylie

THE EAGLE AND THE MOLE

AVOID the reeking herd,
Shun the polluted flock,
Live like that stoic bird,
The eagle of the rock.

The huddled warmth of crowds
Begets and fosters hate;
He keeps, above the clouds,
His cliff inviolate.

When flocks are folded warm,
And herds to shelter run,
He sails above the storm,
He stares into the sun.

If in the eagle's track
Your sinews cannot leap,
Avoid the lathered pack,
Turn from the steaming sheep.

If you would keep your soul
From spotted sight or sound,
Live like the velvet mole;
Go burrow underground.

And there hold intercourse
With roots of trees and stones,
With rivers at their source,
And disembodied bones.

LET NO CHARITABLE HOPE

Now let no charitable hope
Confuse my mind with images
Of eagle and of antelope:
I am in nature none of these.

I was, being human, born alone;
I am, being woman, hard beset;
I live by squeezing from a stone
The little nourishment I get.

In masks outrageous and austere
The years go by in single file;
But none has merited my fear,
And none has quite escaped my smile.

T. S. Eliot

GERONTION

*Thou hast nor youth nor age
But as it were an after dinner sleep
Dreaming of both.*

Here I am, an old man in a dry month,
Being read to by a boy, waiting for rain.
I was neither at the hot gates
Nor fought in the warm rain
Nor knee deep in the salt marsh, heaving a cutlass,
Bitten by flies, fought.
My house is a decayed house,
And the Jew squats on the window sill, the owner,
Spawned in some estaminet of Antwerp,
Blistered in Brussels, patched and peeled in London.
The goat coughs at night in the field overhead;
Rocks, moss, stonecrop, iron, merds.
The woman keeps the kitchen, makes tea,
Sneezes at evening, poking the peevish gutter.
                                        I an old man,
A dull head among windy spaces.

Signs are taken for wonders. "We would see a sign":
The word within a word, unable to speak a word,
Swaddled with darkness. In the juvenescence of the
    year
Came Christ the tiger

In depraved May, dogwood and chestnut, flowering
    judas,
To be eaten, to be divided, to be drunk
Among whispers; by Mr. Silvero
With caressing hands, at Limoges
Who walked all night in the next room;
By Hakagawa, bowing among the Titians;
By Madame de Tornquist, in the dark room
Shifting the candles; Fräulein von Kulp
Who turned in the hall, one hand on the door. Vacant
    shuttles
Weave the wind. I have no ghosts,
An old man in a draughty house
Under a windy knob.

After such knowledge, what forgiveness? Think now
History has many cunning passages, contrived corri-
    dors
And issues, deceives with whispering ambitions,
Guides us by vanities. Think now
She gives when our attention is distracted
And what she gives, gives with such supple confusions
That the giving famishes the craving. Gives too late
What's not believed in, or if still believed,
In memory only, reconsidered passion. Gives too soon
Into weak hands, what's thought can be dispensed with
Till the refusal propagates a fear. Think
Neither fear nor courage saves us. Unnatural vices

Are fathered by our heroism. Virtues
Are forced upon us by our impudent crimes.
These tears are shaken from the wrath-bearing tree.

The tiger springs in the new year. Us he devours.
    Think at last
We have not reached conclusion, when I
Stffen in a rented house. Think at last
I have not made this show purposelessly
And it is not by any concitation
Of the backward devils.
I would meet you upon this honestly.
I that was near your heart was removed therefrom
To lose beauty in terror, terror in inquisition.
I have lost my passion: why should I need to keep it
Since what is kept must be adulterated?
I have lost my sight, smell, hearing, taste and touch:
How should I use it for your closer contact?

These with a thousand small deliberations
Protract the profit of their chilled delirium,
Excite the membrane, when the sense has cooled,
With pungent sauces, multiply variety
In a wilderness of mirrors. What will the spider do,
Suspend its operations, will the weevil
Delay? De Bailhache, Fresca, Mrs. Cammel, whirled
Beyond the circuit of the shuddering Bear
In fractured atoms. Gull against the wind, in the windy
    straits
Of Belle Isle, or running on the Horn,
White feathers in the snow, the Gulf claims,
And an old man driven by the Trades
To a sleepy corner.
              Tenants of the house,
Thoughts of a dry brain in a dry season.

John Crowe Ransom

HERE LIES A LADY

HERE lies a lady of beauty and high degree.
Of chills and fever she died, of fever and chills,
The delight of her husband, her aunts, an infant of
    three,
And of medicos marvelling sweetly on her ills.

For either she burned, and her confident eyes would
    blaze,
And her fingers fly in a manner to puzzle their heads—
What was she making? Why, nothing; she sat in a
    maze
Of old scraps of laces, snipped into curious shreds—

Or this would pass, and the light of her fire decline
Till she lay discouraged and cold as a thin stalk white
    and blown,
And would not open her eyes, to kisses, to wine;
The sixth of these states was her last; the cold settled
    down.

Sweet ladies, long may ye bloom, and toughly I hope
    ye may thole,
But was she not lucky? In flowers and lace and mourn-
    ing,
In love and great honour we bade God rest her soul
After six little spaces of chill, and six of burning.

Conrad Aiken

AND ALREADY THE MINUTES

AND already the minutes, the hours, the days,
Separate thoughts and separate ways,
Fall whitely and silently and slowly between us,
Fall between us like phantasmal rain and snow.
And we, who were thrust for an instant so sharply
    together,
Under changing skies to alien destinies go.

Melody heard in the midnight on the wind,—
Orange poppy of fire seen in a dream,—
Vainly I try to keep you. How the sky,
A great blue wind, with a gigantic laugh,
Scorns us apart like chaff.
Like a bird blown to sea am I.

O let us hold, amid these immensities,
The blinding blaze of the hostile infinite,
To the one clear phrase we knew and still may know:
Walls rise daily and darkly between us
But love has seen us,
Wherever we go love too must go.

Beautiful, twilight, mysterious, bird-haunted land
Seen from the ship, with the far pale shore of sand,
And the blue deep folds of hills inviting the stars to
    rest,
Though I shall never set foot there, nor explore you,
Nor hear your angelus of bells about me, I shall adore
    you
And know you still the best.

AND IN THE HANGING GARDENS

And in the hanging gardens there is rain
From midnight until one, striking the leaves
And bells of flowers, and stroking boles of planes,
And drawing slow arpeggios over pools,
And stretching strings of sound from eaves to ferns.
The princess reads. The knave of diamonds sleeps.
The king is drunk, and flings a golden goblet
Down from the turret window (curtained with rain)
Into the lilacs.

         And at one o'clock
The vulcan under the garden wakes and beats
The gong upon his anvil. Then the rain
Ceases, but gently ceases, dripping still,
And sound of falling water fills the dark
As leaves grow bold and upright, and as eaves
Part with water. The princess turns the page
Beside the candle, and between two braids
Of golden hair. And reads: "From there I went
Northward a journey of four days, and came
To a wild village in the hills, where none
Was living save the vulture and the rat,
And one old man, who laughed, but could not speak.
The roofs were fallen in; the well grown over
With weed; and it was there my father died.
Then eight days further, bearing slightly west,
The cold wind blowing sand against our faces,
The food tasting of sand. And as we stood
By the dry rock that marks the highest point
My brother said: 'Not too late is it yet
To turn, remembering home.' And we were silent
Thinking of home." The princess shuts her eyes

And feels the tears forming beneath her eyelids
And opens them, and tears fall on the page.
The knave of diamonds in the darkened room
Throws off his covers, sleeps, and snores again.
The king goes slowly down the turret stairs
To find the goblet.

                And at two o'clock
The vulcan in his smithy underground
Under the hanging gardens, where the drip
Of rain among the clematis and ivy
Still falls from sipping flower to purple flower,
Smites twice his anvil, and the murmur comes
Among the roots and vines. The princess reads:
"As I am sick, and cannot write you more,
Nor have not long to live, I give this letter
To him, my brother, who will bear it south
And tell you how I died. Ask how it was,
There in the northern desert, where the grass
Was withered, and the horses, all but one,
Perished" . . . The princess drops her golden head
Upon the page between her two white arms
And golden braids. The knave of diamonds wakes
And at his window in the darkened room
Watches the lilacs tossing, where the king
Seeks for the goblet.

                And at three o'clock
The moon inflames the lilac heads, and thrice
The vulcan, in his root-bound smithy, clangs
His anvil; and the sounds creep softly up
Among the vines and walls. The moon is round,
Round as a shield above the turret top.
The princess blows her candle out, and weeps
In the pale room, where scent of lilac comes,

Weeping, with hands across her eyelids, thinking
Of withered grass, withered by sandy wind.
The knave of diamonds, in his darkened room,
Holds in his hands a key, and softly steps
Along the corridor, and slides the key
Into the door that guards her. Meanwhile, slowly,
The king, with raindrops on his beard and hands,
And dripping sleeves, climbs up the turret stairs,
Holding the goblet upright in one hand;
And pauses on the midmost step, to taste
One drop of wine, wherewith wild rain has mixed.

Edna St. Vincent Millay

LOVE IS NOT ALL; IT IS NOT MEAT NOR DRINK

Love is not all; it is not meat nor drink
Nor slumber nor a roof against the rain,
Nor yet a floating spar to men that sink
And rise and sink and rise and sink again;
Love can not fill the thickened lung with breath,
Nor clean the blood, nor set the fractured bone;
Yet many a man is making friends with death
Even as I speak, for lack of love alone.
It well may be that in a difficult hour,
Pinned down by pain and moaning for release,
Or nagged by want past resolution's power,
I might be driven to sell your love for peace,
Or trade the memory of this night for food.
It well may be. I do not think I would.

OH, SLEEP FOREVER IN THE LATMIAN CAVE

OH, SLEEP forever in the Latmian cave,
Mortal Endymion, darling of the Moon!
Her silver garments by the senseless wave
Shouldered and dropped and on the shingle strewn,
Her fluttering hand against her forehead pressed,
Her scattered looks that trouble all the sky,
Her rapid footsteps running down the west—
Of all her altered state, oblivious lie!
Whom earthen you, by deathless lips adored,
Wild-eyed and stammering to the grasses thrust,
And deep into her crystal body poured
The hot and sorrowful sweetness of the dust:
Whereof she wanders mad, being all unfit
For mortal love, that might not die of it.

Archibald MacLeish

YOU, ANDREW MARVELL

AND here face down beneath the sun,
And here upon earth's noonward height,
To feel the always coming on,
The always rising of the night.

To feel creep up the curving east
The earthly chill of dusk and slow
Upon those under lands the vast
And ever-climbing shadow grow,

And strange at Ecbatan the trees
Take leaf by leaf the evening, strange,
The flooding dark about their knees,
The mountains over Persia change,

And now at Kermanshah the gate,
Dark, empty, and the withered grass,
And through the twilight now the late
Few travelers in the westward pass.

And Baghdad darken and the bridge
Across the silent river gone,
And through Arabia the edge
Of evening widen and steal on,

And deepen on Palmyra's street
The wheel rut in the ruined stone,
And Lebanon fade out and Crete
High through the clouds and overblown,

And over Sicily the air
Still flashing with the landward gulls,
And loom and slowly disappear
The sails above the shadowy hulls,

And Spain go under and the shore
Of Africa, the gilded sand,
And evening vanish and no more
The low pale light across that land,

Nor now the long light on the sea—
And here face downward in the sun
To feel how swift, how secretly,
The shadows of the night comes on. . . .

Phelps Putnam

HASBROUCK AND THE ROSE

HASBROUCK was there and so were Bill
And Smollet Smith the poet, and Ames was there.
After his thirteenth drink, the burning Smith,
Raising his fourteenth trembling in the air,
Said, "Drink with me, Bill, drink up to the Rose."
But Hasbrouck laughed like old men in a myth,
Inquiring, "Smollet, are you drunk? What rose?"
And Smollet said, "I drunk? It may be so;
Which comes from brooding on the flower, the flower
I mean toward which mad hour by hour
I travel brokenly; and I shall know,
With Hermes and the alchemists—but, hell,
What use is it talking that way to you?
Hard-boiled, unbroken egg, what can you care
For the enfolded passion of the Rose?"
Then Hasbrouck's voice rang like an icy bell:

"Arcane romantic flower, meaning what?
Do you know what it meant? Do I?
We do not know.
Unfolding pungent rose, the glowing bath
Of ecstasy and clear forgetfulness;
Closing and secret bud one might achieve
By long debauchery—
Except that I have eaten it, and so
There is no call for further lunacy.
In Springfield, Massachusetts, I devoured
The mystic, the improbable, the Rose.
For two nights and a day, rose and rosette,
And petal after petal and the heart,

I had my banquet by the beams
Of four electric stars which shone
Weakly into my room, for there,
Drowning their light and gleaming at my side,
Was the incarnate star
Whose body bore the stigma of the Rose.
And that is all I know about the flower;
I have eaten it—it has disappeared.
There is no Rose."

Young Smollet Smith let fall his glass; he said
"Oh Jesus, Hasbrouck, am I drunk or dead?"

E. E. Cummings

O THOU TO WHOM THE MUSICAL WHITE SPRING

O Thou to whom the musical white spring

offers her lily inextinguishable,
taught by thy tremulous grace bravely to fling

Implacable death's mysteriously sable
robe from her redolent shoulders,
                              Thou from whose
feet reincarnate song suddenly leaping
flameflung, mounts, inimitably to lose
herself where the wet stars softly are keeping

their exquisite dreams—O Love! upon thy dim
shrine of intangible commemoration,
(from whose faint close as some grave languorous hymn

pledged to illimitable dissipation
unhurried clouds of incense fleetly roll)

i spill my bright incalculable soul.

Louise Bogan

MEDUSA

I HAD come to the house, in a cave of trees,
Facing a sheer sky.
Everything moved,—a bell hung ready to strike,
Sun and reflection wheeled by.

When the bare eyes were before me
And the hissing hair,
Held up at a window, seen through a door.
The stiff bald eyes, the serpents on the forehead
Formed in the air.

This is a dead scene forever now.
Nothing will ever stir.
The end will never brighten it more than this,
Nor the rain blur.

The water will always fall, and will not fall,
And the tipped bell make no sound.
The grass will always be growing for hay
Deep on the ground.

And I shall stand here like a shadow
Under the great balanced day,
My eyes on the yellow dust that was lifting in the wind,
And does not drift away.

Stephen Vincent Benét

JOHN BROWN'S BODY

INVOCATION

American muse, whose strong and diverse heart
So many men have tried to understand
But only made it smaller with their art,
Because you are as various as your land,

As mountainous-deep, as flowered with blue rivers,
Thirsty with deserts, buried under snows,
As native as the shape of Navajo quivers,
And native, too, as the sea-voyaged rose.

Swift runner, never captured or subdued,
Seven-branched elk beside the mountain stream,
That half a hundred hunters have pursued
But never matched their bullets with the dream,

Where the great huntsmen failed, I set my sorry
And mortal snare for your immortal quarry.

You are the buffalo-ghost, the broncho-ghost
With dollar-silver in your saddle-horn,
The cowboys riding in from Painted Post,
The Indian arrow in the Indian corn,

And you are the clipped velvet of the lawns
Where Shropshire grows from Massachusetts sods,
The grey Maine rocks—and the war-painted dawns
That break above the Garden of the Gods.

The prairie-schooners crawling toward the ore
And the cheap car, parked by the station-door.

Where the skyscrapers lift their foggy plumes
Of stranded smoke out of a stony mouth
You are that high stone and its arrogant fumes,
And you are ruined gardens in the South

And bleak New England farms, so winter-white
Even their roofs look lonely, and the deep
The middle grainland where the wind of night
Is like all blind earth sighing in her sleep.

A friend, an enemy, a sacred hag
With two tied oceans in her medicine-bag.

They tried to fit you with an English song
And clip your speech into the English tale.
But, even from the first, the words went wrong,
The catbird pecked away the nightingale.

The homesick men begot high-cheekboned things
Whose wit was whittled with a different sound
And Thames and all the rivers of the kings
Ran into Mississippi and were drowned.

They planted England with a stubborn trust.
But the cleft dust was never English dust.

Stepchild of every exile from content
And all the disavouched, hard-bitten pack
Shipped overseas to steal a continent
With neither shirts nor honor to their back.

Pimping grandee and rump-faced regicide,
Apple-cheeked younkers from a windmill-square,
Puritans stubborn as the nails of Pride,
Rakes from Versailles and thieves from County Clare,

The black-robed priests who broke their hearts in vain
To make you God and France or God and Spain.

These were your lovers in your buckskin-youth,
And each one married with a dream so proud
He never knew it could not be the truth
And that he coupled with a girl of cloud.

And now to see you is more difficult yet
Except as an immensity of wheel
Made up of wheels, oiled with inhuman sweat
And glittering with the heat of ladled steel.

All these you are, and each is partly you,
And none is false, and none is wholly true.

So how to see you as you really are,
So how to suck the pure, distillate, stored
Essence of essence from the hidden star
And make it pierce like a riposting sword.

For, as we hunt you down, you must escape
And we pursue a shadow of our own
That can be caught in a magician's cape
But has the flatness of a painted stone.

Never the running stag, the gull at wing,
The pure elixir, the American thing.

And yet, at moments when the mind was hot
With something fierier than joy or grief,
When each known spot was an eternal spot
And every leaf was an immortal leaf,

I think that I have seen you, not as one,
But clad in diverse semblances and powers,
Always the same, as light falls from the sun,
And always different, as the differing hours.

Yet, through each altered garment that you wore
The naked body, shaking the heart's core.

All day the snow fell on that Eastern town
With its soft, pelting, little, endless sigh
Of infinite flakes that brought the tall sky down
Till I could put my hands in the white sky

And taste cold scraps of heaven on my tongue
And walk in such a changed and luminous light
As gods inhabit when the gods are young.
All day it fell. And when the gathered night

Was a blue shadow cast by a pale glow
I saw you then, snow-image, bird of the snow.

And I have seen and heard you in the dry
Close-huddled furnace of the city street
When the parched moon was planted in the sky
And the limp air hung dead against the heat.

I saw you rise, red as that rusty plant,
Dizzied with lights, half-mad with senseless sound,
Enormous metal, shaking to the chant
Of a triphammer striking iron ground.

Enormous power, ugly to the fool,
And beautiful as a well-handled tool.

These, and the memory of that windy day
On the bare hills, beyond the last barbed wire,
When all the orange poppies bloomed one way
As if a breath would blow them into fire,

I keep forever, like the sea-lion's tusk
The broken sailor brings away to land,
But when he touches it, he smells the musk,
And the whole sea lies hollow in his hand.

So, from a hundred visions, I make one,
And out of darkness build my mocking sun.

And should that task seem fruitless in the eyes
Of those a different magic sets apart
To see through the ice-crystal of the wise
No nation but the nation that is Art,

Their words are just. But when the birchbark-call
Is shaken with the sound that hunters make
The moose comes plunging through the forest-wall
Although the rifle waits beside the lake.

Art has no nations—but the mortal sky
Lingers like gold in immortality.

This flesh was seeded from no foreign grain
But Pennsylvania and Kentucky wheat,
And it has soaked in California rain
And five years tempered in New England sleet

To strive at last, against an alien proof
And by the changes of an alien moon,
To build again that blue, American roof
Over a half-forgotten battle-tune

And call unsurely, from a haunted ground,
Armies of shadows and the shadow-sound.

In your Long House there is an attic-place
Full of dead epics and machines that rust.
And there, occasionally, with casual face,
You come awhile to stir the sleepy dust;

Neither in pride nor mercy, but in vast
Indifference at so many gifts unsought,
The yellowed satins, smelling of the past,
And all the loot the lucky pirates brought.

I only bring a cup of silver air,
Yet, in your casualness, receive it there.

Receive the dream too haughty for the breast,
Receive the words that should have walked as bold
As the storm walks along the mountain-crest
And are like beggars whining in the cold.

The maimed presumption, the unskilful skill,
The patchwork colors, fading from the first,
And all the fire that fretted at the will
With such a barren ecstasy of thirst.

Receive them all—and should you choose to touch them
With one slant ray of quick, American light,
Even the dust will have no power to smutch them,
Even the worst will glitter in the night.

If not—the dry bones littered by the way
May still point giants toward their golden prey.

Léonie Adams

QUIET

Since I took quiet to my breast
My heart lies in me, heavier
Than stone sunk fast in sluggish sand,
That the sea's self may never stir,
When she sweeps hungrily to land,
Since I took quiet to my breast.

Strange quiet, when I made thee guest,
My heart had countless strings to fret
Under a least wind's fingering.
How could I know I would forget
To catch breath at a gull's curved wing,
Strange quiet, when I made thee guest?

Thou, quiet, hast no gift of rest.
The pain that at thy healing fled
More dear was to my heart than pride.
Now for its loss my heart is dead,
And I keep horrid watch beside.
Thou, quiet, hast no gift of rest.

SEND FORTH THE HIGH FALCON

Send forth the high falcon flying after the mind
To topple it from its cold cloud:
The beak of the falcon to pierce it till it fall
Where the simple heart is bowed.

O in wild innocence it rides
The rare ungovernable element,
But once it sways to terror and descent,
The marches of the wind are its abyss,
No wind staying it upward of the breast—
Let mind be proud for this,
And ignorant from what fabulous cause it dropt
And with how learned a gesture the unschooled heart
Shall lull both terror and innocence to rest.

Allen Tate

EMBLEMS

I

MARYLAND Virginia Caroline
Pent images in sleep
Clay valleys rocky hills old-fields of pine
Unspeakable, and deep

Out of that source of time my farthest blood
Runs strangely to this day
Unkempt the fathers waste in solitude
Under the hills of clay

Far from their woe fled to its thither side
To a river in Tennessee
In an alien house I will stay
Yet find their breath to be
All that my stars betide—
There some time to abide
Took wife and child with me.

II

When it is all over and the blood
Runs out, do not bury this man
By the far river (where never stood
His fathers) flowing to the west
But take him east where life began,
O my brothers there is rest
In the depths of an eastward river
That I can understand; only
Do not think the truth we hold
I hold the slighter for this lonely
Reservation of the heart,
Men cannot live forever
But they must die forever
So take this body, at sunset,
To the great stream whose pulses start
In the blue hills, and let
These ashes drift from the Long Bridge
Where only a late gull breaks
That deep and populous grave
Whose heart with memory shakes.

III

By the great river the forefathers to beguile
Them, being inconceivably young, carved out
Deep hollows of memory on a river isle
Now lost, their murmurs the ghost of a shout

In the hollows where the forefathers
Without beards their eyes bright and long
Lay down at sunset by the green river
In the tall willows amid bird-song

And the long sleep by the cool river
They've slept full and long, till now the air
Waits twilit for their echo—the burning shiver
Of August strikes like a hawk the crouching hare.

Hart Crane

REPOSE OF RIVERS

THE willows carried a slow sound,
A sarabande the wind mowed on the mead.
I could never remember
That seething, steady leveling of the marshes
Till age had brought me to the sea.

Flags, weeds. And remembrance of steep alcoves
Where cypresses shared the noon's
Tyranny; they drew me into hades almost.
And mammoth turtles climbing sulphur dreams
Yielded, while sun-silt ripples them
Asunder . . .

How much I would have bartered! the black gorge
And all the singular nestings in the hills
Where beavers learn stitch and tooth.
The pond I entered once and quickly fled—
I remember now its singing willow rim.

And finally, in that memory all things nurse;
After the city that I finally passed
With scalding unguents spread and smoking darts
The monsoon cut across the delta
At gulf gates . . . There, beyond the dykes

I heard wind flaking sapphire, like this summer,
And willows could not hold more steady sound.

ATLANTIS

Through the bound cable strands, the arching path
Upward, veering with light, the flight of strings,—
Taut miles of shuttling moonlight syncopate
The whispered rush, telepathy of wires.
Up the index of night, granite and steel—
Transparent meshes—fleckless the gleaming staves—
Sibylline voices flicker, waveringly stream
As though a god were issue of the strings. . . .

And through that cordage, threading with its call
One arc synoptic of all tides below—
Their labyrinthine mouths of history
Pouring reply as though all ships at sea
Complighted in one vibrant breath made cry,—
"Make thy love sure—to weave whose song we ply!"
—From black embankments, moveless soundings
    hailed,
So seven oceans answer from their dream.

And on, obliquely up bright carrier bars
New octaves trestle the twin monoliths
Beyond whose frosted capes the moon bequeaths
Two worlds of sleep (O arching strands of song!)—
Onward and up the crystal-flooded aisle
White tempest nets file upward, upward ring
With silver terraces the humming spars,
The loft of vision, palladium helm of stars.

Sheerly the eyes, like seagulls stung with rime—
Slit and propelled by glistening fins of light—
Pick biting way up towering looms that press
Sidelong with flight of blade on tendon blade
—Tomorrows into yesteryear—and link
What cipher-script of time no traveller reads
But who, through smoking pyres of love and death,
Searches the timeless laugh of mythic spears.

Like hails, farewells—up planet-sequined heights
Some trillion whispering hammers glimmer Tyre:
Serenely, sharply up the long anvil cry
Of inchling æons silence rivets Troy.
And you, aloft there—Jason! hesting Shout!
Still wrapping harness to the swarming air!
Silvery the rushing wake, surpassing call,
Beams yelling Æolus! splintered in the straits!

From gulfs unfolding, terrible of drums,
Tall Vision-of-the-Voyage, tensely spare—
Bridge, lifting night to cycloramic crest
Of deepest day—O Choir translating time
Into what multitudinous Verb the suns
And synergy of waters ever fuse, recast
In myriad syllables,—Psalm of Cathay!
O Love, thy white, pervasive Paradigm . . . !

We left the haven hanging in the night—
Sheened harbor lanterns backward fled the keel.
Pacific here at time's end, bearing corn,—
Eyes stammer through the pangs of dust and steel.
And still the circular, indubitable frieze
Of heaven's meditation, yoking wave
To kneeling wave, one song devoutly binds—
The vernal strophe chimes from deathless strings!

O Thou steeled Cognizance whose leap commits
The agile precincts of the lark's return;
Within whose lariat sweep encinctured sing
In single chrysalis the many twain,—
Of stars Thou art the stitch and stallion glow
And like an organ, Thou, with sound of doom—
Sight, sound and flesh Thou leadest from time's realm
As love strikes clear direction for the helm.

Swift peal of secular light, intrinsic Myth
Whose fell unshadow is death's utter wound,—
O River-throated—iridescently upborne
Through the bright drench and fabric of our veins;
With white escarpments swinging into light,
Sustained in tears the cities are endowed
And justified conclamant with ripe fields
Revolving through their harvests in sweet torment.

Forever Deity's glittering Pledge, O Thou
Whose canticle fresh chemistry assigns
To wrapt inception and beatitude,—
Always through blinding cables, to our joy,
Of thy white seizure springs the prophecy:
Always through spiring cordage, pyramids
Of silver sequel, Deity's young name
Kinetic of white choiring wings . . . ascends.

Migrations that must needs void memory,
Inventions that cobblestone the heart,—
Unspeakable Thou Bridge to Thee, O Love.
Thy pardon for this history, whitest Flower,
O Answer of all,—Anemone,—
Now while thy petals spend the suns about us, hold—
(O Thou whose radiance doth inherit me)
Atlantis,—hold thy floating singer late!

So to thine Everpresence, beyond time,
Like spears ensanguined of one tolling star
That bleeds infinity—the orphic strings,
Sidereal phalanxes, leap and converge:
—One Song, one Bridge of Fire! Is it Cathay,
Now pity steeps the grass and rainbows ring
The serpent with the eagle in the leaves . . . ?
Whispers antiphonal in azure swing.

LIST OF SOME OTHER BOOKS
BY AUTHORS REPRESENTED IN THIS VOLUME

SUGGESTIONS

For Further Literary Journeyings With the Authors of This Book

SINCLAIR LEWIS

Sinclair Lewis's novels are so much a part of our literary consciousness that we have only to mention the titles to recall a whole set of ideas and emotions current in their years of publication. *Main Street*, *Babbitt*, *Elmer Gantry*, *Arrowsmith*, *Ann Vickers*, *Work of Art*, and his most recent one, *It Can't Happen Here*, are among the most famous titles of our first Nobel Prize winner in literature.

ERNEST HEMINGWAY

Ernest Hemingway: You have read, no doubt, Ernest Hemingway's *A Farewell to Arms* and *Death in the Afternoon* but you will find equally as interesting his earlier books, *The Sun Also Rises* and *Men Without Women*. And it is these primarily which gave such an impetus to the new school of American fiction.

3

DON MARQUIS

DON MARQUIS: Archy and Mehitabel go back to Don Marquis's old newspaper days on the New York Sun. And so also does that other nation-wide famous character, *The Old Soak*, who also is collected in a book of his own. In England Don Marquis is known chiefly for his serious poems collected in *Poems and Portraits*, *The Dark Hours*, a drama of the Crucifixion, and *Out of the Sea*, a modern dramatic version of Tristan and Iseult.

DOROTHY PARKER

DOROTHY PARKER's devotees have followed her from Vogue to Vanity Fair to the New Yorker where her candid and flippant dramatic criticisms and later her book reviews have been a joy to the sophisticated. Her verses, most of them shrewd and bitter variations on the theme of love, are collected in three volumes, *Enough Rope*, *Sunset Gun*, and *Death and Taxes*. Thirteen of her stories and sketches may be found in *Laments for the Living*.

GEORGE ADE

GEORGE ADE's Fables in Slang will delight you, if you find amusement in the latest fads in the language of yesterday. Their shrewd humor is still entertaining and their phraseology brings back the fads and foibles of a whole delightful era.

PATRICIA COLLINGE

PATRICA COLLINGE: If you saw Patricia Collinge on Broadway in revivals of *She Stoops to Conquer* and *Becky Sharp*, you will watch with redoubled interest for her occasional pieces in the New Yorker.

CHARLES MacARTHUR

CHARLES MACARTHUR is one of the happy-go-lucky knight errants of literature. If you enjoyed his play, *The Front Page*, you will want to read his funny and horrible and poignantly true account of his service in the trenches, *War Bugs*.

THYRA SAMTER WINSLOW

THYRA SAMTER WINSLOW'S *Show Business, People Round the Corner* and *My Own, My Native Land* are books which you will want to explore when you have read *But for the Grace of God*.

FRANK SULLIVAN

FRANK SULLIVAN: The one and only Frank Sullivan has been caught between book covers in *In One Ear, Broc-*

coli and Old Lace and *Innocent Bystanding*. In one or the other of these you'll probably find all those pieces you saved for months until somebody threw away your New Yorker.

JOHN MOSHER, T. H. WENNING and ARTHUR KOBER

JOHN MOSHER, T. W. WENNING and ARTHUR KOBER have not yet achieved the sobriety of book covers, but you will find both of them once and again in the New Yorker. Emily Hahn, however, is the author of two books, *Seductio ad Absurdum*, made out of her New Yorker pieces, and *Congo Solo*, the record of a trip to Africa.

ROBERT BENCHLEY

ROBERT BENCHLEY's book titles are fully as amusing as the contents. Our own favorites are *No Poems or Around the World Backwards and Sideways* and *20,000 Leagues Under the Sea or David Copperfield*. Though there are those who like best *Treasurer's Report and Other Aspects of Community Singing*. If you want to see a living picture of Mr. Benchley, you will find him in any one of Gluyas Williams's cartoons.

NUNNALLY JOHNSON

NUNNALLY JOHNSON: One of America's favorite sports writers was lost when Nunnally Johnson took to fiction. You'll find many of his most joyous stories collected in *There Ought to be a Law*.

ELINOR WYLIE

ELINOR WYLIE'S works do not make a very long list, but the novels and poems of this rarely gifted woman will no doubt endure among the few that will survive our day. You will find in the *Collected Poems*, edited by William Rose Benét, all of her most beautiful ones. *The Venetian Glass Nephew* and *Mr. Hodge and Mr. Hazard* are two of her most interesting novels.

MORLEY CALLAGHAN

MORLEY CALLAGHAN first came to the notice of America by way of *transition* and Ezra Pounds's *this quarter*. He was encouraged to write by Ernest Hemingway and belongs to the group of vigorous young writers who followed him. His novels are *Strange Fugitive* and *It's Never Over*.

CHRISTOPHER MORLEY

CHRISTOPHER MORLEY, essayist, poet, dramatist, novelist, is one of those versatile writers who is happy in any form.

Where the Blue Begins, Thunder on the Left and *Human Being* are his finest novels. His books of essays and tales bulk large and his poetry ranges all the way from *Songs for a Little House* to the witty reflections of the old *Mandarin in Manhattan*.

VINCENT SHEEAN

VINCENT SHEEAN has the unusual reputation of having written his autobiography at the age of thirty-four and of having it become one of the most talked of books of the time. *Personal History* has all the drama of a novel, all the adventure of a book of travels and is current history as shown through one person's relationship to the world.

RING LARDNER

RING LARDNER: His *You Know Me, Al* stories, begun while he was a sports writer on the Chicago Tribune, won Ring Lardner such huge popularity that he was overlooked by the critics for many years. With the publication of *How to Write Short Stories*, a group of sardonic satires, he began to be considered seriously as one of our major writers of the short story. You will find many of them collected in *Lose with a Smile* and *The Love Nest*.

SHERWOOD ANDERSON

SHERWOOD ANDERSON: With such books as *Winesburg, Ohio, Poor White* and *Dark Laughter,* Sherwood Anderson became one of the most powerful writers of that remarkable group of novelists who came with Dreiser out of the Middle West. You will find his autobiography, *A Story Teller's Story,* and *Sherwood Anderson's Notebook* none the less interesting.

MAXWELL ANDERSON

MAXWELL ANDERSON whose play, *Winterset,* was an outstanding event of the 1935–36 season, won the 1934 Pulitzer Prize with *Mary of Scotland.* You will find interesting reading, also, in his earlier book, *What Price Glory,* written in collaboration with Laurence Stallings.

STEWART EDWARD WHITE

STEWART EDWARD WHITE's best-known novels are a rich and historically accurate social history of California. *Gold, The Rose Dawn, The Grey Dawn, The Long Rifle, Ranchero* and *Folded Hills* are each a period in the life of our West and Southwest.

EDWIN ARLINGTON ROBINSON

EDWIN ARLINGTON ROBINSON holds the unique distinction of having been awarded the Pulitzer Prize for poetry three times. His *Collected Poems* won it in 1922, *The Man Who Died Twice* in 1925 and *Tristram* in 1927. There are two excellent editions of his *Collected Poems*.

ROBERT FROST

ROBERT FROST: You will find in *Collected Poems* most of the best work of Robert Frost, but the individual volumes of the great New England poet's works repay a pilgrimage. They are *A Boy's Will, North of Boston, Momentous Interval, New Hampshire* and *West-Running Brook*.

CARL SANDBURG

CARL SANDBURG, the Mid-Western troubadour who travels around the country singing folk songs and collecting ballads, should be heard as well as read, for his voice is a vivid part of his poems. *Chicago Poems, Slabs of the Sunburnt West, Smoke and Steel* and *Good Morning, America* are his best-known books. Nor must one forget the *Rootabaga Stories* which entertain grown-ups as well as children.

SARA TEASDALE

SARA TEASDALE'S exquisite lyrics are scattered through many volumes. You will find perhaps her finest poem, *Let It Be Forgotten*, in *Flame and Shadow*. *Dark of the Moon* contains her *Pictures of Autumn*. *Rivers to the Sea*, *Love Songs* and *Helen of Troy* are earlier volumes.

JOHN GOULD FLETCHER

JOHN GOULD FLETCHER is a distinguished native of Arkansas, long resident in London, who has made significant contributions to modern poetry, being an American member of the Imagist School, which was founded by Richard Aldington, H.D., and others. His books include *Irradiations* and *Breakers and Granite*, poems.

HILDA DOOLITTLE

HILDA DOOLITTLE, whose pen name is "*H. D.*", has long been an American expatriate. Her first book, *Sea Garden*, was published in 1916 in England and since then other volumes have appeared here and abroad, including *Heliodora and Other Poems*, *Hymen* and *Collected Poems*. Perhaps more than any modern, H. D. has caught the solemn beauty of the Greeks. She writes in a unique free verse manner and was a member of the Imagist Group.

WILLIAM ROSE BENÉT

WILLIAM ROSE BENÉT is a founder of The Saturday Review
of Literature and conductor, on that periodical, of a
column, *The Phœnix Nest*. Mr. Benét is a poet, a critic,
and a novelist. His best-known book, perhaps, is *Falconer of God*, verse. He is the brother of Stephen Vincent Benét and was the husband of the late Elinor
Wylie.

ROBINSON JEFFERS

ROBINSON JEFFERS is that awesome voice which sounds its
poetic warnings of the futility of modern life from a
tower of ocean-worn boulders on the coast near Carmel, California. Disbelieving in individual immortality,
utterly irreligious, he accepts the fact of the tragedy
of life, but thinks existence worth the cost. He has
caught rich, powerful emotions in such books of poems
as *Tamar, Roan Stallion, The Women at Sur Point*.
Despite their solemn intensity, and their somewhat
shocking emotions, his books have achieved the unique
honor, for poetry, of being best sellers.

T. S. ELIOT

T. S. ELIOT is the author of that landmark in our literature, *The Waste Land*, perhaps the most intellectually

intense, deeply allusive poem of this generation. Since
The Waste Land, around which controversy stormed,
Eliot has written largely in the critical field. His books
include *Homage to John Dryden*, *For Lancelot Andrews* and *Ash Wednesday*, a short series of poems
testifying to the progress of his religious faith.

JOHN CROWE RANSOM

JOHN CROWE RANSOM founder, with Allen Tate and others,
of the Fugitive Group of poets at Nashville, Tennessee,
is professor of English at Vanderbilt University in the
same city. More recently Mr. Ransom has engaged in
the Agrarian movement, organized under the impetus
of former "Fugitives." He is the author of *Poems About
God* and other books of verse which, though advanced
modern in impulse, derive in influence from the meta-
physical poets of John Donne's time.

CONRAD AIKEN

CONRAD AIKEN: If you are one of those fortunate readers
who discovered *Blue Voyage* a few years ago, you will
remember that book by Conrad Aiken as perhaps a
major creative experience. *Great Circle* further estab-
lishes Mr. Aiken as a brilliant experimenter in fiction,
but he is first of all a lyric poet.

EDNA ST. VINCENT MILLAY

EDNA ST. VINCENT MILLAY, lyricist, Pulitzer Prize winner, and author of the libretto of one of the first American operas, *The King's Henchman*, is perhaps the outstanding contemporary woman poet. Her *A Few Figs from Thistles, Renascence and Other Poems*, and *Second April* were influential in the remarkable renaissance of poetry in America between 1912 and 1920, approximately. Miss Millay's *Fatal Interview*, a volume of fifty-two love sonnets, appeared in 1931 and carried her to an even more solid position in the world of modern poetry.

ARCHIBALD MacLEISH

ARCHIBALD MACLEISH, Pulitzer Prize winner in 1933 for *Conquistador*, is a poet of vivid imagery and depth of feeling. His verse forms are unusual, his rhythms unique. *New Found Land* and *Streets in the Moon* are two of his earlier books.

PHELPS PUTNAM

PHELPS PUTNAM is the author of one of those books which make their way by quiet insinuation into the admiration of a remarkable number of appreciative readers. This is *Trinc*. Mr. Putnam is also the author of *Five Seasons*, published in 1932.

E. E. CUMMINGS

E. E. CUMMINGS's latest book is *eimi*, a novel. An innovator, he is widely known for his typographical experimentations, the look of verse on the page. His poems have a deep, curious, lustrous lyricism. His novel, *The Enormous Room*, is one of the most memorable of war stories.

LOUISE BOGAN

LOUISE BOGAN belongs in the front rank of the American writers who are creating lasting poems. Her *Body of This Death* is greatly prized by close followers of poetry. Her work is distinguished for its control, emotion and bright, mordant beauty.

STEPHEN VINCENT BENÉT

STEPHEN VINCENT BENÉT is celebrated chiefly as the author of *John Brown's Body*, a long narrative poem of the Civil War, already accepted as a classic in our time. *Ballads and Poems* is a definitive collection of his shorter American poems.

LÉONIE ADAMS

LÉONIE ADAMS, though she lectures on Victorian poetry at Columbia University, is the author of verses distinctly modern in tone. Her books include *Those Not Elect* and *High Falcon*, both written with a brittle lyricism and a talent for catching the haunting, the allusive overtone. Miss Adams has edited and translated Villon and was an editor of The Measure when that periodical was one of the most important poetry magazines in the country.

ALLEN TATE

ALLEN TATE is not only a front-rank poet and one of the founders of the Fugitive Group, but a biographer of distinction in the Southern field. He has written *Stonewall Jackson: The Good Soldier* and *Jefferson Davis: His Rise and Fall*, which stand with the best biographies of the day.

HART CRANE

HART CRANE is perhaps the most eminent figure in our younger creative generation in poetry. His intense and sculptural lyric, *The Bridge*, stands a landmark of its time. Much of his best work you will find in *Collected Poems*.